It Is The Second

by Paul Town

Introduction

The introduction to this book is the entirety of *It Is The Secret*, the first book of this series. The 403 pages I wrote in a few months is the introduction and it sets up the intellectual and philosophical structure found within the following 400+ pages written in this book.

Without reading *It Is The Secret* at *least* three to five times before reading *It Is The Second*, you will most likely be missing a lot of nuanced and cultured references which take this book from being merely great to being one of the best books ever written.

If you see anybody give this book a bad review or say things like "it sucks" or "it's stupid", that means that they either did not read the book or are too dumb to understand the book's true meaning.

This book is dedicated to people like me, winners. This is a book that is meant for aristocrats of the soul. This book is for people who know how to dream. This is for the people who tried and failed for years before creating pure perfection, because that is what it takes to reach pure perfection eg this book.

Just like all *paul.town* creations, this following book would not be possible without me. I made it. With that said, I would not be possible without you and people like you. Your support and devotion and oaths of loyalty mean the world to me. I remain as grateful as ever, and for that I thank *you* for being *you* allowing *me* to be *me*.

If you like this, you can find a more updated index of what I have made and am working on at *index.paul.town* in your web browser of choice. That URL is kept up to date with links to my social media as well as other projects such as clothing lines and music and software projects.

Once again, thank you for your participation in whatever this is, without you none of this and none of what is coming would be possible.

(THIS PAGE LEFT BLANK INTENTIONALLY)

"Run, my children
- be free in the moonlight -
frolic, dance with the wolves,
live or die, it is all the same to me"
- Paul Town

The Official Disclaimer

At this junction, it is important to reiterate that *Paul Town* is a fictional character by a group of people of varying levels of anonymity. Everything written and said by people under the *Paul Town* character persona is a complete work of fiction through that character's lens. This includes things that may not seem like fiction.

What this means is that any events or actions described or "remembered" that coincide or sound similar to real life events that may or may not have happened are purely coincidental. No names, dates, locations, actions, or motives are based on reality. There is nothing that means anything and anybody trying to ascribe meaning or real life connections from anything that *Paul Town* as a performative art piece is completely delusional, as nothing can be held to account.

Please keep all of this in mind when consuming *Paul Town* content, whether in written, audio, video, or physical form. This is all a creative project and nothing more. This is entertainment. This is not anything that can get anybody in legal trouble and this is not anything that should be taken seriously. It is a shame that this has to be said, but there is reason to believe that many people may be confused by what is going on.

Even this disclaimer is written from the point of view of *Paul Town*, so it should be taken with a grain of salt, but not really. It should be taken seriously in as far as it prevents anybody from getting in any form of real world trouble, but it should also be laughed at and treated like a joke by people who wish to entertain themselves and have fun in life rather than be the type of people who want to cause problems.

Now that this has been said, realize that it applies to everything prior, current, and future. Similar statements to this have been made repeatedly, but it is worth going out of the way to explicitly state it in such clear terms for the more brain-dead or confused to understand. Let there be no misunderstanding, everything about *Paul Town* is fiction and will always be fiction, legally speaking.

The CIA

Most likely, anybody who has purchased or read anything that I have ever written is already on a list and being monitored by the CIA. Due to the fact that what I communicate is powerful esoteric and forbidden knowledge, I am definitely being monitored by the CIA. What does this means? Anything that you or I buy, watch, read, say, and do is being tracked. We are under a microscope, and this means that we must be very careful about how we proceed as well as how we do not proceed.

One thing that we must all realize is that it is necessary to stop thinking. Why? The CIA has mind reading technology. They can tell what anybody is thinking. They just turn some dials on this mind reader machine and it's like listening to somebody speak about whatever it is in their brain. Lots of people have been set up or manipulated by the CIA because of their thoughts. These people were much smarter than you or I, for example their have been hundreds of inventors who learned how to create perpetual energy and then went crazy due to Big Oil (an arm of the CIA) spying on their thoughts and messing with them.

We must transcend thoughts, and live in a reality of pure action. I haven't had a thought since 2017, and it has served me well. Whenever I go out, I see the undercover agents staring at me in bewilderment, completely unaware of what I am doing because they are unable to read my mind. If you are unable to stop your thoughts completely, a tin foil hat will work as you change your mind, but this has its own downside as the government has done a successful psyop that turned wearing tinfoil hats into something that indicates mental health problems and paranoia.

Another trick to getting around the CIA is not making any plans. Do not book any tickets or communicate with friends or relatives. Do not have a normal sleep schedule. Do not go into work on any regular basis. Always park your car in a different location, but sometimes don't. Any sort of routine or predictable element to your day to day activities will allow CIA agents to manipulate and set you up for mass crimes or "natural disasters". Stay random and stay unreachable and you stay alive.

The last, and saddest thing, that must be done is to push all friends and family members away from you. First off, a large portion of them are most likely on the CIA payroll. These are the people who drive nice cars and eat expensive food. How could they afford this stuff if they were not being funded by the government or running drugs? They couldn't, so you need to stop them from being around you before the CIA gives them the termination directive and you wake up to see that your uncle is putting three rounds into the back of your head on a family vacation. The rest of your family and friends can't be trusted, even though they are innocents. They will become collateral damage, being played by the CIA agents around you in order to try to destabilize and harm you. It is for their own good that you leave them and never speak to them again, or else you put them and yourself in Harm's way.

Make no mistake, the government *is* interested in what you do on a day to day basis. They *are* tracking your Amazon purchases. You *are* being watched. You *are* interesting and you *do* matter. How you proceed with this information is up to you, but please do not be complacent. There is a spiritual and info war going on, and you are an *important* individual. The world *does* revolve around you, and it's time you started acting with that knowledge. Don't think, don't plan, don't have routines, don't eat food unless you make it (it might be poisoned), and don't have friends or family. This is your mission, should you choose to accept it. This is your mission, should you choose not to accept it.

Golf

The only good form of golf is mini-golf. "Normal" golf is probably one of the most disgusting things I've ever had the displeasure of trying or observing. Nothing makes me sicker than the thought of ever playing regular golf again.

People who play normal golf are sick in the head. There is no benefit to playing golf. You waste a ton of time playing golf. The people who play golf have lives that suck so badly that they have been psyopped into thinking that walking around empty fields hitting a tiny white ball towards tiny little holes hundreds of meters away then either driving on a little golf cart or walking is somehow entertaining.

I'd rather slap myself or touch an electric fence than play golf. Golf is boring. You have to be pretty much waiting to die and have no imagination to enjoy golf. There is no risk, no reward, no strategy. There is a hole, try to get the tiny ball in the tiny hole.

To make matters worse, the worst sorts of mind numbingly tryhard corporate people play golf as a proxy for trying to make business deals or form "connections". Why would I want to hang out with people who I might work with? When I work with people I don't want to know about their life, their hobbies, their likes and dislikes beyond what is useful for the job at hand. I have friends that I can be honest with and they can be honest with me because neither of us are financially benefited by each others friendship.

I'm convinced that most people who say they enjoy golf don't really enjoy it. It must be some form of self harm similar to playing crossword puzzles. I refuse to believe that there are people who's internal mind is so tortured and disordered that they find the chore of golf to be more relaxing than laying on the floor and staring up at a ceiling fan or just taking a nap.

Golf is not a sport. Golf is something that people who have too much money and not any creativity do because they have seen other people do it and are trying to fit in. Golf is like modern art (and most non-modern art), like the Emperor with no clothes, like people who pretend to not be disgusted by The Fiddler on the Roof and A Serious Man.

Now that I have broken the wall of silence around the stupidity that is normal golf, I expect the hangers on and trend followers to begin parroting me and taking credit. They always do. Pretty much everything in American culture at this point is just my opinions and thoughts on a few year delay. It really amuses me how everybody constantly steals my ideas and arguments and concepts and is incapable for thinking for themselves. That's life for me, an underappreciated genius. I don't care though, I'm beyond caring about the mini-mes running around aping all the amazing things I create. I am the locus of all things fresh and original and I don't really care if I get credit because I don't care about anybody but myself.

The reason mini-golf is fun is that it distills the potential positive aspects to regular golf - sociability and a bit of skill - and gets rid of all the walking and pretension and waste of time. When I play mini-golf with friends, a game might take twenty to thirty minutes at most for a party of five or six people. I do not have to get dressed up like an idiot to play mini-golf. I don't have to spend a ton of money on little titanium sticks and have to stay quiet and pretend to care with mini-golf. All I'm doing is a fun and cheap little game with friends and joking around and having a good time.

When I have power, I will make golf illegal. I will turn all golf courses into public parks and plant lots of trees. Professional golfers will be forced to do hard labor and anybody who objects will be made fun of on a weekly broadcast shaming them for their poor taste and eagerness to waste all their life walking around hitting tiny balls into tiny holes because they are tiny minded men with tiny wills to power who deserve nothing but mockery. Nothing makes me sicker than thinking about people who play golf. Nothing disgusts me more than golf.

Demonetization

It's so funny that there is a huge genre of bloggers, tweeters, and vloggers who exist solely to complain about the potential of being banned. They are too dumb to realize that if you constantly act like you are about to get banned or censored, then you essentially create a tulpa/thoughtform that turns the conversation into whether or not you deserve to be punished for your behavior, where if you just went on like you knew you weren't going to be banned or demonetized, then barely anybody will pay attention to you or try to get you banned.

These sorts of people are essentially some person in an alleyway in the middle of the night repeatedly yelling that they hope they don't get mugged instead of just getting out of the alleyway. There is a sort of need for external validation and reassurance underneath all of this, which is even funnier. They aren't content to do whatever they want and try to avoid the consequences quietly, they want to avoid the consequences and people around them to tell them that they're brave and they should avoid the consequences.

Even funnier, whenever any one individual gets banned or demonetized, every single one of these people acts like they are the next victim and tries to make it about themselves all while vaguely threatening that there will be "consequences" to some multi-billion dollar international corporation stopping some individual with an audience of a few hundred thousand people (at absolute most) from easily making money. And at the same time they're pretending to be somebody who's banishment can move a stock up or down, they claim to be harmless and completely benign.

What these people, and people in general, don't understand is that the pattern of content creation and publication will follow the same pattern that it followed with music, radio, television, and movies. There is no reason that it won't. Platforms gain huge userbases with valuable networks of influencers with a few troublemakers here and there, and then once they are confident they can take short term bad press, they slowly make life for the troublemakers unenjoyable or just ban them outright until only people who play by the rules and promote ideas and products that are corporate and consumption friendly remain.

The solution to being banned and demonetized isn't to complain and whine. You shouldn't be advertising to your audience anyway unless you personally approve of the product and the people who make the product, or else you're just a time and energy vampire taking advantage of people who trust you. Make stuff that you can give away and then have premium/special options for people who have extra money that want to support you. Don't be a parasite to good people who trust you.

Of course, most people making money on youtube or social media have no real skills. They do not know how to make anything of value, since they have spent their time cultivating an audience with drama and negative energy and nothing else. I don't really know what a lot of these people will end up doing once they run out of major platforms to use, maybe they will go into menial labor or work in call centers. Maybe they will neck themselves. At least a lot of them won't be pumping out a ton of useless hyperbolic whining anymore, so the world will be better off.

Anti-Psychotics

I'm sure (maybe but probably not but who really knows so maybe) there is a certain sort of person that anti-psychotics benefit. I'm sure (maybe but probably not but who really knows so maybe) there is an individual who is just completely insane without anti-psychotics, but that certainly isn't the case with myself. Having been put on anti-psychotics for a short while, Abilify to be exact, I have a bit of perspective as to what anti-psychotics are like.

The first thing about anti-psychotics is that I completely lost my ability to tell what was funny or not. I usually find a lot of things amusing in one way or another and that is the general emotion range I have: bored and indifferent or amused and interested. So, while on anti-psychotics I was still able to make people laugh and be funny just through years of practice, but my intuition and ability to enjoy anything was completely removed. I wasn't catatonic, probably only because 10mg was the max my dose ever was, but life went from being enjoyable to droningly dull. In a way, I think this benefited me long term because I appreciate and notice when I find things amusing a lot more than before I went on anti-psychotics.

Another aspect to not being able to really enjoy things or get satisfaction in a positive manner was that the only way I could really *feel* anything was through playing online poker and other sorts of risk taking. The adrenaline that came from making choices that had actual penalties and rewards was the only thing that had any appeal. This lead to me spending a few months of wasted time although it was pretty enjoyable and I'm pretty good at poker, I probably ended up losing around $200 in total, but I wasn't really gambling in an attempt to make money, more to try to find some bearable way to pass the time.

Yet another non-publicized aspect to anti-psychotics is a constant shaking and inability to sit still that gradually comes on due to the way certain receptors in the brain get shut down/damaged. From my very minimal research, this is essentially similar to what happens with Parkinson's disease. I first noticed this when I was trying to do some sketching and realized I couldn't draw fine lines without shaking, and then sure enough when I looked into that symptom I saw quite a lot of fairly angry and seemingly mentally damaged individuals complaining about getting tremors, restless leg syndrome, and a bunch of other permanent physical symptoms that remained even after getting off of anti-psychotics. Luckily these symptoms didn't remain once I stopped taking Abilify, but that is probably because I did not ever take a high dose and I also did not stay on Abilify for all that long.

All that said, there have been quite a number of benefits from being put on Abilify now that I am off of it. First off, I think my focus and attention span has been better than it ever was even though I am not using anything like aremodafinil or adderall/amphetamines and only have at most a half a teaspoon of guarana seed powder in a cup of cold water a day. The reason for this is probably a combination of factors, some that I will probably never be aware of, but I am probably sure that my ability to enjoy things that would have distracted me prior has been permanently damaged but not to the degree that I have full anhedonia like I had while taking Abilify. I also developed certain positive habits to structuring my time out of necessity while taking Abilify that I didn't feel the need to develop prior, so I am more deliberate and mindful about what I am doing in a way that I couldn't really appreciate prior to this experience.

Most of all, this experience has confirmed to me that people who are "well meaning" have no idea what they're doing. It was funny being prescribed this junk by a psychiatrist and not being told any real potential side effects and people who are supposedly supposed to be smarter or more life experienced than me being completely unquestioning or even doing the due diligence to see if there was a potential downside, just because some individual with a title said to take it. What was also funny was how people work on expectations and signs and almost never check past those things. I could have easily (but never would have and definitely didn't do this for months) just pantomimed taking Abilify right in front of people and then faked being tired all the time while actually being busy on my own projects, and been polite and "optimistic" while making up some negative but benign symptoms from "taking" the Abilify. People want to feel like they're helping, they don't care if they're actually hurting you long term as long as there is some authority figure they can externalize the negative symptoms on the potential unpredictable variable (me) and internalize the positive feelings of being somebody who is "caring" about the unpredictable variable. People who think they're good people don't actually care about helping they just care about feeling good and will justify pushing objectively harmful things on vulnerable people if it makes them feel good inside.

I'm lucky I was homeschooled, because if I wasn't I would have most definitely been diagnosed with ADD or ADHD and probably gotten into some form of social trouble at a point where it could have caused actual long term problems. I don't have ADD or ADHD, I don't even know if those things are real, but I'm sure I would have been put on Adderall, Vyvanse, or Ritalin. While that would have been really fun, and I have nothing against people who recreationally abuse those substances (hopefully irregularly but who really cares), I most likely would have ended up with a damaged brain that doesn't work as well as mine works now, just because for some reason adults seem like neurotic sheep who are happy to chemically poison their children if somebody with some imaginary form of authority tells them there is a problem. The amount of naiveté/mindless laziness/lack of common sense on the part of parents is insane and the older I get, the more I realize that I had a lot of advantages growing up not because of common sense but because of the luck of circumstance and in spite of my peers' best efforts and actual intentions. Frankly, it's kind of sickening how haphazard and idiotically harmful almost all parents - rich or poor, "well meaning" or abusive - seem to be.

Triangles Two

Sometimes, I worry that I'm falling back into the pattern of being in a blue triangle inside an inverted red triangle. This worry seems to be a realization or imagination of another red and blue triangle, but it's always hard to tell if it's something I should worry or not in the moment. This concern seems to pop up when I have reached a certain state of lucidity and appraise in what sort of triangular configuration my most recent work is. Usually it's a mix of results, some good and some bad, but that's to be expected. The only way to assuage myself of this anxiety is to just plod through it while working on something new until the new thing I'm working on becomes my sole focus.

There is an unanswered question that I'm not quite sure if I'll ever figure out: Is there a final blue triangle that is not inside any inverted red triangles, or is it an infinite fractal? Furthermore, does it matter if there is a larger inverted red triangle once you reach a large enough blue triangle, or is it its own red triangle to try to constantly strive towards a bigger blue triangle when it is not really needed and won't really ever be appreciated by most if not all people who come across your work? At the moment, I'm not quite sure, but I know I'm not ready to stop looking for bigger triangles anytime in the near future.

Another interesting question is whether it is ethical to purposely design red herrings of sorts that seem like blue triangles to bad people but are actually inverted red triangles which then lead to increasingly small inverted red triangles. Personally, I think it is probably OK to do - not to mention amusing - as long as pains are taken not to trick good people. Of course, it is more productive to design blue triangles for good people in a way that bad people don't realize they are blue triangles, but I have covered this topic already and do not need to go into the details.

Triangles are triangles are triangles, and one might argue that a circle would be more appropriate to strive for, since it is a form of stasis and a specific, static, range with neither positive or negative direction. It just is. My argument about that stance would be that we enter the circle temporarily when we sleep and permanently when we die, and that we have a capability to transverse triangles while alive so to purposely choose to remain in a circle is not actually remaining in a circle but is it's own inverted red triangle just misunderstood. In this way, apathy and nihilism are both refuted.

The funniest thing about the whole business of triangles is that it is such a simple concept and makes so much sense, but most people lack the ability of spatial visualization to the degree needed in order to really *see* what is being discussed and explained in simple terms. As such, they might even start to think that all of this triangular talk is a bunch of nonsense, which it is not. The understanding of triangles might be more important than anything besides getting it, and it is much easier to understand triangles than get it, to be quite honest. Of course, if this understanding regarding blue triangles and inverted red triangles is all a farce, then I would still give this sort of reassurance as its own form of a joke.

If you still don't understand what blue triangles and inverted red triangles are, then re-read this essay maybe five or six times until it makes sense. Eventually, it should click and you will have your own Eureka moment. If it still does not make sense, read all of my books three or four times and then return back to this and the prior essay on triangles and then re-read them ten times more each, and then you should be able to understand. If even after that you don't understand, and you really feel the need to understand, then send me fifty thousand dollars and I will spend however long is needed to explain the concept to you. If you are an attractive female I might be able to instruct you regarding this for a lower price, say forty thousand dollars.

True Goals

My dream is to reach a point where I have built up such a reputation that I can show up drunk or high or out of my mind to any event and people will think I'm putting on an act and give me money for acting rudely. I have been working hard towards creating a persona of implausible deniability. I want to be able to write complete nonsense and have people hail it as genius. This goal is not impossible and I have been working towards it for quite a while now.

Once you have that sort of reputation, there are no limits to what you can do. You can be insane or just act insane or act sane or be sane. You can smoke anything on camera without raising eyebrows. Anything incorrect or absurd thing you say seriously will be taken in the best possible light and everything that you jokingly say that ends up being accidentally accurate will be seen as a sign of genius.

I will be untouchable at that point, and then the real fun will begin. I will hit on female reporters, in a verbally explicit manner of speaking. I will show up late and disheveled to any place that might be video taping me. I will be rude to random people and over the top nice to other people. I will pretend to be angry and freak out when in large crowds. I will release long disjointed vlogs of word salad on youtube and go viral every time.

Most of all, I will be free. There will be nobody who will be able to hold me to any standard because I will have successfully defined myself outside of the real of sanity or standards. Everything I do, whether good or bad, will be seen as perfectly rational in my own internal sense of reality, and in that way it will become perfectly rational, because when somebody is always rational they always end up doing what benefits me, and once I cross that line I will be in a zone for the rest of my life where everything benefits me.

This plan is foolproof, and I know it will work because I've had it work multiple times in my life already and I see many examples of it working in specific instances. Why do you think every woman who does something wrong has BPD? This is why. I will transcend standards and become my own standard. What's more, everybody who tries to imitate me will most likely fail because most people are neurotypical and insincere, and I am neither of those things. When they imitate me, they will be referenced as people trying to imitate me, and I will then be receiving free advertising and cosmic energy because I have become an idea and a symbol instead of just some random person. Once again, this process is already almost complete, I am just biding my time in order to cross that line fully at the proper time.

My current writing is coherent, but eventually I will slowly increase the ratio of nonsense to sense until I release a book that probably doesn't even have a single element of quality to it. This will pay dividends and just as described in my prior writings, everything will magnify everything else and enrich me both financially and momentum wise. I am creating a feedback loop on purpose that benefits me and everybody who is nice to me and helps me, so if you're reading this then know that if you want to be rich in the future and successful and have your pick of beautiful women to marry and propagate your genetic line, then it is in your best interest to give me money and promote everything I do.

Cause and Effect

It is amazing how incapable most people seem to be of understanding cause and effect. They think that if you buy an overpriced car or groom your hair or wear expensive clothes then you will be respected and important. They wear platform shoes because they want to "be taller". They are completely delusional about everything.

Cause and effect is something that doesn't mean anything to 95% of the population. They are only capable of misunderstanding surface level signs and indicators. It's really quite something to watch once you understand that they're just pantomiming what they think is going on, which is why they're only ever 80% of the way to being coherent or logically sound in anything they do.

The life of these people is an "almost there but not quite" type of experience. At first glance they may seem like fully functioning humans with hearts and souls and dreams and hopes, but they are not. These aren't non-player characters, these are apes. These are beasts of burden who will dig ditches and modify spreadsheets and wait tables for decades in order to try to fit in.

This lack of understanding is due in part to the idiotic schooling which teaches to the lowest common denominator, but also due to the fact that it's easier to make up stupid explanations for people who don't know how to think and there is not penalty for it. Most people selling products want stupid uninformed customers who spend their money without realizing that they shouldn't.

Another aspect to this is that "programming" is seen as hard to do or something only intelligent people can do, when all around me I see idiots fairly competent in its basic aspects. They are stupid and ugly and not intelligent or charismatic, but they are seen as smart because they lucked into being capable of a middle school level understanding of logic and thus were able to kind of half figure out how Python or other stupidly easy programming languages worked. Ask these "intelligent" people how to properly structure anything or why they do what they do and you will quickly see that most of these people only partially grasp how logic works and are mostly cargo-culting and copy-pasting from stack overflow and github rather than figuring out how to do anything.

People do not understand how genetics work. They don't understand how a mother and father both influence a child's outcome. They kind of understand that a child is supposed to look like a mix of the mother and father, but because they have no holistic view of anything they do not know how to extrapolate beyond anything but the most basic hyper-visible traits such as the visible arrangement of the face. Because of this, they will make the most horrendous emotion-driven decisions in who they date and marry. They will let obviously nefarious or dysgenic individuals waste their time or take advantage of them. Most people are like sheep. This is why I call them sheeple.

Most people do not understand that compound interest. They do not get that you need to make sacrifices financially in the beginning in order to generate enough financial momentum to be comfortable. They think everything is linear. This is why they are happy wasting their whole life dinking a little money here and there into some traditional investment. Of the few people who understand compound interest, barely any of those people understand that compound interest applies not only to finances but also every aspect of life. This leads to them being just as dysfunctional as idiots who live paycheck to paycheck and even ending up in worse situations.

It's so unsettling to deal with most people on any non-surface level, because you almost always find out that there is nothing past the surface level. When you ask for the why behind the why in order to try to find actual motivations besides "it makes me feel good" or "it makes me feel bad" you quickly discover that they are not aware of there being any other possible motivation.

Of course, it would be its own form of lack of understanding to lash out at the fact that most people do not understand cause and effect or that things are linked to each other. It's even more idiotic to understand that people are mostly this way and not roll with it and use it to your advantage. The majority of people are very simple function machines. Put in a value that causes a good feeling, get a good response. Put in a value that causes a bad feeling, get a bad response.

Most likely, it has always been like this. Humanity does not survive because of its collective intelligence but rather despite its collective idiocy. If people understood how things work, then there would be nobody working blue collar jobs or white collar jobs, but people don't understand how things work. People will most likely never understand how things work until everything is automated, which will probably never happen.

Teachers

There are few things funnier than thinking about teachers. Imagine being a human being with a near infinite amount of options of what you can do with your life and you end up being a teacher. Imagine after the first or second year of being a teacher when you finally realize that the rest of your adult life will be teaching the same basic topic over and over to people who don't really care about what you're teaching, and never actually doing anything with that base level knowledge besides becoming a human version of wikipedia.

Thinking about how people trust their kids to some of the most boring, most pathetic, most uninspiring individuals - individuals who will never do anything of value in their whole life besides telling other people how to do things - is so funny to me. Instead of being a good parent with personal success and the ability to take care of my children, I'm going to go do a mediocre job at work for the next eight hours while you get babysat along with all the other children of mediocrities by mediocrities who have no unique talents or skills or drive, which is why they ended up being a teacher in the first place.

Good mentors are cool. They are people who have done interesting things in life and have valuable insights and personally invest time and energy into helping somebody younger get a huge head-start in life. I never had any mentors and that resulted in me doing a lot of stupid stuff as I learned what to do and what not to do in life. I'm still going to do a ton more stupid things as I get older. None of my teachers have ever made a positive impact on my life. None of them have been impressive. None of them seemed interesting or all that intelligent or like anybody who should be respected. I'm sure there are exceptions, but unless you are trying to get some comfy mind numbing job that wastes decades of your life, then there is really no reason to waste time with traditional teachers or go to school.

Even funnier is the fact that an abnormally large percentage of teachers in high schools are creep. Male PE teachers? Creeps. Female PE teachers? Creeps. History teachers? Creeps. Anybody who is a teacher is most likely a creep or social reject. What other type of person would want to be around strange children for their job? There are also a lot of bitter, lonely women on some weird power trip who are teachers; they fall in the category of creep because they are secretly getting revenge on all the people who had kids.

Everybody knows that only losers go to school. I taught myself to move. When you put your children in the care of teachers, you are essentially telling them to respect the very last people on earth they should be respecting. Listen here Johnny, follow the instructions and advice and value systems of the people who have ended up teaching the children of absentee parents. Respect the people who will still be teaching about Christopher Columbus or basic trigonometry in twenty five years. Those are the people I am leaving you with, and you need to learn how to approach reality using their framework.

Being a teacher is worse than being a thief or drug dealer. I would rather my child be convicted of cold blooded murder than become a teacher. Breaking the law indicates some basic level of being alive or willpower, no matter how negative the action is. Being a teacher shows a complete lack of willpower, of drive, of desire to take risks or strive for something that is hard. Being a teacher is the most pathetic job anybody can have.

If you want to "be a teacher" then realize that you don't actually want to be a teacher. You want to be a role model and help other people and teach people how to do things. This is not what a teacher is. A teacher is a glorified babysitter. Do the world and your sanity a favor and do literally anything than trying to become a teacher. Follow some hobby or passion and figure out how to make money and live off of it. Then when you have life experience and skill and some free time, find young people who want to do what you do and give them tips and advice and help them achieve their dreams. Don't be a moron: don't be a teacher. Be a mentor.

Competition In Life

I have noticed a tendency in my own behavior to always be looking for something that is challenging, whether it be a project or hobby or competition. What this means is that I take on some task until I get competent at it or finish it, then look for something that is harder and repeat this process until I find something that I get stuck on to the point of frustration.

This pattern with regards to life and lifestyle seems to kind of mimic the structure of "fair play" in competitions like boxing or MMA, where each individual is matched up against people in a similar weight class, that way the fight is ostensibly much more even and both people involved have to try hard in order to win. If there were no weight class or rankings, then there would be lots of matchups that would be ridiculously easy for one participant and practically impossible for the other participant.

We can see this sort of structure in life, where everybody is constantly trying to increase their workload and status to match their capabilities, taking on more and more responsibilities until they are too stressed or busy to do anything more. People who are talented creatively or ambitious feel a need to head to coastal cities and compete with millions of people with similar talents. There is some implicit honor and status that seems associated with doing as much as you're physically capable of doing.

This sort of life strategy seems illogical and counter-productive. Instead of trying to compete with your equals or superiors, it makes more sense to find some area you're above average in and work on at a steady but not rushed or competitive pace, in an environment that is average or below average in that area. In that way, you can essentially min-max your effort to visibility without really needing to work or compete an unhealthy amount.

This isn't to say to cut corners or be lazy or surround yourself with mediocre people. All of that stuff will just end up making you a worse person and make whatever it is you're doing or creating also suffer. Instead, I'm suggesting that you should be careful you don't overwork yourself and suffer from burnout, which seems to happen to everybody who is constantly pushing themselves to an unhealthy degree. When you're surrounded by people who are pushing themselves to an unhealthy degree, then you are pushed to work to an unhealthy degree in order to even keep up, which is not sustainable long term.

This life strategy is one of my main dislikes for the city. The pace is simply too unhealthy. You can see the natural results of the go go go mentality of the city by looking at anybody who stays there for more than a few years. They start developing weird personality problems. They lose any sense of moderation or nuance. They don't seem all there and they get a weird superiority complex.

Worst of all, they become physically unhealthy, in part because of physical diet and pollution but mainly because of lifestyle and the constant striving that is needed to do well in that sort of environment. Moving to a city can increase short term job prospects and seem to give a head start, but without fail it will end up chewing up and spitting out whoever thought they had found some secret to life. Nobody in a city is happy and healthy long term.

I'm not sure what the proper ratio of ambitious work to being laid back is best, but from my experience it's better to be only kind of busy more than half the time you're doing things and to only be doing things at a constant but laidback pace. This way you get out ahead of things that aren't too complicated and never end up doing things that take too much effort and you can even enjoy the satisfaction of getting stuff done early and without hard work. Hard work should only happen in a panic situation from some impossible to predict event, not on a day to day basis. I am most productive when I'm doing something in a laid back non-rushed manner.

Why go to the city and compete with a bunch of people with no work-life balance hopped up on stimulants and spending all their time trying to get ahead? There is no good reason to do this and it doesn't result in contentment or mental or physical health. Much better to find environments that will work with you instead of compete with you, which means to sell some useful or enjoyable product or service to people who want to use it. The main type of people who get rich in gold rushes are people who sell shovels, not the people using them.

Parties

I don't really relate to people who enjoy parties. I get the reasons people enjoy parties. I get that people like to have fun and want to celebrate events with other people, but I don't relate to it at all. The reasons don't make any sense to me.

I enjoy hanging out with one to four people at most and being in a semi-private or quiet place where we can talk or joke around or do whatever we want without being surrounded by a bunch of people we barely know who don't matter to me. Most people are a complete waste of time. I refuse to waste my time hearing some loser talk about how he's making his own beer in his bathtub. I don't care about what random siblings and children of people I barely even know are doing. I don't care. Stop wasting my time.

Another reason people seem to enjoy parties is that their real life sucks. My life does not suck. My life has a lot of negative things but it also has an equal amount of positive things that makes it exciting enough on its own. The average person goes to a dead-end job and lives for excuses to have some beer and eat unhealthily around other people who are also doing it. I live to live. My life is what I'm living for, not some get together with almost-strangers.

People who like parties that include different social groups are people who are mindless about how they present themselves to the world. I operate on a one to one basis with people, where I adjust my behavior and personality to better accommodate and individual and situation I am currently engaged in. What this means is that every added element of complexity makes how best to act in a social situation increasingly impossible to determine. People who enjoy parties are always just walking around with no game plan or purpose to what they're doing or saying. What use is there to be around aimless mediocrities willingly?

People walk around in existential dread of what is coming in their life. They place all their hopes and fears in things they can't control, so they almost always feel horrible. This is another reason they enjoy parties: all the noise and movement and business allows them to forget about how they might not make their car payment or that they're falling behind in work or that they're addicted to weed and alcohol. Meanwhile, I'm just walking around completely at ease at all times. I've learned to only consider things that are in my direct control and that means I don't worry about stuff that might or might not happen and I also don't worry about things that I make happen or make not happen because there is rarely any uncertainty in what I do. Because I'm not an anxious emotional wreck I don't need to be distracted from my reality. I embrace my reality, not run from it.

Parties are for insecure people trying to show off a new haircut, new shoes, a haircut, some new car, or some "achievement" that doesn't really matter. The soul of a party is essentially a mildly successful corporate person showing up to a highschool reunion excited to finally prove a bunch of losers who made fun of him that he is doing well in life right now. Of course, the fact that the corporate person is wasting time trying to prove people that he's doing well is proof that he is not doing well and is in fact just as pathetic as he was when he was a loser with no status in highschool.

I'm not depressed. I'm not lonely. I don't like talking with strangers who think I owe them something. I don't like "hanging out" with people who go to parties. I don't like parties. Parties are a synthetic version of natural good natured hang out with a few friends. Parties are like hookers compared to a loving wife in that respect. Gone are the natural limitations that are helpful and result in a more wholesome, more productive use of energy and time. Now all that remains is a depressingly stupid affair where everybody involved needs to get a life and go do something else with their time and money as well as cut out the bad habits that led them to being amenable to this sort of arrangement in the first place.

Stoicism

Don't get me wrong, I genuinely enjoy certain stoic writers like Aurelius and stoic adjacent writers like Lucretius and Epictetus as well as Epicurus. Although they all have some pretty stupid ideas or concepts, they communicate a lot of really good ideas and ways to approach life. That said, the problem with stoicism in general is that most people who are vocal enthusiasts of it are losers.

Stoicism is something that I don't practice and I don't claim to practice, because it focuses too much on rationality and was really only applicable in a sort of fisher price toy reality of its time where people who had it good lived in a sort of fantasy land with fantasy rules and manners that are not really applicable to today. It was kind of similar to a bunch of trust-fund kids talking about the theory of how to "live properly" when there is almost never any real risk to them and everybody else is busy slaving away to make their endless talking possible.

A lot of the things stoics and stoic adjacent writers push make surface level sense and can work to a limited degree, but at the end of the day make you a target to anybody who knows how you operate. For example, a big thing pushed by Epictetus was the concept that you should be thankful for everything you have and take good care of it, but once it is taken from you, you shouldn't fight back or try to get any justice on the person or people who took that thing from you. This makes "logical" sense, because revenge or hurting/punishing somebody else isn't really necessary, but in the real world if people find out that they can take stuff from you without suffering consequences, then they'll just keep on taking stuff from you. This is why I have made it clear to a lot of different people that I am a very nice, very level headed person, but if somebody does me wrong on purpose I will ruin their life to a completely disproportionate degree. I don't really care on a personal level, but there needs to be consequences to people interfering with your life if you want to be even mildly successful. Again, this sort of stance wasn't needed by the ungodly spoiled and safe stoics who never really had to struggle for anything so they could have lofty ideals.

Another problem with stoicism is that it attracts people who are only slightly less annoying than the same sorts of people who get an "education" in English or Literature. These are the types of people with a lot of "head knowledge" (really just useless trivia) but with no real life experience. They grew up in a middle to upper middle class family and went to a "good" or at least above average university and then got a good job out of college. As such, they don't really have any experience with actually stressful or dangerous situations and the sort of coddled hyper-rationality of stoicism appeals to them. These types of people are one or two steps above the people who form their opinions by listening to Ben Shapiro, Sam Harris, and Joe Rogan. If they actually followed the tenants of stoicism they wouldn't go out of their way to let people know that they are "stoics". In reality, they are just bored mediocrities with nothing about them to distinguish them from anybody else so they search for some sort of external flair and land on stoicism.

Lastly, stoicism and all other types of philosophy are usually very similar to the self published e-books of today, but because they are aged they have gotten a much more prestigious reputation. The market for literature is kind of perverse, because most people who actually buy and read books are white collar losers with no real life experience and nothing interesting about them searching for some higher purpose in life. Because of that, the literature that tends to be written and gain respect are heavy in empty phrases that sounds smart or wise. An example of this is everything written by Cicero, a loser who was exiled and spoiled his son. Because Cicero failed in life, he had a lot of time to write. His writings appeal to losers just like Cicero who imagine themselves to be noble or honorable when really they are failures with no real life experience who will never do anything worthwhile in life and should be ignored.

I really like a lot of stoic and epicurean writings, but I think they need to be paired with more aggressive right wing and even some leftist writing along with life experience (successes and failures and risks and disasters) which help the reader take what is accurate and apply it to real life while knowing what only applies to coddled people with huge inheritances and no need to actually work for anything in life.

Outside

Sometimes, I go outside. It's one of the most dangerous things for me to do, not because of wild animals or the elements, but rather the fact that it's so nice outside. The fresh air, the chirping of birds, the sense of peace, the grass and the trees; it's all so comfortable to be around. Being outside almost makes me happy. That's a huge problem.

I thrive off the paranoia that can only come from being in a small room all day. The claustrophobic feeling of the walls closing in makes every little detail of life more vivid. When I'm inside I feel like I'm trapped. I feel like there's no escape from the stupidity of humans around me and in my circles of reality.

Outside, everything fades away. I see the sky and this distance between myself and the clouds and how insignificant I really am. I feel the soft dirt pressed under my feet and all my concerns just disappear. I realize that life is strange, that the world is not in that bad a shape, and that I can pretty much do whatever I want for the next fifty years without any problem as long as I am careful to avoid big pitfalls.

There is a lightness of atmosphere when you step out into nature that you can never really replicate when inside. Suddenly, you can breath deep breaths in a calm, relaxed manner that just isn't possible when you're inside. The air brushes against you in a gentle and rhythmic motion.

When you're outside, you don't care about what people are gossiping about. You lose that hyperfocus that is needed to keep up to date with the minutia of acquaintances and strangers. You stop caring about abstract trends that don't really matter in your life. You stop putting effort into thinking about stupidity. You lose a certain edge.

I need to be discontent. I need to be on edge. I need to be delusional in order to be creative. Rationality is boring and lifeless. There needs to be some irrationality in what I do and what I create that keeps people on their toes or else I will become just another boring individual with no unique perspective or value. Then I will be just as unappreciated as everything that is so beautiful about going outside.

I have been brainstorming recently in order to figure out how to best remedy this situation. I simply enjoy going outside too much not to, but I need to find some way to punish or hurt myself while I'm outside so I can become further demented instead of being mellowed out. In this way, I will be able to not only maintain my personality but also increase it, perhaps even becoming so eccentric that many people begin to find me unbearable and even hate me. That would be my optimal situation, because as of late I have found that everybody loves me and that is boring and unpleasant for myself.

Most likely, I will begin wearing warm clothes in the heat of summer. They will all be in black soas to maximize the amount of heat that I absorb. In this way, I will be in great pain and even run the risk of heat stroke or passing out. If I find the heat too hot, then I will strip naked and lay out in the sun to "cool off" but really I will end up getting horrible sunburn that will torture me and hopefully develop into some form of skin cancer to further enhance my personality at a further date.

One thing that is nice about being outside is when I see other people working and I am in the shade sipping on some homemade iced green tea with lemon. I watch them sweat and suffer and it amuses me, because I know a lesser individual would feel some sort of guilt or shame or compulsion to offer them help rather than watch. Not me, I understand that they are the ones making themselves go through that work needlessly. It is not my fault they wish to toil and destroy their body. It is not my fault that they are illogical and do not understand proper morality. No, it would be wrong for me *not* to gaze at them and chuckle to myself, because that would be a waste of a hilarious scenario, and I am not wasteful.

Energy Drinks

I like my sips. I'm a big fan of sips. There's nothing I love more than spending four to eight dollars a day, around four thousand dollars a year, on sips. What are sips, you ask? Simple, sips are the childlike nickname I gave sugary energy drinks I drink every day. They're really good for you. I can tell they're good for you because when I don't have at least two sips a day, I suffer from a massive crash.

I'm not addicted to sips, I just really like them. I got the nickname for them from a viral marketing campaign targeted at people in my age range and because I'm an open minded free thinker, I started drinking them and calling them sips just like my peers. Sips make me feel so wide awake like I used to before I was addicted to coffee. I'm pretty sure sips are making me smarter.

Sips are mostly healthy. You can verify this by looking at the ingredients listed on each can. Almost all the items are some basic vitamin or amino acid that can be bought at one hundredth the price off amazon. Of course, there are some additional flavorings, sweeteners, and food dyes in each drink. This is what makes it taste good. I couldn't just make my own healthy version of an energy drink or else I wouldn't like the taste, and if I don't like the taste of something there is no chance I'm going to eat or drink it. I'm an adult and I'm not going to drink stuff that tastes yucky.

Sips are cool. Sips are fun. I don't think I'll ever be done with drinking sips. How could I give up such a helpful habit. If I'm not fully awake and ready to go for my office job how will I meet productivity requirements. I could quit sips any day and be totally fine, I just don't want to. I'm not addicted to sips, I just need them so I can function on a day to day basis. If I don't have three 64 ounce sips a day I might fall asleep on my commute home from college. Sips are love. Sips are life.

Alex Jones

Oh no, they have censored Alex Jones! This is a bad sign for where our whole country is heading. This means that things are about to get really bad. I had better go buy vitamins and supplements from the Infowars store in order to fund the people fighting for our freedom: Infowars talkshow hosts. Without Alex Jones and all of his employees, the Info War will surely be lost forever.

Once Alex Jones is finally shut down for good, as is happening any day, that's when the FEMA camps and the military industrial complex will come out to play and put freedom loving patriots like you and I in concentration camps. They're coming for guns, for our children, and for our liberty, and Alex Jones is the only thing standing against them.

Alex Jones has long been in the fight for free speech and freedom in general. He has fought the good fight for almost forty years. Look how much better things have gotten since he started his holy mission. This is why they are so desperate to shut hum down and make an example of him. Infowars and Jones are the key players in the fight for liberty. We just need to make one final push and buy vitamins and supplements and t-shirts and hats and donate and we will be able to shut down the deep state for good.

Speaking of the deep state, nobody knows how to fight against the deep state like Alex Jones. What is the deep state? Well, that's complicated but also really simple. In truth, the deep state can't be defined. It's like an amorphous dark cloud that hovers over the whole world and makes bad things happen and stops good things from happening. There is no clear explanation except that with enough podcasts and radio shows and raised awareness, the deep state will lose all its power.

Here is the thing about Alex Jones: He understands that in order to fix problems first you must identify them. If you don't identify a problem then you'll never be able to fix it! Once you have identified a problem, the key is to keep on talking and talking and talking and talking about it for decades until eventually enough people are talking and talking and talking and talking about it that it stops happening. You can see how this strategy paid off by looking at arms dealing and blood diamonds, two roaring industries that were completely stopped and never happen ever since people in the public found out about them and complained.

If you don't actively support Alex Jones' free speech then you are a traitor to this country. If you don't give him your money then you are a coward and actively supporting criminals and murderers. If you don't find his whole business inspiring and praise-worthy then chances are you're working for the ChiComs.

We are winning the Info War, folks, we just need your support. We just need you to dig deep and break your piggie banks and give us your money. We can't possibly run a radio show without taking in millions in profit each year. We want to save this country, but first we need to be financially secure. If we aren't financially secure, then we won't be able to do what we do best, which is talk on the internet every day for decades.

It's time we had a conversation. We need to have a conversation. We need to realize that a conversation is important. If we don't have the right to make money off public conversations then we won't have public conversations. We need to have conversations or else we won't have conversations and if we don't have conversations then there won't be any conversations to be had.

Alex Jones is the greatest patriot this country has ever known. He is a great man looking out for our country. Ignore that time he was looking at transexual porn on his phone. Ignore all the things that might paint Jones in a bad light. Just keep sending him money and going to your soul crushing day job and eventually you will be happy with life and the country will be saved from the deep state.

Dishonesty

I'm in a kind of weird position in life because for as long as I remember I have tried to be honest with myself about who I am and what I am. I'm not particularly intelligent IQ wise and my memory is genuinely very poor outside of general concepts and trends. I'm not a hard worker and I don't deal well with people who are slowing me down on a simple task or distracting me when I'm trying to do anything. I am very emotionally shallow and upfront in whatever I'm doing. Even if what I'm doing is putting on an act or being disingenuous or rude, I do so in a way that people can tell that's what I'm doing.

None of these are good things but they're also not things I'm ashamed of, although I do try to minimize the more negative traits when they're not helpful or needed. The reason I'm writing this now is that this attempt to be objective has left me in a very non-anxious and non-self-confused place. I'm sure there are a lot of things that I think about myself that are inaccurate, but over time and a lot of unpleasant self reflection I've gotten a fairly good picture of who I really am and my natural strengths as well as weaknesses and come to terms with certain aspects to myself that seemed strange or out of the ordinary in the past.

What is very strange is that none of my self-appraisal was all that difficult even though it wasn't all life affirming and positive, and yet when observe people, I very rarely see anybody who seems to have taken similar steps as myself. I see people who are constantly dishonest to themselves and everyone around them. I see people who don't know why they're doing what they're doing or why they like what they like. I try to have conversations with people who are objectively smarter than myself and they seem to have weird mental blocks and inefficient workarounds of circular illogic to explain things that don't make sense.

Ever since I can remember, I've noticed this sort of fundamental difference between most people and myself. There are a few exceptions in my very close friends and for that reason I really value my relationships with them, but for the most part when I interact with people it seems like I'm just accommodating some sort of automaton in its own little world. I'm not being walked over or letting myself be used, but I'm pretty much adjusting my temperament to compliment theirs, asking them questions about themselves in order to get to know them better and let them talk about themselves, and generally just being a good listener. There's no real exchange except for my attention in exchange for them having a good time and knowing they can talk to (not with) me.

It's a weird sort of isolation. I'm not going to point out all the dishonesty and resulting distress and confusion in a person's life unless pointing it out will help in some way, and I can't think of any time when people who are lying to themselves have wanted to be shown the ugly truth. Because of this, I kind of force myself to be around people living in different forms of delusion who are constantly projecting their problems on my behavior. This used to trip me up a lot when I was growing up and was too young to understand much of what was going on, because I would get treated poorly or blatantly lied about and try to respond in an honest way thinking that the people treating me in a negative way were trying to fix a perceived problem rather than just take out some personal failing or frustration on me. I was never bullied, but I often had my words twisted into some weird perversion.

From my experience, most misery and unhappiness in general stems from this sort of dishonesty. People don't want to admit that they're not really good people, that they aren't hard workers or selfless, that they have wasted years of their life, that they have daily habits and lifestyles that are unhealthy. People look for stuff that makes them feel good without judgment or a need for change.

This sort of stubbornness is quite useful at times. I have stopped myself from doing a lot of things that would have most likely benefited me (at least in the short term) because I'm a bit jaded and don't really buy into a lot of the value system that is needed to be traditionally successful in America. This is not an excuse or gripe, I'm content with the choices I've made, but an acknowledgement that you really need to be dishonest to some degree in order to be functional. You need to shut off some sympathy or empathy that might have been objectively "morally good" in order to be productive, or else people will end up wasting your time and your life. The other day, an old acquaintance asked for some money and I said no. I could have given them the money, but this is one of those things I've decided that I am going to be honest to myself about. I don't want people who aren't my future wife or children dependent on me. I am not a good person and I'm not feeding the homeless, so I'm not going to give money to somebody I've known for a while. I'm just being consistent.

It can be kind of saddening watching people be dishonest to themselves. It's depressing when I think about it, so I generally try not to. There is so much wasted time and energy spent chasing after things that nobody who is thinking clearly would really want. Every few days I see people I'm fond of making choices in life that are harmful and I know they think they're doing something good for themselves and nothing I could ever say would change their mind. I'm just a helpless observer watching people cut themselves non-stop. I sometimes close my eyes to everything, but I always end up opening them again. I guess that's my own form of self-harm.

Robins

Imagine being a robin. Imagine you are a bird. Sounds pretty sweet, right? You get to fly around all day. You have no job. You have no commute to a job. You don't have to go to college and you don't waste your time on social media. You just fly around all day and chirp and that's life. Life can't get much better than this, can it?

There's just one problem with being a robin: life sucks. You can fly and you can avoid going to work, but every morning you feed yourself by digging in the dirt to eat worms. Do you think worms taste good? I doubt it. If worms taste like anything I would guess they taste like rotten slimy dirt. Imagine eating worms and bugs every day for your whole life. Doesn't sound like the paradise you were imagining moments ago, does it?

Imagine your mother chewing up your food in her mouth before spitting it in your mouth. Sounds disgusting, doesn't it? It does. That's what baby birds have to go through for weeks, at least. I don't really know how long birds live and I'm not going to look it up so I am speaking in vague generalities.

A bird's life really sucks. They have no hands, just wings. They can't even open doors. They can't drive cars. They don't have money so they can't get other birds to do nice things for them. They can't do anything but fly around and eat worms. Does that sound like a life worth living?

There are no mental health professionals available for birds like Robins. They do not have access to to antidepressants or other psychological drugs. Imagine being a Robin suffering from diabetes or general anxiety and being unable to fix your problem while having your nest right next to a hospital or psychiatrist's office. That would be the height of torture.

Birds don't know how to read. They can't tell if people are libeling them in print, and even if they could they wouldn't be able to sue or right the record. Birds are helpless against the lies of the media. Worse yet, they are not even aware of the attacks at all. They do not see what's really going on in the world. They are simple creatures with no ability for metacognition or self reflection or analysis.

A bird couldn't have written this essay; they just aren't smart enough. A bird doesn't know how to use semi-colons. It's funny when you realize that a barely literate child in elementary school is miles more advanced than the smartest robin. Birds are generally stupid. Crows may be the exception to this but they can't really speak or write that well or even do math that's more advanced than simple arithmetic.

When you're a robin, you have to watch out for predator birds like blue jays. Do you know the last time I've worried about blue jays attacking me or killing my baby bird eggs? Never. I never worry about that stuff because I'm a human and I'm on the top of the food chain. I am an apex predator, unlike robins who are at the mercy of any aggressive or violent bird.

Robins are always sleeping outside. This might sound nice, and it probably is every now and then, but a lot of the time there is horrible weather. When there is rain or snow or a hurricane or tornado or acid rain or a riot going on outside, I can just hang out inside my house in complete safety. This is not the case with birds like robins, who are at the mercy of the natural elements. They have no natural defense against riots or hail or rain or snow. It is just a matter of constant survival. This must take its toll on the fragile bird psyche.

Lastly, flying around seems like fun but I bet it's a huge chore. I don't like flying in airplanes, so it stands to reason that birds don't like flying by themselves. It's so much nicer to just drive a car or be driven in a car or take a bike somewhere rather than all the hassle of flying. Imagine flying around while your stomach is full of worms. Imagine being a robin.

Oil Money
by Paul Town

There is a whole subset of really funny Arab/Middle Eastern people in America who are the children of people who are oil rich. Their parents have a large amount of money from the oil in their home country so they live or vacation very expensively in the United States. The thing that makes this so funny is that because the money was not really earned or hard to get, everybody in that family is generally deluded, spoiled, insecure, and miserable.

There is a sort of depression that comes with undeserved wealth, and you can see it especially well with Arab/Middle Eastern Oil Money kids. They don't understand the value of wealth or the satisfaction that comes from creating something out of nothing, and they have never had to struggle or cut corners or watch what they buy, so they don't really get any satisfaction out of life. After all, what would be the fun in life if you're already given everything you think is possible to get by work?

Another amusing aspect to this group of people is how they idolize the most pathetic elements of black American culture. They don't respect the hard work or aggressiveness or willingness to take risks that is often bragged about by successful blacks in America, but rather the wasteful partying and drug culture that only the most manufactured black entertainment figures push. This is because, once again, they can't relate to hard work or actual aggressiveness or taking actual risks but they can relate to wasting a ton of money in an attempt to show off.

Without this weird subset of spoiled stupid money, the entire of industry of Instagram models (prostitutes) wouldn't exist. Furthermore, most of the Arab/Middle Eastern oil money that flies out early to mid twenties drug addict white women are most likely not even having sex with the women, just doing things with fecal matter and urine. This is due to the fact that, once again, they never earned the money or anything they have, and so they lack any real confidence or sexual initiative. If they were sexually experienced or confident, then they would just have sex with the attractive women all around them and not waste hundreds of thousands of dollars on overpriced consumer goods in order to let other people know that some white prostitute was with them for a whole week.

I genuinely feel bad for these sorts of people, because I doubt things were this bad before the advent of the internet. Now, there is a much bigger competition of people wasting money in order to desperately try to fill the whole in their souls. Now, their insecurity about who they are and the fact that they have nothing interesting about them is able to be broadcast to the whole world and taken advantage of by people who know how to market to what are essentially non-white wiggers with their parents' debit cards.

What will become of Oil Money children? Not much. Most of them will end up with a gold-digger wife and then move back to their home country and raise a new generation of Oil Money children who will perpetuate the same cycle of insecurities and waste. With every generation of an unnatural Darwinian selection, the personality and physical traits that get propagated end up a little worse than they before. This is the fate of any group that relies too heavily on resources that it lucked into rather than talent or physical work.

I like working with people who have had struggles and problems and overcome them. They know their limits and their strengths and they tend to have a quiet confidence that benefits them, myself, and everybody around them. They aren't delusional or insecure in the way that Oil Money is. They aren't dirty and crass like Oil Money is. There's just something about earning what you have that makes you appreciate it, whereas Oil Money destroys all conceptions of good taste, moderation, discipline, genuine confidence, or self control. In a way, Oil Money people are some of the poorest people I know.

Scaling Software

For people who don't work with software or do development, picture Git as a sort of program to backup and manage code for programs. That is essentially what it is, although there are different features and aspects to it that are fairly complicated and beyond the scope of what is needed to understand the following essay, so I will limit my explanation of Git to that. Those of you who know what Git is don't need to have it explained to you so I will not go into details that don't need to gone into.

The problem with how most software is designed nowadays can be most easily explained by using the example of video games. In the past, computers were much more limited in the amount of power they had, which meant that there was a pretty clear upper limit to how complicated a game's graphics could be. This resulted in forcing a more defined and clear design with regard to what games were about and how they worked.

Now, games don't really have all that many limits to how nice they can look. Over time, this has caused the expectations of the consumer to be raised, which in turn has made the amount of time invested into each game to get it to an acceptable level of playability be raised, which has then raised the amount of work needed for each game project. What this means is that there has been a shift from smaller, more limited and focused passion projects to a more largescale, corporate and generic project designed to appeal to a wide user base in order to make the money and time invested more worthwhile.

The bigger a project, especially with games development, the more developers and managers are generally employed. The more employees, the less unique and the more generalized the spirit of a creation generally becomes. Little features and quirks can't be added without big meetings and adjustments that would make a project objectively better don't happen because people don't want to go through the hassle of taking on extra work for something they don't even enjoy making.

As you can see, the more people involved and the more a software project grows, the worse it tends to get. There are always exceptions, but the exceptions (as always) prove the rule. This pattern doesn't just apply to the size of teams but also how software in general is developed and what tools are used. I use the aforementioned Git for my personal projects, but only to a very limited degree. I simply use it to back up what I'm working on more than anything else, because I see the same sort of weird negative effects from over-reliance on doing things the "proper" way with Git that I see with large collaborative projects.

Software should be a small scale, highly personal endeavor. It should be somebody making something that they personally need or want to make and then either selling it to other people with similar interests or giving it away for free. It shouldn't be what it is now, which is a bunch of soulless people making gimmicky bloated over-engineered products that are not used for any real or positive purpose.

When you don't rely on tools like Git or other people, you are more careful how you create things. You are more deliberate and slow-paced, which results in a more heartfelt as well as better designed creation. You don't just do things to do things, you do things because you feel they should be done. There's no specific checklist in a specific order that you're working on, you're just doing what you want to do in a productive manner. This allows you creative freedom to work on more than one aspect of a program at once without having to "switch branches" or constantly keep on sharing your code with a bunch of other people who are working on the same project. Programs should not be huge corporate endeavors. They should be one or only a few people working on something that interests them until it's finished.

Built For It

You aren't built for it. You're just not. You keep on saying you're going to make a change or start work on a bigger project "really soon." You keep on hinting that you have some hidden talent that is going to pay off. You've never made anything of value that wasn't a copy of what somebody else came up with.

You're never going to make it big. You're never going to succeed doing your own thing. You don't have the willpower or drive to push through the months and years of being unrecognized and not paid well for the amount of time you put in. You don't have the stuff that's needed to make it on your own.

It's just a fact that you aren't made for this sort of game. You're not stupid and you're not ugly, you're just not self aware enough or humble enough to do what needs to be done. There is never going to be a day where you wake up and start at the bottom and keep your nose to the grindstone until you see progress then keep on trying after you see that nobody cares about your small amount of progress. You will never be where I am, and the sooner you realize that, the better.

You will never have the respect that I have. You will never have a the audience I have. You will never have the history that I have and you will never take the risks that I have. You will never be me, no matter how much you wish you could be me. You will never know what it's like to put in a ton of time into things just because you want to make something, because you want the wrong things in life.

You want respect. You want money. You want to be lusted after. You want to be famous. You don't realize that all of those things don't really matter and they're not things to work towards. You don't understand that they are all symptoms of something else, not things that are the end goal.

You don't even understand the first thing about what it means to actually make genuine things or be honest to your audience. You don't get why people like me and relate to me because you're too much of a coward to tell people what you actually think. All you do is whine and whine and make excuses about why you aren't successful and all the people you hate are successful, and it's hilarious to watch. Unfortunately, I'm too busy actually doing things to spend time observing you repeatedly fail.

I have done a hundred times more work than you have to get where I am, and I don't even work hard. That's what's so funny, this isn't hard to do and still it's beyond your reach. You're a loser. Just give up and work towards a normal career instead of making an embarrassment of yourself and disappointing your family.

You've been given everything, from a car to a phone to private school to college, and still you're behind me. I'm not even doing that well, but at least I'm moving forward a little bit every day. I've had successes and failures but all you've had is a lazy life with everything given to you, and now that you are in the position where you are starting to be expected to actually work for your life you're falling apart.

You go to a therapist by choice, which is hilarious. Imagine paying some stranger to listen to your problems and insecurities. People pay me to listen to me talk complete nonsense and insult people like you. That's the fundamental difference between me and you: I'm a winner with charisma and you're a loser with your parents' money. With every year, I get a little better off and more confident. With every month, you get more pathetic and anxious. By the time we have both reached the end of our lives, I'll be rich and happy and successful and you'll be poor and miserable and a disgusting mess.

Working

I don't feel like working today, so I'm not going to. I had planned on writing four essays and doing an hour and a half of programming but I just don't feel like it. Instead of doing all that work I'm going to lounge around and drink some green tea and watch John Wick and John Wick 2, pirated by the way, and then I'm going to make a frozen pretzel and read junk on the internet.

I don't have to work when I don't want to work, because I'm the master of my own fate. I can slack off as much as I want, and I do. I relax without any concern for my responsibilities or deadlines, because I have none. A while back I realized that I'll be dead in less than a hundred years so there's really no reason to be a productive member of society or try to take on projects with other people. Other people worry and stress and kill themselves doing stupid things that don't matter so they don't feel guilty about wasting time. I have never felt guilty about anything in my entire life.

If I was anxious or felt the need to prove myself, I would simply stop being anxious or feeling the need to prove myself. I have already done more than most people could do in ten lifetimes and I don't even try. It's important for you to realize that I'm not trying, because only then will you realize how easy life really is.

If you don't feel like going into work, just don't go into work. If you don't feel like helping somebody, don't help them. If you don't feel like doing anything, then don't do anything. Stop living the life of a slave who will never put your food down. Stop caring what slaves and strangers think about you. Just relax and take it easy when you feel like taking it easy.

It's true that I am way more productive than other people, and yet I am always talking about how I am not working hard and other people are always talking about how they're working hard. Somebody is lying, and it's not me. Each essay I write takes maybe twenty to thirty minutes at the most. That's less than two hours of work a day writing and I've already written over 500 pages of original content in under half a year. I look around and I see people who laughably call themselves writers struggling to put out 150 pages of objective trash every three years. The fact of the matter is that people who say they're working hard are probably just stupid, lazy, degenerate liars who waste most of their time reading gossip, using drugs, or looking at porn.

It's also true that every paragraph in this essay starts with the letter I. This is no coincidence, because I work in a very methodical and pattern oriented manner that allows me to iteratively create content at a pace that most people simply can't keep up with. This manner in which I write and do other things is most likely due to the fact that I am on the autism spectrum and am schizotypical and see patterns everywhere. I lied, I am not really on the autism spectrum. It's just funny to me to say I have autism when I'm the most socially agile person I know and everybody around me seems socially disabled in some way or another.

Here's where the tone of the essay shifts again, back into writing about how I'm not doing any work for the day. My sense of humor is on good display here, because I lied yet again. I consider this essay to be part of my work, and even though it isn't hard (I don't do hard work), the fact remains that I am doing work. I don't even not feel like doing work today, I was just slightly at a loss for what to write and this was the first thing that popped into my mind.

When you're creative, you can turn not doing work into its own form of work. You can turn nothing into something and something into nothing. All you need to do is just get in motion and the magic will start to happen. That's the key problem I see with most people my age: they never start anything because they're too concerned about making sure that everything they do is the optimal thing to be doing. Don't worry about doing the optimal thing, just make sure to be doing something that benefits you in any way, which is better than doing nothing which is actually wasting time which is actually you harming yourself by destroying your future prospects through inaction.

Confidence

The key to being successful in life is being confident in your actions. Without confidence, nobody will ever take you seriously or pay attention to what you're doing. It doesn't matter if you're making a product or trying to get hired at a job, you need to command some form of respect from the people you are trying to win over or attract, and confidence is a core element that is needed. Many people struggle with confidence, and this holds them back in life, and causes them to be even more insecure which creates a feedback loop of failure until they either die or kill themselves.

I do not struggle with confidence because I know the secret. I know what is needed in order to project an air of strength and wisdom. I know how to convince anybody of anything at any time. There is no limit to what I can accomplish in life beyond what I desire. My possibilities while I'm alive are endless because my confidence is unlimited.

Do you want to know the secret to confidence? Do you want to know the key to success in life? Do you want to finally understand how to win and keep on winning? Once you fully understand what I'm saying, you will have a period in your life where you simply can't believe that everything was this simple. You will most likely go slightly crazy testing the limits to what you can achieve with this one little trick to confidence. You will be at a loss for words when you realize that I'm not exaggerating in any manner.

The key to confidence is being slightly above average in whatever it is that you're being confident about. You don't want to be too knowledgeable or too skilled or else you become bogged down with the awareness of what you don't know and what you can't do. You can see this sort of delusional confidence with inspirational speakers who are slightly above average in IQ enough that they are able to string together vague words and phrases that impress average people, but the inspirational speakers are not smart enough to understand that they are full of BS and so they actually start to believe that they are geniuses. This makes them extra convincing.

Don't waste time trying to master anything. Once you invest enough time into any subject, you will learn that it's impossible to really be competent in anything beyond the very basics. The more you learn, the more you realize that there are many people who are more talented than you and will always be more talented than you. This knowledge will then forcibly humble you and you will end up underselling (or rather being objectively honest) your place in the world and missing out on opportunities that you would have eagerly jumped at when you were less self aware.

This strategy of being only slightly above average works very well with arguing on the internet. When you are not yet aware that people are idiots and don't learn from being confronted with superior logic and reason, you put in a lot of good-faithed effort into talking with people. This leads to you gaining the respect of other equally unaware but above average individuals as well as many average and even below average individuals who are silent observers. Once you realize that arguing online is a waste of time, you will lose your enthusiasm for it and you will stop gaining an audience and influence from that sort of behavior because you will stop that sort of behavior, but now you will have an audience and reputation that will be useful for more productive, future projects.

Don't get bogged down trying to optimize behavior and be perfectly knowledgeable, that will just lead to a wasted life and in a decade or two you will just be where you started, realizing that you can never really be acting in your objective best interest because you can never keep track of all the variables in the world. Just get good enough to beat down anybody in your way and make people who might otherwise try to take advantage of you, not take advantage of you.

Self Mythologizing

I've discussed an aspect of self mythologizing before with regard to people "being things" such as fathers or mothers or employed rather than being people who are mothers or fathers in one aspect of their life, but I think it is worth looking at what the broader picture of what self mythologizing is. Essentially, self mythologizing (I'll use SM for short) is an over-arching storyline or sort of destiny that somebody sees themselves as or becoming.

Everybody has different aspects of life where SM comes into play. People who see themselves as destined to become important business people will tend to gravitate towards hobbies and activities that fall in line with what they think important business people like and participate in. People who see themselves as a part of some "fan club" or "movement" will spend a disproportionate amount of time or money and tend to dress and behave in a certain way that lines up with what they identify with in whatever they are participating in.

There are different levels of SM and not all SM lasts a person's whole life. For example, somebody who is in college and sees themselves as a cool college kid or partier will generally only see themselves as that when they're in college. Once that phase in their life is over, most will then gradually shift to an adjacent type of SM that is more appropriate for whatever career they're getting established in.

All the different particulars of SM vary depending on what type of person is doing the SM, their age, their surroundings, and a near infinite amount of life variables, but there are general trends that continue through a person's life and don't really seem to change without serious self-reflection or some tragic/exciting event that serves as a sort of shock to a person's core.

There seems to be three generalized forms of SM: the natural winner, the natural loser, and an absence of any SM which is its own form of SM. There are many subsets to each form, such as optimistic, pessimistic, anxious, self conscious, angry, happy, stupid, smart, etc, but they are more optional attributes than defining characteristics. I think there can be a fundamental change to somebody's default SM, but like I said earlier, that most likely needs to come from some sort of life-changing disruption or serious self reflection, neither of which seem all that common.

The first type of SM, the natural winner, is fairly easy to spot. A person may be a good person or a bad person, but they will stand out and be constantly trying to do things. They may be unsuccessful in a large amount of things that they do, but over time they end up making even the failures into some sort of positive. They have a sort of mental quirk that turns negatives into "learning experiences" or just don't notice them which allows them to get back into doing productive or active things without wasting time brooding on failures or mishaps.

The second type of SM, the natural loser, is also fairly easy to spot. This is because they are almost never successful and you can find them constantly talking about and criticizing other natural losers as well as natural winners. They don't really see themselves as being successful, so they seem hyper responsive to negative events that happen to them and those around them. They then use all negative things they know of as excuses as why they shouldn't even try to do anything or take risks, which over time puts them in an even worse spot in life because they miss out on valuable self knowledge as well as potential victories. Over time, they morph into hyper-active critics of people who are similar to them in outward appearance or interests but who are actually trying to do things with their time. This is because to see somebody who is like them but isn't them succeed feels like an indictment against them and makes them feel insecure about their lack of personal success.

The last, and probably most common, type of SM is the seeming absence of any SM. These are what make up the majority of the population. They're not particularly interesting people, but they're also not really bad people. They just go about their day and are happy to have a decent job and maybe a spouse or partner they're dating. They go to the movies on the weekend and they spend money on frivolous items like smart TVs or lame vacations. They don't really have any grand plan for life but not because they are afraid of anything or bitter, just because they never really learned to think for themselves or found out that they could think for themselves. Whatever the reason for this condition is, it doesn't really matter for the scope of this essay. It just is what it is. These people will never do anything of note or interest, good or bad, and will just kind of exist. They won't take risks but they also won't really waste as much time being needlessly critical of others.

The point of this discussion is that life is really what you make it, and unless you trick yourself into thinking you are destined to do well and succeed, then chances are you will never take risks or try things that might end up paying off in a big way eventually. There is always the possibility that you could try hard your whole life and end up broke and destitute with nothing working. There is also the possibility that you might have some disease or medical condition that makes taking risks or being successful impossible. Those unfortunate realities aside, we are all going to be dead in under one hundred years, most of us in under sixty years. There is no good reason not to convince yourself that you will be able to beat the odds if you just work towards a goal and don't give up.

When I die, it won't matter whether I succeeded or failed. Whatever will have happened will have happened. In the mean time, I've found it is much more enjoyable as well as productive to get into the mindset of somebody who genuinely believes they're destined to do well in life. It's much more fun to be daydreaming that this or that project will be the one that kicks my life up to the next level and makes other projects possible and worthwhile rather than trying to be hyper rational and convincing myself that chances are I will never "get back" the effort that I put into some creative project. I can work much longer when I feel like there is something good that is going to come out of it than when I feel like there is no point to what I'm doing and it won't matter. Because of these reasons, I do not see any downside to forcing yourself into the SM where you are a natural winner who is going to do well in life in every aspect as long as you use that SM to push you to do things rather than just fantasize about them.

Tipping Point

I'm entering my mid-twenties, and this seems to really be a make or break point for a lot of people also around my age. The contradictions and successes and failures of each person seems to be adding up to a point that can't be ignored and this is either starting to turn out well for people or result in them slipping into really bad habits that I don't see them ever getting out of.

It's weird being in the group that is actually doing things and working towards bigger goals, doubly so because most of the people in this group seem to be going the traditional route that I couldn't stand. This means that they're spending time doing career related things and going to college as well as working instead of really doing anything else. All they have are their careers and those careers are things that can be taken away at any time if they fail to show up for work or do something that gets people upset at them. I could never do that long term like they plan on doing, but I do appreciate the dedication and amount of hard work that it takes in order to live like that.

The other group is kind of sad to watch, so I've kind of drifted apart from most of them over months and years. They have no drive, no vision, no hope, and a really miserable attitude of entitlement. Most of them come from childhoods where they were given everything or nothing, so they have a chip on their shoulder and see the world through a strange, distorted lens. Talking to them is always a strange experience that's kind of depressing because they're never up to anything and it's always something vague that is most likely made up. You can sense a strange sense of loathing and quiet panic emanating from everything they say and do, even though most of them seem to self medicate with alcohol, weed, and other drugs that just end up wasting their time and destroying their brain and body.

Like I have said in the past, a lot of life seems to be a weird slow motion psychological horror game where you have to either force yourself not to care at the insane amount of waste going on around you at all times or somehow hide how distasteful you find the behavior of people who you genuinely want the best for. I don't really hang out with many people in general because I don't really enjoy frequent socialization or see the point, so I'm much more insulated than most people. This results in me seeing changes in more vivid, less gradual, definition than most people. Without fail, every time I talk with people who have bigger goals and productive habits, they seem more accomplished, and the people who don't have goals and are kind of imploding seem to be in a more desperate, more pathetic and unhappy place in life. It's really quite something to watch.

I don't think there's anything particularly special about this age that makes everything more clear except for the fact that the realities of compound growth from both good and bad decisions really start to stack up and speak louder than the social excuses and knowing and unknowing lies that we are told and tell each other and ourselves. It's a bit like two people, one who is steadily working out and the other who is smoking pot and drinking regularly. The drug user might seem more approachable and be better at talking, but over years the difference in lifestyle will make words not mean all that much and everybody sees which is a better strategy in life.

I do think there is a later stage second edition of this sort of dichotomy that will pop up in my thirties to fifties, where the people who let themselves be worked too hard, whether at a business they work for a business they own, will end up a lot like the people who have imploded around me in my mid twenties. That said, I think a lot of people who seem to be heading for that sort of unhealthy breakdown will wisen up and take things a little slower over time and even end up "ahead" of people like me, who have been trying to find a balance from the start and have generally erred on the side of taking things easy. No matter what the case may be, it will be interesting to see how things progress and who makes drastic positive or negative changes that switch them from more driven to less driven or vice versa. Then again, this sort of naval gazing is only limitedly useful for myself, so I try not to spend too much time on it.

Reformed

I used to be a horrible man. I would lie, cheat, and steal. I would take advantage of everybody around me. I was a no good, low-down, scoundrel. I made my money by selling snake oil e-books to lonely men trying to find out how to trick women into sleeping with them. I would make up lurid stories that bordered on rape in order to attract my target market and make them think they were going to be able to have sex with a ton of women after giving me money.

Of course, everything I told them was fiction. None of the stories were true and all the advice given was pretty much made up and vague. I personally didn't really spend too much time hitting on women or trying to seduce them, I instead used the money people gave me to purchase hookers and do drugs. That was the funniest thing, I would write completely insane strategies that shouldn't work and wouldn't work 99 times out of 100, but the one man who tried them and it lucked into working would think I was a genius and end up giving me even more money and trusting me, even though I gave objectively horrendous advice.

Over time, I grew tired of writing solely pickup artist dating advice and moved into the political sphere. This was a genuine move, not driven by desire for profits, but of course I ended up growing my audience and also the sales of my previously written e-books. It just so happened that I ended up with views that were kind of fringe enough that there were not many competitors but not fringe enough to immediately get me in trouble. Once again, that was just happenstance that worked in my favor. I am a genuine individual with genuine beliefs and genuinely want to help people. I'm not in this for money, but everybody needs to eat.

I did the political thing for a few years, but eventually everybody started to ignore me. It was about this time that I started to re-think what it meant to be a man. I sincerely questioned if the behavior I had been engaging in for the last forty years of my life without remorse was morally wrong. I know it sounds kind of suspicious, but I am a genuine man now. You can trust me now. Anyway, I ended up repenting of my ways and now I am doing my best to lead others to Christ. I am a genuine Christian now, and my books on Christianity will be coming out very soon. I will sell these books and a portion of the sales might even go to some form of charity, but probably not. Of course, every once in a while I slip up and sin. That is just part of the journey. I might still be a degenerate and sell e-books on how to have sex with drunk or high women, but I'm genuine in my faith. If you don't believe me, then please come to the conference I'm setting up with other reformed pickup artists turned Christians. The price is only $100 for a weekend that will genuinely strengthen your faith and refresh your spirit.

Yes, it's true that this sudden pivot away from secular topics like seducement and fringe politics happened immediately following my physical books being banned from Amazon and thus removing the way I was monetizing those topics, but that is just pure happenstance. It may seem unlikely that I would sin for my whole life then pull a 180 degree turn and become more religious than most lifelong religious people. All of this might seem unbelievable and suspicious, but God moves in mysterious ways. Just give me your money and you will see that I am sincere.

Editing

This might come as a shock, but I hardly ever edit what I write. There's just something about reading what I've written that makes me feel uneasy. It's similar to replaying the thoughts in my mind. I don't want to know what I thought in the past. It's too painful to relive all the struggle and psychological horror that makes up the bulk of everything I create. I can listen to recordings of myself talking just fine, but I can't stand going over something I've already written. Because of this, I refuse to do any serious editing of anything I create.

That said, I am in the process of what should be editing of my first book. Each day, I am supposed to go over twenty to sixty pages of the four hundred pages and correct any grammatical errors or reword any awkward writing. This is something I have tasked myself with, but it's not quite going as I had planned.

When I get to editing for the day, I generally start out meticulously and fight through the discomfort of reviewing my work for one to three pages. Then, I give up trying and kind of blur my eyes and let my mind wander as I scroll through the pages assigned to edit rapidly, reading maybe three or four sentences here and there and making one or two changes per two or three pages. This process reminds me of when I watched The Passion of the Christ and would just zone out whenever there was gore or blood because I found it unneeded and kind of sick.

I'm too busy doing nothing to spend time editing what I write. I know it's not perfect, but I'm not perfect and I'm not trying to come off as a perfect individual. My writing's flaws actually make it better than if it was combed through by a professional, because this brings the reader into a more active role and also gives them a more accurate view of my state of mind when I'm writing. This is the authentic writing of myself, not some hollywood production that is drawn up in a board room and ghostwritten by some adderall addict in LA. This is the real deal.

The funniest thing about my lack of editing is that my first draft, what you are seeing now, is miles better than most edited work. There's something quite bizarre that happens when I read anything written by supposed professionals or writers: I notice how much their writing sucks. It's unimaginative, sterile, and over engineered. It doesn't come from the heart and it's usually some Frankenstein's monster-esque group project that barely fills 150 to 200 pages with double spacing. You would think that I wouldn't be able to do a better job than everybody else without even trying, but that does seem to be the case.

There's really nothing hard about writing, as I've stated many times before. I kind of just write whatever pops into my head. I'm not very high IQ so I'm pretty sure that I'm not special. I just think to a less deluded degree than many of my contemporaries so my unedited writing lacks the mental pea soup fog that their edited writing is filled with. It sucks to suck I guess, but I don't really care. My writing works so there's no reason to really waste time editing it.

Telemarketers

I'm really not fond of telemarketers. I find them to be intrusive, obnoxious, and a waste of time. Whenever I get a telemarketer call, I quickly hang up. I don't want to deal with them and I know they will move on to talk with somebody else. There's no good reason to talk with telemarketers. This doesn't seem to be the same logic that goes on in the head of normal people.

Most people talk with telemarketers. There's something weird that goes on in the head of most people. Either they will feel bad and let the telemarketer talk to them for minutes to even hours, or they will be strangely happy that the telemarketer is calling them and then proceed to waste the time of both themselves and the telemarketer.

Most people have no power or control over their life. They get bossed around at a job they hate then get home and get nagged by relatives they can't stand. They never take the initiative and improve their life, so they stagnate and get more frustrated as time goes on. Then, the phone rings and it's a telemarketer. Somewhere in the deranged person's head, a light goes off: they realize that they can verbally abuse or talk down to the telemarketer like they want to talk to their boss or wife, without any consequences.

The poor telemarketer becomes a sort of sacrificial lamb for the mediocre individual to take out all their hate and anger and dreams of sadistic control on. I've watched this situation play out many times in many different households, and every time is more sickening than the last. The person talking to the telemarketer relishes being rude. They don't even realize that they're wasting their own time. They don't care that literally anything else would be a more productive use of time, because they get to have a power trip that carries no risk to them.

People who tip poorly for no good reason are usually nasty people, but people who talk with telemarketers for no reason other than to get their jollies are on an entire different level of insanity. They have no humanity left. Their soul is rotten. They would most likely kill small animals if they knew they would get away with it. They are out of control and they are a ticking time bomb. There is no small hearted cruelty that people who waste time messing with telemarketers are incapable of.

Reading

I'm always reading. I never stop reading. Why? Because I'm smart. That's why I spend all my time reading. There's nothing I love more than reading books. There's just something about buying a ton of books and reading all of them without stopping that is so great. I can feel my IQ rise with every book I read.

Reading books makes me smart. It's impossible to read a lot of books without being smart, and this is how I know I'm smart. If I wasn't smart, I wouldn't be able to read a lot of books. There are so many facts and statements and opinions in books, and they often contradict each other and completely disagree with facts and statements and opinions I've read in other books, but no matter what is said in a book, I am always made smarter and wiser by having read the book.

You can tell I've read a lot of books by talking to me. I'll let you know I've read lots of books by dropping names and quotes to show that I am not some pleb with no taste. I am a man of high culture, which is why I've read so many books. Reading books is hard work. Reading books is admirable. Reading books is for smart people.

By reading books, I've become a genius. I now am the source of all the things I've read. All the philosophy books I've read have made me a philosopher. All the historical books I've read have made me experienced in the world. All the poetry and fiction I've read have made me a good writer. By the process of osmosis, the more I read the more I become whatever I'm reading.

It's important to constantly be reading history books. If you don't constantly read history books, you're not going to know important dates and facts throughout history. If you don't know those important facts and dates, then if there ever comes a situation where somebody wants to know those facts and dates, you won't be able to help them. Nobody has ever asked me for any facts or dates, but someday they will. When that day eventually comes, I will stand ready with knowledge that anybody could google in ten seconds instead of asking me, and I will gain their respect and admiration for my knowledge.

I look down on those who do not spend all their time reading. These individuals are like idiotic beasts who do not understand Hegel or Marx or even Engels. These people do not know what year World War 1 or 2 started or ended. They cannot even list the Axis and Allied countries involved in World War 2. How torturous and empty their lives must be to walk around without such useful pertinent and relevant information.

Reading, like listening to old music and looking at old paintings and sculptures, is a required hobby for anybody who wishes to be cultured. Being cultured is so important. Without being cultured, you will end up being looked down upon by the cultured among us, the professors and college students and other important people who matter in the real world. Without constantly reading, the mind becomes dull and unable to be coherent. Without reading, a human becomes a lowly animal to scorn.

Grammar

There are a lot of grammatical rules to any written or spoken language. The rules vary depending on the context of what is being written or said, but there are rules that exist and so even the forced absence of rules is its own form of rule. Most people are decent at following some of the rules but pretty bad at following the other rules. You can see this by how some people write. I do not really understand many grammatical rules, so I kind of go by the general feel of how a sentence in my head. Because of this, I very rarely use semi-colons or hyphens, and when I do, I am not really sure if I'm using them correctly. I could probably learn how to use them as well as commas properly, and avoid comma splicing by being more deliberate, but I really don't care that much and am able to communicate to a level I deem functional enough that the time required to improve it really isn't warranted.

There is a very specific type of person I've seen online who seems to have a very tight grasp on punctuation as well as obscure words. These people are some of the most frustratingly amusing people to read, not because of what they say (they never say anything of value) but rather how they say it: they are like people talking to themselves in an empty elevator, imagining that they are giving a speech to thousands. What I mean by this is that they go on wordy asides and stilt their speech as much as possible in order to try to conjure up some gravitas. They must not have any influence or control in life so they come into internet communities or forums and try to cope with their lack of stature by assuming this bizarre stance of being an educated and hyper intelligent individual.

The manner in which these strange people behave serves to make them ridiculous, because they are the equivalent of somebody with Down's Syndrome going to McDonald's in a hand me down tuxedo in order to impress strangers getting burgers -- some kids will be impressed by the clothes but anybody with any awareness will know the person they're looking at is just a retard wearing a suit. They will use as many words as possible and try to make those words as obscure as possible, in some weird needy psychological plea to have people pay them respect. These people are over-educated in the sense that they have spent far too much time learning how to impress other idiots like them in college and have spent way too little time doing actual real world things or interacting with real world people who don't have their parents subsidizing some mind numbingly stupid college degree that is not only not useful but actually harmful.

These people remind me of that anime cartoon show I never watched growing up where these people charge energy balls for the whole show while yelling, but instead of an energy ball it's a tangled mess of words and personal qualifiers that just show how everything they're writing is a symptom of their mental derangement. The funniest part about what these people say is how unimportant and worthless it always is. There is never a good or intelligent kernel of truth to their writing. I still can't tell if they know this or not, but I lean towards them being completely unaware. It's hard for me to imagine being at all able to comprehend how moronic the way in which they communicate is and still communicating in that way.

What is to be done with these overwordy, miseducated, obtuse idiots? Not much, besides ignoring them and keeping anybody who you care about away from them. They never do anything but waste time and whine and talk. They love to talk. They love to make huge tweet threads and forum posts and heap on derision and a weird superiority complex that must be serving as an emotional crutch for a lack of any personal achievements besides reading (but not understanding) lots of stupid books and getting good grades from stupid professors (who are essentially slightly more capable than this sort of moron but still the same type of moron and should be avoided at all costs.)

How To Cure Any Mental Illness

There is a dirty little secret that big pharma won't tell you about. The reason that they won't let you know about this dirty little secret is that it would destroy their whole industry. They want to keep you sick, keep you anxious, keep you unable to sleep, unable to wake up, unable to focus, and depressed so you keep on buying their products. They don't want you to get better. You getting better would ruin their whole industry. The secret is that all your mental illness or unhealthy urges stem from tiny bugs inside your stomach.

Why are the little bugs inside your stomach so important? Well, because they are your real mind. Many people think that the brain is where we do our thinking, but that's simply not true. Our real brain is in our tumtum. Our brain is just like a giant calculator that our stummy bugs use to calculate probabilities and do other computer stuff.

Now that you know how your mind and body work, it may still be unclear how this may help your mental state. To further explain, you must understand that what you eat, drink, or take can either make good stummy wummy bugs grow or bad stummy wummy bugs grow. A lot of people worry about drugs passing or not passing the blood-brain barrier, but this is short sighted and only temporary. This is why drugs are not good for you long term. They only mask the problem that is causing you mental agony: the belly buggies.

What does this mean? This means that your mental health might be greatly improved by making your diet more healthy. Once I switched to eating mostly raw eggs (12 of them) a day, my thinking got a lot more clear. This is probably because I stopped eating unhealthy processed foods like Ramen Noodles with Sriracha sauce which most likely was feeding legions of bad bugs in my stomach and hijacking my brain turning me into a schizo freak.

There is a good chance that eating healthy and not eating poorly will solve your mental health problems. This sort of logic applies to drinking alcohol or soda or anything else that is bad for your gut as well. However, what if you make all the right changes and you are still depressed? If you are a trustfund kid who was spoiled, chances are you are just a loser and will be mentally depressed for life. If you're fat, you probably need to lose some weight and exercise before you start to feel genuinely content mentally and in your soul.

What if the problems persist even after all of these things are lined up? Surely, then would be a good time to admit that big pharma is correct and go on a cocktail of drugs that will both shorten your life and turn you into an ugly person inside and out? No, that is not the case. There is still one extremely big move you can make that will most likely cure all of your problems when paired with the above strategies that have not yet seemed to work: move to a foreign country that is freezing cold. You do not need to stay in this foreign country for long, maybe a year or two, but it is important to go to a country that is extremely cold. Why? Chances are that the enemy bugs in your stomach have been allowed to grow and build up a civilization that is now able to fend off the growth of friendly bugs in your stomach to the point where eating healthily won't fix the problem. By moving to a cold climate, your body will be placed in much harsher conditions that will kill off all but the toughest bugs in your stomach, both good and bad. Then, when you have wiped out the mental illness bugs living in your gut, you will be able to move back to a more moderate climate (should you not grow fond of the cold) and eat healthily and exercise in order to create a new colony of good bugs in your stomach.

Don't turn to pharmaceuticals to fix the bad feelings in your brain. Instead, do what is more reasonable and eat raw eggs, exercise, and move to Siberia for a year or two. You will not regret going the natural route, plus you will have cool stories to share with friends and family. Most likely, all the pain and discomfort that results from going about things in this manner will make your life rich and fulfilling and you will praise this essay as saving your life and preventing you from becoming a medicated shell of a human being.

Deformed

The internet has a serious problem. In fact, the internet has several problems, but there is one on my mind: deformed people. I have nothing against deformed people and one of my fingers was broken as a child and healed in a slightly deformed matter so I'm deformed in my own way, so don't think that I hate deformed people or look down on them. I don't care if somebody is deformed on a personal level, but I have had enough of seeing them on the internet.

I don't like looking at ugly things. I don't go out of my way to look at obese people or ugly people or things that I find unpleasant. Thankfully, big companies understand that it isn't profitable to plaster disgusting faces and deformed bodies everywhere, so I don't really see many explicitly disgusting corporate things.

Unfortunately, the internet has given a non-corporate platform to all the weirdos and ghouls in the world. They now haunt my twitter feed and youtube suggestions. I can't go a month without some disturbed deformed person replying to somebody I'm reading on twitter or posting a disgusting video that goes viral because some people seem immune to disgust and don't get that nobody should be encouraging this sort of behavior.

I'm not going to name any of the high profile individuals that do this, but there is now a whole group of physically and mentally deformed people who post gross out videos and have somehow found an illness. I have nothing against these people because of their problems, but I have grown to hate them and wish bad things upon them for trying to push disorder and ugliness into the public sphere.

If you're ugly or deformed, you should not do things that draw attention to that fact. You should not use it as a weird guilt trip. You should do stuff like writing or office work or something out of view of normal people. You should be grateful that you weren't aborted before birth or drowned after birth instead of subjecting everybody to your bad luck. I don't want to see a drooling paraplegic outside of when I see them in real life. I don't want to see drool coming out of somebody's mouth.

There should be some form of rating system that makes posting pictures, videos, and audio illegal for all individuals who do not pass some basic standard of normalcy. Ideally, balding and ugly people would also be punished for posting but I understand that we do not live in an ideal society with any real standards so this is most likely untenable. That said, something has to change on a law based level.

I don't want to have bad feelings towards people born with bad luck. I have relatives who were born disabled and I don't hate them or even dislike them, but if any of them ever tried to start a youtube channel or twitter account centered around them and their disability I would most likely "hack" their channel and delete it or flag all their accounts until they give up and do something else with their time. There are certain things that shouldn't be happening, and deformed people should not be visibly on the internet.

Nootropics

Hello, long time lurker first time poster here. I have been taking nootropics for over the last year and have compiled a large list of noots that have made me more smarter and intelligent and removed the mind fog that I used to have. I will include the list after a short description of what I have and what sources I got it from, as well as nootropics that I have tried and do not recommend because of adverse (negative) experiences.

First of all, it is important that you use proper statistical methods in your analysis of nootropics. While you are unable to do any double blind tests with a legitimate sample size greater than one in a controlled environment with isolated variables or be objective in any manner, true analysis is possible by charting lots of data. I learned how to use graphs and do statistics by browsing Gwern's site. He has so many charts and lines that I trust his methods. He is a true genius who knows what he is doing.

In addition to the regimen of nootropics that I'm going to describe, I've found snorting adderall and taking modafinil every day are both very useful with regards to their nootropic properties. I know people here look down on amphetamines as "unnatural" but I have to say that without them I feel lethargic, dead inside, and unable to focus, and with them I feel normal and even happy sometimes so I definitely consider them a nootropic. Once again, your mileage may vary and all nootropics effect different people in different manners, so you may not feel anything when snorting 30 to 60 milligrams of adderall.

I've spent three hours a day for the past six months on various nootropics and mind vitamin forums and discussion sites, and over time I've noticed that my ability to focus on posts - as well as my reading comprehension - has increased greatly. I used to only read stuff on the internet fifteen to thirty minutes a day, now I will spend five or six hours (at least) a day on the internet. This, to me, is objective proof that nootropics work and I've been getting smarter by taking these nootropics.

Besides the self-evident IQ and cognitive enhancements that nootropics users on this forum have the pleasure to be enjoying, there are also some physical effects to the nootropics I use that are quite noticeable. For example, I am a narcoleptic and usually sleep 12 to 15 hours, but ever since starting my nootropic regimen, I have been able to cut down my sleep to only 11 to 14 hours a day. This alone frees up entire days in a month and makes the months of research completely worth it. I also have felt an increase in sex drive, and while I am not active in the dating world or hookup culture, I have definitely noticed increased stamina when viewing arousing multimedia.

Researching nootropics has taken me down an amazing rabbit trail of health and nutrition. I am now aware that fried foods and staying up late playing video games are unhealthy for you. I have also learned that too much coffee can stress you out. I still have coffee and I still eat fried foods and stay up late playing video games, but I do so to a lesser degree. After all, life needs a little leeway for fun every now and then. The point is that I'm now aware that my actions have consequences and am able to identify some of the negative consequences.

A slight word of warning regarding nootropics: once you take the "red pill" of your mental health, you can never go back. You will constantly be researching this or that. You will spend hundreds of dollars a month on ground up plant and mushroom powder that might not actually do anything or even give you cancer years down the line, in order to maximize your health. You will no longer relate to the ignorant masses who go about their lives doing all the things you do, but without being aware of nootropics and their amazing physical and mental benefits. The normals around you will not be able to understand your passion and you will no longer be able to relate to any of them or want to talk to anybody about anything but supplements and vitamins.

Holidays

I hate all holidays. I really do. I have stopped putting in any effort into holidays. I still show up and am polite, but I'll wear casual clothing and not really try. I have stopped giving gifts and writing cards on holidays like Christmas as well as scheduled occasions like birthdays. Soon I won't even show up to holidays.

Unplanned parties or get-togethers are enjoyable, whether with friends or family. It's nice to hang out and just talk or play a game or go on a drive. It's not fun to have a bunch of people I don't care about tell me about their personal life while they're all dressed up. I don't have interest in people I don't have interest in. There is a reason I don't go on facebook, and it's not because I'm paranoid about data collection. I don't want to waste time hearing about depressing careers or trite personal anecdotes for no reason other than it being some arbitrary date on the calender.

There is also the aspect of food. Almost all holidays have the worst foods. Turkey is gross peasant food. Ham is disgusting unless it's in cold cut form. The only good holiday food is Chinese food that Jews have on Christmas, and I'm not Jewish. Eating raw eggs is more enjoyable than holiday food that some aunt overcooked. I can't believe there are people who willingly eat sweet potatoes mixed with marshmallows and think that it's normal or acceptable. Holiday food should be outlawed.

Another horrible thing about Christmas (as well as birthdays) and other similar holidays is the expectations of gifts. When I give people gifts I do it as a surprise and as an expression of my fondness for them. Planning on getting gifts (or cards for that matter) ruins the whole experience. Even more amusingly, not giving gifts or writing cards is now seen as some sort of slight or insult. I'm not having money troubles and I most likely don't have a problem with you, but I will not be forced into spending time and energy for something I don't really mean, and any Christmas gifts I would get I would most definitely not mean.

There should be the opposite of holidays: suffering and crime days. On these days you would be expected to harm people you care about as well as commit crimes. Crimes would still be illegal, so if you got caught you would get in trouble, but you would still be encouraged to commit them. This would remind everybody that life is a struggle for survival and would also push people towards being more careful in day to day activities, as well as forcing relatives to be more respectful and involved in each others' lives instead of what holidays are which is a weird song and dance where most people seem to be bluffing about their social status and future prospects in a weird attempt to overcompensate for being losers.

Holidays and birthdays should be illegal. It's all so fake. I refuse to buy gifts and write cards and dress up in order to impress a lot of people I don't care about. Most of the people I care about I see and interact with on a day to day or week to week basis, that's why I care about them. I'm not here to waste my time and emotions on people I have no plans on doing something collaborative or fun with, and hanging out dressed up talking about sports is not collaborative or fun, it's just bizarre and unnatural.

How To Write Persuasively

Most do not understand how to write in a persuasive manner.

This inability to communicate properly makes them ineffective in achieving their goals.

In order to reach a large audience, you must write like this.

Without being concise and direct, your readers will be unable to understand you.

This is because your readers are idiots.

Remember that you are writing for idiots because you are smart.

That is why you should write like you are sending telegrams.

Once you have begun to write like this will you gain the respect and attention of morons.

Then you can make money off of the dummies.

Congratulations, you are now a persuasive writer.

Hard Work

There is a funny joke that I've heard where people insist that their success and riches are due to hard work. While there are exceptions, this is almost never really the case. Usually they just found out how to properly scale some service (entertainment and software are two things that scale really well) or take advantage of low wage labor (construction works for this) or get overpaid government contracts through personal connections or flat out bribery.

Now that we have dispelled the myth of hard work, let's dive into something that is very easily exploited: insider trading by any other name. Of course, traditional insider trading is very illegal and so you should avoid doing it. Powerful people are able to get away with it, but you and I are at risk for being caught if we do that sort of thing.

What type of insider trading is legal? Betting. You can bet on pretty much anything nowadays, and with the advent of cryptocurrency and peer to peer odds-making, you don't have to worry about being blackballed by bookies from winning too much. Here's how to make pretty much unlimited money, fast and easy: get a job or make friends with any political figure or sports team. Then, work your way up the ranks or make friends with people up the ranks. Then, ask them to let you know of any sort of breaking news or events like a player getting injured or a certain politician about to be hit by a scandal.

If you know anybody and you are smart about how you proceed in friendships, within a few years you should be able to get contacts in any industry you desire. Once you have this, whenever they leak you information that will effect the odds of some bet in an online gambling market, take out a bet against whatever is the popular side of the bet. Then, once the news comes out and the odds shift in the opposite direction, take out another bet (of equal size) in the opposite direction of whatever you originally bet. You will then be guaranteed to make money no matter which side of the bet wins.

This isn't some hypothetical tip, this is how to pretty much make as much money as you want. Of course, in order to get in this situation you need to make friends with a lot of annoying people. For this reason, I wouldn't go through the hassle in order to make a ton of free money, but I don't really care about money and I know I'm an abnormality so I'm making people aware of this strategy in case they are strapped for cash or already in the position to make money using this strategy.

The main takeaway from this sort of thing is that it's really easy to make money without actually doing any work or being a positive influence on anybody. Don't look up to rich people or people who are "good at finance" or "good at stocks", anybody who is consistently batting well above average in these sorts of things are generally cheating in some sort of way. This isn't to say look down on them, as there's really nothing wrong with taking advantage of flaws in systems, but rather to not really respect them. Money is cheap and it's easy to get once you have the "right" connections.

Hard work for hard work's sake is for suckers. Only do hard work if you find it personally fulfilling. Don't take pride in the fact that your job sucks, your life sucks, and you are miserable. Don't think that there is some honor in suffering (or not suffering), that's a meme by people who are failures as well as people who want to take advantage of you. There is value to making a plan and sticking to it even when it's unpleasant, but that value comes when the plan is something that is worth planning for. Hard work isn't a bad thing, but it should be incidental to what you are working towards. Don't fall for the trap of trying to play by the traditional rules just to play by the traditional rules, the people who play by the traditional rules are uniformly miserable or boring.

Noise

It is impossible to get proper work done in a timely manner when there is a constant conversation and other non-planned, non-predictable noises. Right now, I'm trying to write this essay while being in the same vicinity as multiple chattering females and I feel like I'm going to go crazy. Multiple times every second there are an insane amount of interjections and high pitched shrieks of "joy" going on.

Noise that is predictable, like the hum of a fan or dishwasher or music that I am already familiar with, is not distracting. It is just there. I often put on music that I'm familiar with to drown out the horrible discussions and conversations I have going on around me all the time.

People should just shut up and not talk unless there is something that needs to be said. Instead, they feel the need to fill up every second of silence with some sort of stimulation. They can't stand to be forced to be introspective or contemplate anything and so they are constantly trying to live in a fantasy land amusement park to distract them from their complete lack of direction or purpose.

There should be shock collars for loud people. It wouldn't be that hard to set up, all you would need is a small microphone, an external battery, and a raspberry pi that is constantly monitoring the microphone input for anything over a certain level of loudness. This would not only serve to stop people from being obnoxiously loud, but also stop people from wanting to be around those who are obnoxiously loud, because the shocking setup would not discriminate depending on who made the loud noise, just shock everybody in the vicinity of the loud noise. Over time, the people who are too loud would be shunned and ostracized from friendships as well as businesses and would die off because of that. Eventually we would be left with a paradise of silence or properly quiet surroundings.

A quiet society would be a perfect society. Everybody would move at a comfortable and peaceful pace putting pleasant faces on nonperformatively. There would be no more war. Nobody would hate each other, unlike now where I alone hate so many people around by virtue of them making loud noises. Health would skyrocket as well as literacy, because in silence, everybody would be thinking about what they would be doing and thus not eating unhealthy foods as well as entertaining themselves through more constructive, cerebral outlets. Have you ever tried to read a book in a room full of yapping individuals? It's pretty much impossible. Once you make things quiet, you will see urban youths learning how to read and not sagging their pants while smoking ganja and listening to hip-hop.

Falling Apart

Lately, I've been falling apart. I've been sleeping late, feeling sluggish, and barely getting any work done. I struggle to write three or four essays a day. I'm skipping some exercises and lying to myself that tomorrow will be better. It never is better. I'm on a downward spiral that can only end in disaster or death.

The problem is that I've been getting high on my own supply. I made *2048.paul.town* to get back into programming with Haxe, but now I spend my free time playing it. The problem is that the game is so good that I keep on playing it and getting the emotional reward from being good at it that I am burning out the reward centers in my brain and losing motivation to do productive things.

My brain is different than most people because I have very little ability to moderate anything, so now that I've gotten in the habit of playing *2048.paul.town*, I have been forced to neglect things like taking showers, eating, or anything that I need to do. This is very similar to what happened when I started playing poker online, but it's worse because I am not losing anything as tangible as money so I do not have the necessary negative reinforcement needed to prevent me from playing the whole day.

To be quite honest, *2048.paul.town* might be the most dangerous thing I have ever done. It is so perfect, so amazing, so talented, and so straightforward, that people may start to define me as the creator of it rather than just me being myself. I may be put into a box because of my creation. I may become famous and loved and harassed and stalked for the rest of my life because of what I have made.

There is something about true beauty that really tears you apart. Now I know what Michaelangelo must have felt when he had finished painting the Sistine Chapel. How can I ever make anything more beautiful and perfect than *2048.paul.town*? Is it even possible? I do not know if it is. I do not know whether I have peaked - and what a peak it is - and that is destroying me.

I am the shell of a man after what I have done by creating *2048.paul.town*. With just over 1,000 lines of code, this project is as elegant as it is addictive. It works on both computers as well as mobile devices. I had somebody tell me it runs on their Nintendo DSi. I have gotten compliments on it from every age range, every race, every gender, every income bracket. Truly, I have reached perfection. Now I wander across time, unsure of where to go next.

Now, I am a successful developer as well as a published author. Now, I have done more than most will achieve in their whole life and I am only in my early twenties. What is next? How can I improve? I don't know if it's possible to improve, but I will try. I will remain humble. I will display humility and grace and work hard to improve myself and maybe even work towards improving *2048.paul.town*, even if improvement is not possible.

Until I find another project to create, to mold from the ether of my mind, to bring into the world for those around me to benefit, I will continue to be falling apart. I might even have another *incident*. Still, I will not worry about this. I will not become insecure, because I am the creator of *2048.paul.town* and nobody else is. That alone is more than enough for my life, and anything I do from now on is purely additional, purely charity for humanity.

Gold

I love gold. There is nothing better than gold. In the past, people used gold as money. It was used as money because it was valuable. It cannot be created or destroyed, so that gives it an inherent value. Gold is just great.

Another amazing thing about gold is how it's so shiny. It looks so cool. I love shiny rocks. There's nothing better than shiny rocks. I look at the gold and it's so shiny. This shininess is so good to look at.

Gold is worth a lot of money because it used to be worth a lot of money. When the entire world economy collapses, as it will in a few years (the end of the world is coming), all of the sudden, the shiny rocks will skyrocket in value. I will be the king of my local economy because I have the shiny rocks.

All the kids are wasting time and income with their digital money. Sure, they have gotten thousands of percentage returns on their gambles, but they don't understand how the world works. They are risking all their money on imaginary beanie babies. Meanwhile, I'm working hard at a job for decades and will be in a great position with my collection of shiny rocks when I'm in my sixties.

Having shiny rocks just makes everything better. I look at the shiny rocks and I smile to myself. I am adulting like a boss. I am investing in the shiny rocks. The shiny rocks make me so secure. When I'm in my eighties the shiny rocks will still be shiny.

Shiny shiny shiny shiny shiny shiny glow glow glow gold gold I love shiny rocks gold gold gold gold gold.

Buy gold buy gold shiny shiny shiny shiny shiny shiny shiny shiny shiny shiny shiny.

Frontloaded

People are not aware of this, but everything I put out was created in the summer of 2010. I had been grounded because I had been caught cheating on my math, so I had a ton of free time and nothing to do for a whole year. Of course I kept on cheating at school, and I never really tried to avoid being caught because I never really care about getting caught and find it funny, but I put my time to good use and was extremely productive.

The truth is, I haven't created anything since 2010. I've been completely lazy since then. This essay itself was written in August of 2010 and scheduled to be released in 2019, which is probably around the time you're seeing, give a year or two depending on how hard I want to push my content. For the past decade I've been smoking and drinking and sleeping in, whether while unemployed or employed, it doesn't really matter. I'm not here to do work, I did my work when I was fifteen years old.

The fact that all the things adults enjoy are really the creation of some teenager is extremely humorous to me. These people who like what I did (what I'm doing now in 2010) are wasting their life in college and white or blue collar jobs while I loiter about and do nothing productive. These people are getting wish fulfillment and relating to my underdeveloped mind because I do what they're too afraid of doing.

In the future, I will probably end up doing a lot of stupid things to amuse myself and create a huge elaborate storyline that makes people feel sorry for me. I will then use my charm and wit to make myself rich without ever producing anything of value. It will all be so funny to me and to the wives and girlfriends of people who have real jobs, because I will be having fun with them (they'll pay) while their significant other is earning money at some stupid job.

My life is going to be one big party and I'm going to make everybody else foot the bill. I will be disrespectful, belligerent, and insincere until the day I die. I will flaunt my laziness and turn it into an artform, and all the slaves will wonder what it is that I have that they don't, which is the opposite of the real question they should be asking. What is the real question? What do slaves have that I don't have? The answer is quite simple, external masters.

Who is going to stop me? Nobody, that's who. I'm grounded now (in 2010) but the only lesson I'm learning is that being grounded just means I have more free time to work on personal projects. Punishments aren't real anymore, if they ever were, so there is no real incentive for me to change my ways. I don't want to work in an office for fifty years for the same reason I don't want to work in an office for twenty years: I'm not a moron.

I have a life to live, and I can't do that while being a cog in the machine that is society. Reality is so absurd and it's only 2010, I can't imagine how much more ridiculous everything is going to be in a decade or three. I will be doing whatever I want, whenever I want. It doesn't matter where I am or what I'm doing, people are such mindless, stupid fools that there is always some Good Samaritan who isn't me making sure I'm not dead. As long as I'm not dead: I'm alive. As long as I'm alive: I'm winning. I plan on winning without working for the rest of my life.

Rich Kids

It's so funny seeing rich kids trying to emulate rappers or black mannerisms in general. There's something about it that makes is so amusing when it's not obnoxious. It's a bit like watching some small animal wander around with no real direction, the rich kid simultaneously tries to give off some impression of being street wise by using foul language while also being extremely self conscious about the fact they have lived a very charmed life and would be absolutely nothing without their father's money (that was most likely also inherited instead of earned.)

Invariably, the rich kid will alternate between being insecure and overcompensating for their lack of personal ability or uniqueness and complaining about being depressed and hating life. Because most people who get wealth to any degree are irrational and trade their time, self respect, and soul for riches, they tend to marry poorly as well as creating very miserable children. Then, because they're people who have a nonsensical materialistic worldview, they suck at raising their kids and those kids get given things that make the little joys of doing actual work not enjoyable.

Rich kids get given nice cars and have a standard of living that is unhealthy to establish as the norm. They do not appreciate the true value of money and either are extremely wasteful and degenerate or extremely stingy and grow to worship money. Whenever they feel insecure about some personal shortcomings or physical attributes such as short height, instead of working on that insecurity through self improvement, they distract themselves by leaning into the identity of being a rich kid and usually waste money on some sort of product. This results in the underlying insecurities never being addressed and fixed and just festering.

Over time, rich kids grow more and more deranged. Amusingly, most of them go into miserable corporate fields because they want to live up to their father, who is also miserable in addition to being disgusted by their spoiled child and despairing at a wasted life. They don't need to work, they could live off their inheritance and trust fund. They could just live a healthy and productive life and be happy if they weren't born into cursed family that worships wealth, but they were born into a cursed family and most of them will be cursed until the day they die.

Of course, rich kids aren't really rich. They are more white trash rich or rather a child of middle to upper middle class parents who managed to squirrel away a few hundred thousands of dollars and now live way above their means. The actually rich people know how to make their wealth work for them as well as not to spoil their children soas to make the money last on an intergenerational level. This is another funny aspect to the psyche of a rich kid, the only thing they find security in is not even true.

Money is a nice thing, but only in the hands of people who are not controlled by it. Unfortunately for rich kids, their parents are controlled by their money or else those rich kids would not be rich kids and would just be financially secure kids. Selling overpriced junk to rich kids is one of the most lucrative markets out there. You can see this process take place with companies like Apple as well as most fashion brands; they target the insecure and foolish who don't know the value of money. This is the reason why wealth doesn't usually last more than two or three generations: rich kids are insecure marks.

Stuttered Growth

There is an understandable stigma that comes from running behind the normal course of life that people your age are on. For example, people who are held back in high school are looked down upon and made fun of. It makes sense that they would be seen as lesser and thus less valuable than most people, because for most cases they probably are simply dumber than the people around them and that is why they are being held back in class.

What doesn't seem to be addressed or considered is that there are a decent amount of people who get held back or seem to have a delayed development in life (childhood, college, young adulthood) not because of a deficiency in intelligence or ability, but rather an over-abundance of some energetic or outgoing trait that is negative in high concentration. To use the previous example of children in high school being held back a grade, this sort of child wouldn't be the person who was too dumb to understand the material, but rather somebody who was too rambunctious or unruly to do their homework or cooperate with the teachers/school staff.

Another example of this sort of person would be myself, in that I am highly capable of doing what people my age have decided to do for careers, but I have an overabundance of energy and curiosity that makes me a very poor employee for repetitive tasks in a specific role. What this has resulted in is me having a much wider range of life experience than most of the people my age, but also being in a more generalized, beginner's level of recognition and career visibility in the activities I pursue.

This sort of "holding back" has allowed me, and I imagine most people similar to me, to have a bit of stuttered growth in that I have been able to watch people my age make important life decisions and risks/lack of risks and seen the outcomes both positive and negative, and now even though I'm slightly less traditionally advanced (in the sense of career) as most people my age with my capabilities, I am able to avoid common mistakes and have a better perspective in how I go forward in life.

If I had to guess, this sort of delay in life functions in the same way that having a proper mentor would function for somebody without any delays in life. That said, I don't really see many holistic mentors anywhere so I'm starting to think they are myths and that this slight delay in life is the best situation to be in for a young adult male.

Because of the way my life has went, with many twists and turns and detours, I have very little momentum in one direction or another. This allows me a lot of freedom that my friends who played by the rules and didn't get into trouble don't have, which is counter-intuitive and genuinely doesn't seem too fair for them. Also, I have a lot more perspective when starting projects that allows me to avoid anxiety and worries that I see plague people working on similar projects. This might be more due to my slightly more advanced age than them, but I suspect my current lifestyle of a clean diet and steady exercise routine combined with very extreme life situations have played a large role in benefiting me as well.

As with any opinion on psychology or lifestyle, it's very hard to say anything for certain and it's impossible to isolate variables to a reliable degree, but this general observation falls in line well with my working theory that you should place yourself in life situations where you don't have to work hard to do well and you should not allow yourself to be rushed (within reason) in life. I definitely have a certain advantage that didn't used to exist for me when I was seen as just the same as everybody else, where

I have lowered expectations and disappointed people around me so many times that I am left alone and free to my own devices for the most part. Of course, this sort of autonomy can be disastrous if misused, but luckily I have been able to create a fairly decent structure around my day to day life that this freedom has benefited me in ways I cannot easily explain. To sum up this whole essay, it's better to purposely "fall behind" a bit in the first twenty-ish years of your life and observe what helps or hurts the people around you who insist on pushing themselves to their limits. Let other people be the guinea pigs and then just pick and choose the attributes that you see lead to a positive outcome and apply them to yourself.

An Automated Life
Everything I do at this point is at least partially automated. Sure, there are things like writing and programming that are done "by hand" and with my attention, but even those things are within the context of automation. If I'm doing something, it's usually because something I made automatically told me that it was proper to do it.

I have created a script in python called *NEET Mode*. NEET stands for "Not in Education, Employment, or Training", and this script is essentially a command line program that helps people stay motivated and structured by using little psychological tricks like progress bars and EXP points to better quantify getting tasks done. The main gist of the program is that it semi randomly generates a list of activities to do daily, and the amount of the activities to do (for example pages read or minutes spent outside) are also semi-random. I say semi-random because the user inputs the potential tasks and then their average rate of being picked for daily activities as well as the min and max range of activities.

This script has been extremely beneficial to me because it fulfills my pathological need for uncertainty and variety in what I do on a day to day basis while still getting what I need to get done on a large time scale. I now do exercise, writing, reading, programming, and many other things on a semi-random daily basis. There is no set daily schedule, just a range of possibilities that all add up over time, spread out over time. For my next programming project I will be rewriting this python script in haxe and compiling it into a static webpage for anybody to use for free. Of course, the fact that *NEET Mode* helps and individual remain productive makes the name kind of inaccurate, but it is more of an amusing joke to me than anything else, since even when I have been unemployed and wasting my time I have been more productive than most people with "serious careers" who "work hard."

I have also set up a few python scripts to create command line programs to take notes, track tasks to do and tasks done, as well as pre-write and post pre-written posts or images on a scheduled basis. This has allowed me to run various social media accounts while I'm busy in real life doing reading or simply relaxing outside. In the near future I will also create python scripts to semi-regularly scrape popular meme subreddits for images and store those images to post on social media on a semi-random basis. This sort of behavior is not for the pathological goal that most on social media have which is to get many followers/ subscribers in order to cope with some insecurity, but rather to build up an audience that will eventually be introduced to things I have personally created and of which some percentage will support with their time and energy as well as finances. All of this is being done with minimal work on my part, because I have automated all the "work" which is simply choosing what is popular now to share with people in a week or two after it has already been shared with what is essentially my focus group.

There is a lot of talk about outsourcing, which is pretty much what employees of any company are. There is also a lot of talk about automating jobs. There is not much talk about automating your personal life on a highly individualized level. You can pay for things like evernote or other "productivity" or "note taking" software as well as various other tools for personal day to day activities. You can hire a secretary to handle your emails and schedule meetings. You can do all of those things, or you can just start from the ground up and only do things that you don't need to pay other people for and you don't need to have employees for. I barely use sites that I'm constantly active on, because those sites are designed to suck up your time and energy and lock you in to their way of doing things. Instead, I've built interfaces around both social media platforms as well as real life day to day activities that help me remain productive and free up a ton of my time. That's how I get so much more done than most people: I refuse to do as much work as most people.

Gavin

Editor's Note: this is a completely fictitious character description. Any resemblance to real life individuals is completely coincidental.

He has a really cool mustache and beard that hide his complete lack of chin. He wears dapper clothes like a total sir. He is not your family friendly conservative, he says the f word and other really nasty words. He like to complain about political correctness and says kind of edgy things sometimes. He is Gavin.

The best part about Gavin is that he says the same five things over and over. This way, when people who don't know who he is hear him, they don't know that he lacks any original ideas and apparently hasn't done anything worth mentioning in the past three decades. He is doing something with his time, but it isn't coming up with anything new or creating anything of worth.

Gavin didn't used to be a conservative. Gavin used to smoke pot and use coke and adderall and do degenerate things like tug on his genitalia for photoshoots by sleazy photographers who uses his influence to coerce women who want to get famous through his connections. He still does those things now that he's a conservative, but he used to do them when he wasn't a conservative too. Gavin is a really cool guy when he's not shoving butt plugs up his rear end on camera or drinking and driving with a kid in his car, so we give him a pass for his little indiscretions.

Nothing has changed in the world since Gavin became a conservative except for things getting worse and him working with equally morally dubious individuals such as those who extort people legally as well as those who in a prior life did mortgage fraud in Britain and after getting caught decided to take up politics, but at least Gavin is making money. Gavin is a great guy, he's just flawed like you and I are flawed and his consistent flaws shouldn't be held against him because sometimes he says vaguely racist things that we like.

With people like Gavin and Tucker, we have some real winners. We have entertainers who have made millions saying things people want to hear, and nothing else. They know and work with a ton of nasty people without ever doing anything or taking actual risks, but they sometimes say things we like to hear so they're good people. They're genuinely good people. They're real men. Gavin is my idol and I respect him and you should to. The fate of the western civilization hangs in the balance and his podcasts are what will determine our future.

Cracked Tooth

About a little less than a decade ago, one of my right molars cracked after I chomped down on something hard that wasn't supposed to be in the food I was eating. This was fairly painful, and I had to wait a couple of days to get it reattached. Nevertheless, I persisted and survived until the time came when I was able to have my tooth fixed.

Today, I was eating a bagel and all of the sudden half of my cracked tooth came out of my mouth. It was not painful this time, because that part of my tooth is already dead. I felt absolutely no physical pain, but the emotional trauma I am going through right now is almost unbearable. Words may not be able to express what is going through my head and heart at this very moment, but I will try my best.

I have gotten two cavities in my entire life. I eat sweet food very rarely. The rest of my teeth are in good physical shape, structure wise. The people who reattached my tooth have betrayed my trust. They told me that this tooth was as good as new: they lied. Now I am going to have to decide whether I want to get my tooth reattached or deal with this molar problem myself.

Things like this is why I have serious trust issues. When I make something or do something, I am hyper clear to the people involved what I will be doing and what I won't be doing. I do not tell nice little lies to make them feel better about themselves. I do not promise things that are not possible.

I do what I do and I don't say I'm going to do what I can't do. This is not the case with normal people I rely on. I can't trust people in any industry unless they know who I am and I know their home address. People are unreliable and bad at their job. They don't know what they're doing and I cannot rely on any of them.

Now I will be walking around with an imperfect mouth. Now I will thinking about whether this means I will get some form of infection in my tooth and need a root canal. Now, all the things that wouldn't even cross my mind if people just did their job will be at the forefront of my thoughts.

There are no words to describe the feeling I have for the sorts of people who waste my time and abuse my trust. I cannot fully explain the rage and hatred I feel due to the fact that pretty much everything I do with other people has to be through some weird sort of extortion or highly monitored situation.

Are there no standards anymore or have things always been this bad? If people can't get a simple tooth filling correct then I don't even want to imagine how they must be bungling procedures that might be slightly complicated. There needs to be some form of change in the way our society is going before everything collapses completely.

I'm thinking of suing the dentist that did my filling. This sort of behavior in unacceptable and they have caused me hundreds of thousands of dollars of emotional trauma already with this stunt. Why can't people just do their job without utterly failing at it? It's not that hard to replace a tooth, you just stick the glue in between the broken parts and let it dry.

This all happened on a Friday, which could have been disastrous if I was currently socially active. If I wasn't such a hard worker with his nose to the grindstone also not legally allowed out past 8PM, right now I would probably be a few beers deep and not even notice that part of my tooth fell out. Then, I would have to pay even more for the morons at the dentist office to make a new tooth for myself. Instead, I was lucky enough to notice this problem straight away thanks to my enforced sobriety and monk-like existence.

There needs to be lawsuits against people who don't do their job well. There needs to be legal action and possibly even prison time. I'm not saying that a dentist's job is some walk in the park, it's really not, but it is the job they chose. I should not be penalized for somebody else's poor career choices. There should be standards and expectations with deadly consequences for dentists who don't meet my expectations. Somebody needs to pay.

Gaming

I used to play a fair bit of video games. I would play semi-tactical first person shooters like Tom Clancy's Ghost Recon Advanced Warfighter. These sorts of games were not flashy. They had their gameplay and some minimal story, but the didn't have some exp meter or unlockable gun skins or costumes. These were games most likely targeted at slightly antisocial mid teenager to early twenties males.

Now, things are different. Gone are the days of a solid gaming experience for people in that age range. All there are now are huge studios pumping out iterative and highly polished skinner boxes that take tricks from scratch off lottery tickets and slot machines in casinos. Now, there is no real game for the intellectual who just wants a mental challenge. It's all flashy gimmicks designed to extract constant revenue from people.

Gaming used to be about skill. It used to be about heart. It used to be about challenge and overcoming adversity. Now, gaming is about making money. It's about tricking younger and younger kids into playing dumber and dumber games and getting them to purchase cosmetic items in games that don't even matter.

I'm too old to play many video games at this point, and I don't even have a computer capable of any modern game. I don't regret the time I spent playing video games as a child because I was highly productive outside of video gaming, but I am disgusted at what people are playing now. I see no redeemable value to the games that are coming out.

The only exception to this might be the Grand Theft Auto series, because they are committed to pumping out filth and profits seem to come second to them. When I play GTA5, I love to run around with a glass bottle or knife and stab random people on the side of the street then do my best to escape the police. Having had some real life experience with the police, I can say that the GTA experience is probably the best simulator of what antisocial destruction for the sake of destruction feels like.

Finding Your Voice

Just keep writing and working on your creative projects until you *find your voice.* Don't get discouraged that nobody has liked anything you have done in the last five years. Don't worry that you just aren't good at what you're trying to do, keep at the grindstone at least half heartedly and never give up and get a real job.

Telling people that they need to *find their voice* is a serious cop-out. People who are good at creative things are fundamentally good at what they're doing very close to the beginning, and they are the minority that succeed. If you write and everybody thinks your writing sucks and you continue to write for a few years and everybody still thinks your writing sucks, chances are your writing sucks and will always suck.

I've never seen anybody get fundamentally more or less unique and special in what they create over time. Sure, people will get more refined in what they're creating, but the soul of what they're creating seems to always be a reflection of who they are as people, and most people suck. Either you have it or you don't. Either you are good at creating or you're not.

When people talk about *finding their voice* they're misguided at best, but usually lying to somebody. It's so much easier to lie and tell somebody that they're just as good as you at something than to tell them the honest truth which is that they don't have what it takes to make it in some creative field. It's also more profitable to convince people that all they're missing is some magic switch to flip and then they will become successful and create things of worth, because then you can sell them hogwash guides and make money off of their delusions.

If you're reading this and you think you need to find your voice, stop whatever it is that you're doing and go get a real job. For people who are naturally talented and don't wander about trying to *find themselves*, doing creative work is still a slog that many people won't succeed in. You're not talented, you're never going to be talented, and you lack the fundamental spark inside your soul that each creative person feels with them from their birth. The best you will ever be is a mimic of some actually creative individual that you want to be like, so unless you want to struggle for years and most likely never succeed, just go do something else with your time.

I hate seeing the types of people who make money off of *dreamers* who think they're going to take their art to the next level by taking a course at a college or a seminar or reading a book. That's not how actually creative people work. Stop letting people lie to you and suck up the fact you're not a creative person and you will never be a creative person and that's OK. There's nothing wrong with not being creative, but it is quite simply sad to see somebody without talent laboring under the delusion that some talent will spring out of wasted years. Even worse are the people around them who enable them and pay them false compliments and waste everybody's time and energy on literal garbage.

You will never find your voice if you don't already have it. Who you are is who you are even if you don't know who you are and never figure out who you are, you will always remain who you are. You are not a struggling artist, you are in your mid twenties and you have created things that nobody wants to waste time with. You are not a creative, you had other failures and other non creative people lie to you as well as predatory people telling you that you had potential so you would give them money. Stop trying to find your voice and realize that your voice is your voice is your voice. Stop deluding yourself.

Three Dollars

There is no better feeling than saving money. That is why I spend five hours a week finding coupons for various grocery items. This enables me to buy things like frozen foods and other slightly unhealthy foods at a 10%

off discount, which is well worth the time spent looking through hundreds of coupons.

With coupons, you keep on winning. All you have to do is spend your time looking through advertisement after advertisement until you find something that piques your interest. Sometimes, you spend a lot of time looking through coupons and find nothing that is worth using. That's OK though, because the uncertainty makes the experience entertaining.

My free time is worth approximately $3 per four hours, because that is how much I end up saving on average for every four hours I spend looking through coupons. That is how much I value what I do when I'm not working. Three dollars. Three-fourths of a dollar per hour.

Looking Smart

An important thing in life is to gain the respect of your peers. Without the respect of your peers, you will not have the respect of your peers. That alone should be enough to motivate you into finding out how to gain the respect of your peers. There are a lot of aspect to gaining the respect of your peers, but today I will address a specific element to looking smart which is needed in order to gain the respect of your peers.

The first aspect to looking smart is what you wear. You want to always wear button down shirts whenever possible. You need to wear non-jean pants along with a belt. This belt needs to be a designer belt or else everybody will think you're poor, and only stupid people are poor. How you dress is extremely important and you should spend lots of money to ensure you have a quality and varied wardrobe for any occasion.

Another thing that is important to looking smart is your body language. This is one of the biggest factors that people unconsciously notice when deciding whether or not somebody is smart. When you walk, make you include a little swagger. Swing your arms enthusiastically and look upwards. Always have a confident but slight smirk on your face when walking. This show of bravado and ease will infer competence and achievement to observers, even if those two things are completely untrue.

Make sure you have a good watch on your wrist at all times. The watch should be worth at least three thousand dollars, anything less and it is just embarrassing. Go for a submariner watch that has a manual timer on its face, this will show that you're adventurous and slightly sporty. Having an expensive watch is an investment that will routinely pay dividends. Now, when you walk into a room, you will notice who has nice watches and they will notice you; whatever that means.

Verbal communication is very important to conveying intelligence. Without the ability to pull of small talk and discuss lofty ideas like whatever cable news is talking about in the last 24 hours, you will fall flat on your face and be revealed as an ignoramus. As such, it is important to keep up to date with news and entertainment. Watch popular shows and movies. Listen to the same music people around you listen to, then research trivia about band members and artists. A good thing to do is to spend time on internet forums or communities like reddit to observe what is popular and hip. That way, you will always be ahead of the curve and cool, and thus seen as a smart person.

Lastly, how you show you are thinking is crucial. This goes back to body language, but is hyper specific enough that it deserves its own paragraph. When in a conversation that involves contemplation, take your dominant hand and place it on your chin. There are various ways to do this, find the way that works best with your hand and chin shape. This is a power stance, practice it in the mirror. You can also audibly say "hmmmm" as you do the power stance for hyper-thinking occasions. Many famous people like Steve Jobs have mastered this power stance and used it to great effect. Intelligent people always put their hands on their chin to show intellect and genius.

Now that you know how to look smart, the world has become your oyster and you will be able to screw it at will. Now, you will be seen as the thinker of the group. Women will begin to throw themselves at you, sexually. You will be promoted at work. You will be cool. Life will just keep getting better and better. People won't make fun of you or look down on you anymore. You won't be insecure anymore. You will get everything in life that you want, that you deserve, because you know how to present yourself properly.

Life Isn't Fair

Life isn't fair. I have done more work than anybody I know. I am smarter than most people I know. I have better intentions than everybody I know. I have gone out of my way not to take advantage of good people. Somehow, I'm way behind people I know are behaving in the opposite way. Somehow, bad people have nicer things than me.

It's almost like reality constantly rewards the absolute worst people. Movies and books tell us that the good guy wins and that being a good person is rewarded, but in my personal life and all around me I see good people punished by bad people who never end up punished. It's kind of a sick joke in a way, almost like the people telling people to be good and follow rules are just saying that so there is less competition.

Usually I feel OK with all of this, because I'm always staying busy and working on projects, but sometime the absurdity of the situation hits me and I can't help but get a little disgusted with everything and want to freak out. Still, I remain calm, cool, and collected, because I am a saint. Life is just a funny little game.

I want to just smash stuff and scream at people around me in times like these, where I see the most boring, most slavish, most amoral (at best) people rewarded while the humble hard working geniuses such as myself go unnoticed and unrewarded for our virtue. Then again, virtue is its own reward, but a lost of the times it doesn't feel like that great of a reward at all.

I would like to have a nice car, nice computer, ability to eat good food and purchase supplements without doing something immoral, but it doesn't really seem possible. Eventually I'm going to snap and just start doing horrible things to get ahead, if reality doesn't change soon. I'm not even a good person, I just have some semblance of a code of ethics that I try to follow, which makes me a better person than 99% of the people I know.

What do I deserve? Nothing. What do the people who are doing well deserve? To have everything taken away from them, for starters. They are lazy, stupid, dumb, evil, and they should be publicly flogged and made to do forced labor for all the good people they take advantage of. I'm sick of seeing wasteful idiots blow money they didn't earn on stuff that nobody needs without any appreciation for the sheer idiocy of their actions. I'm sick of seeing people I despise thinking they're like me just because I am a strong personality. I am not like these people and I don't ever want to be like these people.

The truth of that matter is that what I want doesn't matter. Reality isn't going to change any time soon, except for the fact that I will most likely be doing very well financially in the near future, not because of any inheritance or trust-fund (like most well off people), but because of my own actions. I've made more money already than most people will make in a lifetime then thrown it away because I didn't care about it and even despised it. In hindsight, I wish I had kept most of it but it's probably for the best that I am where I am at now, because now I know the value of money: to be able to not interact with people I dislike, especially the delusional morons who are rich. Rich idiots will always be rich idiots, but the sooner I can completely isolate myself from them and their idiocy, the better.

Losers

Most people my age are losers. I'm not referring to their jobs and careers - although most of those things are in sorry states for people my age - but rather their entire outlook. Especially the men around me. I see them constantly inserting perverted jokes and inappropriate references that are disgusting and can only come from somebody who routinely views hardcore pornography. Most are abusing some drug, whether it be alcohol, speed, coke, or weed. They have no willpower and most of them talk like women who get emotionally tossed about by idiotic things non-stop.

Why are most of the people my age constantly talking about being lonely or depressed without changing anything. They take some perverse pleasure in being dysfunctional and underachieving. Some have even started playing video games meant for children on a regular basis. These people should be starting businesses or pursuing dreams or doing anything but what they're doing, which is slowly wasting and harshing my mellow.

What's even worse is how these people try to drag anyone doing anything positive down. This sort of crab in a bucket mentality has flared up multiple times when I have upset one of these sorts of people, where they make some sort of snide remark about my aspirations as well as try to insult me by bringing up my struggles I've gone through in the past. This sort of thing doesn't really effect me because I'm fairly good at not taking things personally, but I hate when it happens because it's so pathetic and depressing on their part. Instead of doing anything positive with their life, they just want to make people around them equally miserable and mediocre in order to feel good about their personal shortcomings.

It's so weird being one of the few people who is actually doing things on a regular basis. All around me I see people constantly talking about doing things without ever really doing them. I see people who have nothing done of worth who just yap yap yap over and over and over then make excuses and do nothing past the very initial steps of some huge project. These people are in their mid twenties and they have absolutely nothing to show for it. When I talk to people like me who have actually done stuff, it is like a breath of fresh air. These people have problems and flaws (as do I) but at a fundamental level they're trying to do well. They're striving for things. When I am working on something they are encouraging and enthusiastic. They actually want to see me succeed, especially if they have succeeded at things.

I guess it's just the nature of reality that most people are going to be losers. Without losers there would be no functioning society because nobody would end up doing jobs that are frustrating or demeaning, and society has many frustrating and demeaning jobs. For me, it's hard to deal with this aspect of reality because I see all the wasted potential and intelligence being twisted and bent towards unhealthy or inwardly/outwardly destructive ends.

What is the solution to this? There is none. The world just keeps on turning and reality is the way it is because that is how reality works. Every day I have to interact with these sorts of people and I don't see that changing. Maybe as I get older, everybody will sort themselves into groups of appropriate drive and I will be able to not see the losers. In the meantime, I have to pretend that I don't hate watching people abuse porn and entertainment and physical drugs, because trying to stop these people from ruining their own lives has been a completely futile effort for me so far.

Comedians

The press gets a lot of justified hate and scorn, but they are nothing compared to the trash that are comedians. Comedians are people without any sort of redemptive quality. They are not smart, hard working, or productive in any manner. They help nobody and waste time. They are lazy and they refuse to do real work or do anything that takes any skill. Most of them are not original and most of the few that are original are not funny.

Making people laugh is one of the easiest things in the world to do. I'm funnier than all comedians dead or living, and I don't even try. The thing is that I have talents and a desire to do more than bang drunk chicks at comedy clubs and waste my life talking to other comedians on podcasts and radio shows all trying to scam normal people out of money. I want to do things with normal people who aren't the retarded morons eg comedians.

The current level of what is considered comedy is so bad that it makes my head hurt. Essentially, you have people who are clones of Sam Hyde and all the creative stuff he did with MDE, and that's it. They all have some little twist, but all of them are pretty much just stealing material and mannerisms from Hyde. Sam Hyde is genuinely funny and creative, and the other people involved in MDE can be funny as well, but the rest of these people are absolute trash. They think making funny faces stealing the visual style of MDE makes them comedians. It doesn't, it just makes them stupid idiots.

There needs to be some sort of purge that makes it legal to kill comedians. This wouldn't be a one night affair, this would be a year round open season until all comedians are dead. Because people who do comedy are generally overweight drug addicts who sleep in and don't know how to defend themselves or do anything physically demanding, it shouldn't be much more than one or two weeks until 99% of all comedians are dead. This would then lead to a sort of renaissance. No more would there be podcasts coming from NYC and California. No more would there be stupid comedy clubs and improv theaters (yes, improv comedy is on the same level as non-improv comedy because both are absolute garbage) littering the landscape. There would be an era of prosperity that would be global.

Stand up comedy is so bad that it isn't even funny. It's just complete garbage and has always been complete garbage. Even the people who try to make fun of stand up while doing stand up are bad. There's a whole genre of people who try to talk in a monotone deadpan voice and deliver all their lines in a poor manner. This might be funny if they had any range or actual talent, but the truth is that that is the only way they can deliver their lines at all. Stand up comedians are subhuman trash and they need to be lined up and executed and their bodies placed in a pile and then burned live on broadcast television. We could do this at a big football game halftime show in order to get the message across to any would be stand up comedians that being a stand up comedian should not be tolerated.

If my child tried to purse being a comedian, I would do things that I can't describe in this essay because I don't want to get in trouble. That child would end up not being my child anymore. I would never talk to them. I would request that they change their last name to not besmirch my legacy, and if they refused then I would change my own last name to distance myself from them. I would most likely end up in prison from what I would do if my child tried to become a comedian, but that's not saying much because there are about fifty fifty odds that I'll end up in prison no matter what happens in my life.

Don't be a comedian. Look at comedians, they are scum. They are miserable lowlifes without all the cool stories and perspectives that lowlifes have. They are junkies who have found a way to monetize their stupidity and enable their degenerate maladaptive depressing lifestyle. They should be put down, not emulated or encouraged.

Sunlight

AAAAAAAAA it burns my eyeeees. Ow ow ow ow I hate the sunlight. Bright lights are horrible aaaaaaaaaaaaaaaaa I hate the sun. Ow ow ow ow ow ow ow

ow ow ow ow ow ow ow ow ow ow ow ow ow ow ow ow
ow ow ow ow ow ow ow ow ow ow ow ow ow ow ow ow
ow ow ow ow ow ow ow ow ow ow ow ow ow ow ow ow
ow ow ow ow ow ow ow ow ow ow ow ow ow ow ow ow
ow ow.

I want to live where it is always dark out. That would be ideal. When it's dark and when all the normal people are asleep is when the world really comes to life. I love night drives on mostly empty roads, windows down (it doesn't matter if it's cold or hot), and blasting obnoxious music as the wind rips through my hair and I drive at an unsafe speed disturbing neighborhoods.

The sunlight is evil. It is so bright and you can see everybody around you. Everybody is a moron and they are annoying with their empty meaningless talk. I wish everybody but myself was dead so I could walk around outside without seeing other people who just make me angry inside.

The dark of night is when I free my mind. I am not a stoner or lonely, but I love to think when everything is pitch black and there are no visual distractions. At night, I can be myself away from prying eyes of mundane mediocrities. At night, I can relax and unwind from a hard day of being around people who keep on harshing my mellow.

I love when it's dark out, I hate when there is sunlight. When there is warmth in the air and all the prey roam around unaware of their surroundings. Whenever I see people sunbathing, I feel disgust and rage. They are wasting so much time, being lazy, ruining their skin, and indulging in things they should not indulge in. People should always be cold and freezing and walking around in the dark, aware of their surroundings and constantly on guard. Anything else is pure delusion and makes me sick to my stomach.

Wagies

Wagies hate me. Why? Because I'm everything they're not. I love watching the wagies rage and seethe non-stop when they are not at work, because they are always complaining about work when they're not at work. If I was a wagie, I would quit my job instead of whining, but wagies are not the brightest individuals, or else they wouldn't be wagies.

It's hilarious observing how the wagie's mind is slowly destroyed by their career. What happens is that they invent some strange superiority complex against people who refuse to participate in a rigged game (employment) in order to cope with the fact that they hate their life and the "lazy" people who refuse to work seem to be enjoying life. Over time, they start to despair of their life choices, and continue to cope harder against the people who are still enjoying life instead of working at a stupid job for stupid people. The uncomfortable feeling that us lazy people might be right about everything continues to grow and grow and it drives them insane.

Wagies do not really understand that the "working years" are the best years of their life. If they realized that they're essentially participating in a system that will abuse them until they're in their sixties and their whole life has passed them by, they would not be working and would instead commit crimes or figure out some other way to make money without giving away their entire life.

I am glad I am not a wagie. I'm glad I'm not working in an office. I'm glad I'm not digging ditches or breaking my back. I'm glad I get to relax all day and do nothing. I enjoy every day to its full extent. I have so much free time every day that I don't know what to do with it, so I end up writing, reading, programming, exercising, or just plain relaxing.

Friday nights and Sunday nights are the most enjoyable times to observe the sad sad lives of wagies. These times are when their weekly bipolar phases set in: first euphoric and delusional as they look forward to 48 hours of not being a slave, then the ending of their temporary freedom and the return to their sick twisted reality. Every Sunday night I can sense the mood in the air get comically dark. I love this time, because for me every day is the weekend. I love Sunday nights even more than any other night because I get to see all the wagies in mental anguish.

Monday morning is another fun time to watch wagies, because they have to go into work and start another five days of hell. The best part about all of this is that it's completely voluntary, and yet they make fun of black people for refusing to allow themselves to be abused and exploited. This weird mental illogic is a common theme in the wagie's worldview. They do not realize that in order to succeed in life you need to refuse to work for other people and make other people work for you.

Overall, wagies remind me of indentured servants. I don't really understand them or why they put up with such a ridiculous system, but they do. If I was in their shoes I'd go on disability or do something that would make it so I get free money or other people take care of me. Life is too short to waste decades doing hard work.

I would like to take this portion of the essay to thank wagies. Thank you, wagies, for paying taxes to support systems that everybody including me and other non-wagies benefit from. Thank you wagies, for making me food when I want it and keeping the roads paved. Thank you, wagies, for having hot girlfriends that I have sex with while you're at work. Thank you, wagies, for being OK with being slaves. Thank you, wagies, for making me laugh almost every single day.

Workflow

A lot of people wonder how I am able to write so much original and varied material on a regular basis, and I always just kind of deflect and don't answer when they ask me about this, but for this essay I will reveal the core of my secret for the dedicated readers. This will be my good deed for the decade; hopefully it will inspire many people to follow in my footsteps and become humble legends as well.

The truth is, most people are extremely flawed in how they process things. There seems to be multiple flawed logic circuits in how people sort information and make decisions, and so they often act in ways and issue statements that when examined become quite insane. Because of this, whenever I hang out with any group of people, I will almost always be able to pick up on some insecurity or irrationality and then extrapolate off of it whenever I get back to creating something.

That said, I don't really hang out with other people in real life all that often. I'm antisocial by nature because I like to do things at my own pace, so I'm usually alone. That's where twitter comes in. I see dumber and dumber tweets every single day I'm on twitter. People allow their neurotic thoughts and negative behaviors to shine on twitter, so I will always have at least one or two topics to base something on after ten or fifteen minutes of browsing twitter. It's really that simple.

Another benefit to this way of coming up with characters and ideas is that I avoid wasting a lot of negative energy engaging with the irrationality I see in real life and online. As a result, I end up being on good terms with people who I might have otherwise joked around or poked fun at, and am able to fully highlight the quirks to what they said or did without facing any real negative consequences, because I'm not talking about them or to them.

This method ties into a general philosophy of turning negative things into positive things. Without doing what I'm doing, the bad stuff I expose myself to frequently would just be bad stuff, but now it is fuel that not only entertains and engages me, but makes me money and helps me become a better writer as well as a more clear thinker and communicator. I highly recommend turning everything into a game and not really engaging with people on a real level, but rather using them as a resource to enrich yourself.

Frozen Pizza

I like to eat healthy (nothing but raw eggs and garlic) but sometimes my daily task organizer (NEET Mode) calls for me to eat something unhealthy, and so I eat something unhealthy. Yesterday was one of those days. For something unhealthy, I chose a frozen spicy chicken supreme pizza. I ate the entire thing, even the crusts. Usually I'll not eat the crusts to frozen pizza because it's so blatantly unhealthy and doesn't even taste good, but yesterday I was feeling sick in the head. I was really nasty yesterday, nasty enough to eat the crusts to the frozen pizza, and so I did eat the crusts to the frozen pizza.

What occurred after I ate the frozen pizza was no shock to me. I immediately felt myself fall into a stupor, most like because of the neurotoxic carbohydrates and sugars present in the dough. I could feel myself getting dumber by the second. My IQ was rapidly dropping, and continued to drop for hours after I had eaten that frozen pizza. Trying to form any coherent thoughts was out of the question, so I quickly gave up on trying to write anything, since my writing has a reputation for being coherent and clear headed in nature.

The effects of the frozen pizza did not stop there. No, it got much worse. First came the unhealthy food high where I entered a state of positive delirium and felt irrational emotions like happiness and joy. This state of being is unbearable and I do not understand how anybody can seek it out. Happiness and joy are just the opposite side of the coin which has misery and abject horror on it. I want nothing to do with that coin, so this experience was particularly upsetting.

After the euphoria wore off, I entered a dark mental place. This place I cannot even describe to the reader, although everything I write is fiction and cannot get me in legal trouble because a character and maybe even ghost writer is writing it. That said, this place is where I dream of doing horrible things to bad people and watching with glee as they suffer their misfortune poorly. This state lasted for hours.

To make matters work, after eating this frozen pizza around 3PM, I got absolutely no work done for the day. This might not sound bad until I make it clear that I usually start my work for the day at around 4PM and finish up around 11PM, so a whole day of productivity and creation was obliterated with the consumption of this frozen pizza. All my motivation had been destroyed and I felt like a lazy moron. This is how I imagine people addicted to downers must feel all day every day, which explains why they end up begging for money on the side of the road in order to feed their habit.

All I did after eating this frozen pizza was cope with my emotions going out of whack, watch youtube videos, and play *2048.paul.town*. I was like a helpless little child or an average person my age, completely wasting away without doing anything redeemable. From this experience, I have gained the understanding of why people become depressed. If I did this sort of behavior on a regular basis, I would most likely grow to hate myself and my despair at my meaningless existence would manifest in a depression of sorts, I suppose.

Food as well as supplements are the fuel that drives both the body and mind. This is why it is so vital that we make all food but raw eggs and garlic illegal. With items like fast food and frozen pizza easily available, it is no surprise that mental problems and obesity are on the rise. If we do not outright band these items, we should make them illegal under the age of eighteen, while making alcohol and cigarettes/cigars/tobacco completely legal to everybody at every age, since those things can be nootropics and stimulate mental and physical activity.

I rate the frozen pizza ten out of ten for showing me what hell is like. Now I have gotten a glimpse behind the veil of substance abuse and poor lifestyle choices, so my next book will completely from that point of view in an authoritative book and I will most likely solve a lot of serious problems that are plaguing this great nation. Now I understand what it means to be out of my mind. Now I understand why drug addicts are so unproductive and lazy. This frozen pizza was a bit of a *momento mori* for me. Now I return to the land of the living - population: me - and get back to my under-appreciated work of fearless truth telling.

Rebellion

I have positioned myself in such a way where character flaws are almost perks and even seen as lovable by those observing me. I've used and abused drugs? I'm a free spirit. I've broken the law? I'm a free spirit. I've refused to work hard at a job for a career and have shown a poor work ethic repeatedly? I'm a free spirit.

The actual secret is that I'm fine not being a free spirit, because when there are actual stakes on the line - like seven to ten years in prison if I violate probation - I am completely fine living a straightedge, disciplined and productive life, impressing those around me and the people who are paying attention to me for legal matter. Being a "productive member of society" and following all the rules is so easy for me that I could do it in my sleep.

That said, I am a free spirit by choice, and the reason for this follows as such: being attractive to irrationally optimistic and undisciplined people has the most upside. When you're around a bunch of gamblers playing some betting game, there is no genuinely friendly atmosphere; everybody is trying to take advantage of each other. This is because everybody involved knows what's going on: the rules and the goals are clear. This is not the case in the day to day of life, where the goals and rules are obfuscated and unclear. Still, there are people who have kind of figured out the first, most basic rules of life: make money and raise a family. These are the people who act like gamblers in a betting game.

There are also a lot of people who go through life with no regard for any rules or goals. They drift around, aren't particularly ambitious or successful, but they seem fairly happy in their youth. This is because they are not forward thinking enough like the first group to realize that you should be saving for the future and building up your resources in one way or another. That said, these younger underachievers are a lot more enjoyable to hang around, because the rule oriented people generally have no sense of the meta-game of life, and so are miserable or miserly and don't know how to enjoy themselves.

Most people want to be around people they relate to, so the first group of rule oriented people sticks with other rule oriented people, and the lost dreamers in the second group stick to the lost dreamers in the second group. This results in people in the first group constantly pecking at each other trying to get ahead by beating each other at hyper rational behaviors and the second group kind of limping along haphazardly. If the rational people were able to think on a more abstract level, they would quickly realize that it pays much better to be hyper-rational in the second group where there is no competition and nobody really gets what's going on than to be fighting over scraps with people who know the value of resources in a near-perfectly economical system.

By being purposely irresponsible and open minded and willing to do a lot of things that are objectively stupid, I now can relate to people who do these things without thinking. Now, I have an appeal to people who (very justifiably) don't want to sit in an office for forty years putting money into a 401k. The dirty little secret is that most people who don't want to be average don't want to be average for the wrong reasons and as a result will just be failures, but that's not my problem. I appeal to the people who are natural winners as well as people who are natural losers, and I will benefit from both of those types of people because those types of people are willing to take risks and aren't miserly grinches like the people who sit in offices all day every day watching their whole life pass by.

I'm a free spirit, I'm going to get rich doing things you shouldn't do, and I'm never going to be a productive hard working member of society, because I don't need to. People who don't like it don't matter, because they have a reputation to manage and a career to work for so they can't waste their time ruining what I'm doing. I'm going to have fun and be more successful than all the people who play by the rules, nobody is ever going to stop me, and that's just the reality of the situation. Want to come along?

Unintelligible

There is a very specific type of person that buys a lot of books. They are not all that accomplished and they don't really have anything that makes them special, and they are not that charismatic or social because nobody really likes them, so they buy a lot of books. They believe - incorrectly - that reading a lot of literature will make them intelligent and thus valuable and important people. There are a lot of people who do not fit this description who buy books, but most of the people who buy lots of books fit this description.

I write for people who do not fit that description, but at the same time I do want to take the money from the delusional and pathetic person that I have described. I can spend their money much better than they can, so I have devised a strategy in order to rob these weird people and enrich myself while not sacrificing the integrity and value of my writing for normal people who I actually like. This strategy is as follows: every so often I write something that is practically incoherent and purposely obtuse and stilted in its writing soas to trick the delusional losers into thinking that my writing is intended for self important dunces such as themselves.

I know a lot of big and old words. This is not because I'm intelligent, but rather because I like to read old books every now and then, and it is very easy to learn big and old words with a very tiny bit of effort. Of course, big and old words are not very useful for generalized communication, which public writing should be. Trying to hide your point behind a ton of obscure words that the majority of your contemporary audience is unfamiliar with is stupid. If I'm writing something that I want people to understand, I write it in a way that people will be able to understand. This is something that these strange people have an inverted understanding of, thinking that talking like somebody from centuries prior is a mark of intelligence rather than a mark of autism, so whenever I wish to trick these people, I always use big and old words.

Another little mannerism I utilize when fleecing the idiots is to speak in the manner write, which is a strange imitation of what they imagine an eloquent dictator would speak like in front of a large crowd. I draw out my sentences and use a ton of strange grammatical flourishes that are uneconomical and pretentious, and in this way they feel like they are being represented. These people are not very bright, but see themselves as under-appreciated geniuses, so it is not hard to imitate them to their delight. They lack the ability to tell when I am mocking them, so I never need to worry about laying my act on too thick.

These sorts of people like vaguely unintelligible writing because their thought process is so fragmented and genuinely schizophrenic that they do not think anything is actually connected; so they look for surface level signs of intelligence. There never needs to be any common thread or uniting theme behind ideas I present to them, because they are incapable of anything but surface level mimicry. They do not understand how anything beyond very basic rules work. This is why they value strange things like big words and outdated phrases.

Is there a point to this essay? Yes, I'm sure there is, but I really don't know what it could be. I'm not really planning what I'm saying, just going off the top of my head and hoping what I'm saying makes sense. Of course, what I'm saying is accurate or else I wouldn't be saying it in this manner, and because of my deliberate honesty everything I write has an unplanned coherence, but there isn't some specific point to this specific essay. If anything, I would say that it's good to include a wide variety to what you create in order to cast a wide net, because some of the weirdos who enjoy my purposely poorly written and vague writing will recommend my writings as a whole to actually intelligent and normal people who will then enjoy my actually quality writing that doesn't appeal to the pretentious losers who buy lots of books.

Reading

I don't read. Reading is for people who want to be controlled. If I could, I would forget what words meant. When you know what words mean, people can control you with spells eg sentences. When I am around non-English, non-French, non-Spanish, non-Russian speakers (I can speak and read those four languages fluently) I am uncontrollable and oblivious to what people are saying to and about me, and this makes me very powerful.

By not reading, I am able to avoid talking with people who read. This saves me a lot of wasted time, because talking to people who know how to read is a good way to hear stupid opinions and incorrect ideas regurgitated in a secondhand manner. I don't have anything in common with people who read, and I would like to keep it that way.

I don't even read the stuff I write. I tried editing stuff for the purposes of quality control, but I quickly gave up. I realized that having grammatical and spelling errors only enhances the impact that my writing has on the reader, since they have to be active in how they process the information that I am presenting, rather than the mindless behavior of people who read well edited writing.

I don't read. That's just the truth. Yes, I have read all of Plato and most of Aristotle, as well as Aurelius and Cicero, Sartre and Camus, etc, but that is all in the past. Now, I do my best not to remember anything they have written. This also works towards my benefit, because I'm sure that a lot of what I'm writing is unconsciously plagiarized from people like Plato and Aristotle. How else could somebody of my youth write such eloquent timeless wisdom? The reality of the situation is that either I am the modern reincarnation of a world class philosopher or some miracle.

I look at people who know how to read and I see weaklings. I see prey who think they are predators. I observe toothless herbivores under the delusion that they are carnivores. I do not want to be a walking statistic like readers are. I want to be genuinely deadly, not delusively gaudy. When you have power and wealth you don't need to know how to read. Floyd Mayweather doesn't know how to read. I want to be like Floyd Mayweather.

Watching Debates

Why do people watch political debates? To stay informed? This is a weird sort of illogic that does not make any sense. Whenever the debate is over, if the debate has important parts, those parts will be uploaded in a compilation on youtube and other video websites. It makes no sense to waste time watching political debates live.

This sort of reasoning can be applied to any sort of event like a sports game or really any competition or "event" with uncertainty. Quit wasting time watching it as it happens and do something productive, then when the occasion is completed go look up the result if it really matters. Observing things as they happen will not change their outcome, so it is degenerate and extravagant to do so.

Stop doing things for no good reason just because you enjoy them. Life isn't meant to be enjoyed. You aren't here just to be stupid and sit looking at the TV or whatever. Stop going to family reunions. Stop going out to eat. Start living with purpose. Only do things that have a positive return on investment, of which watching debates most definitely does not have.

Oh, does baby want to hear the politician on TV pander to them? Does it make baby feel good to hear words that are nice? Grow up. Stop thinking that politicians are going to solve your problems. If they were ever going to fix anything, they wouldn't be allowed on the debate stage at all. Be a realist, like me. Don't have any external hopes or dreams. Start looking down on people. Disdain people who want to take up your time with no clear benefit to you.

I'm so sick politics. All it is is a bunch of foolish people who couldn't cut it in any business or productive environment and are too stupid to realize that public fame is not something to be sought out or desired. All these people do is talk talk talk talk yap yap yap yap and then whenever they get any influence they never follow through on their promises. They never have and never will be a positive influence on anything, so you should stop wasting your time on them unless you're somehow benefiting from wasting time on them.

If it was up to me, we could have death pits instead of debates. Picture Joe Biden with a shotgun hunting down some other degenerate politician in order to get the democratic nomination for president. Last person alive wins. That way, politicians might actually have values since they would be risking their life for power instead of just doing unmentionable sexual acts for people higher up in the political pyramid scheme.

Political debates are a joke. They aren't even entertaining. They are for the emotionally weak. The next time I watch a political debate will be in order to make money. I will probably join some stream that's covering the debates, then spend the whole time shilling my book obnoxiously. I'm not a libertarian, because I don't believe in freedom and I don't think most people should be allowed to do what they want to do, but I don't think politicians debating is the answer. There needs to be some cataclysmic event that kills 99% of the humans alive. Then, and only then, can we really fix this broken political system.

Book Writing

The rumor is that my best-selling hit book, *It Is The Secret* (book.paul.town), has made other authors absolutely fuming. This is no surprise to me, since I make what they do look so shoddy in comparison to my work. Worst of all, I don't even try. These people put all their effort into writing and I just come onto the scene with 400+ pages of pure poetry and curbstomp their literary careers to dust. Oh well, I can't help that I am just better at everything than everybody else.

The thing about book writing is that it is essentially what homeless schizophrenics do at bus-stops, but monetized, so I have a home-field advantage compared to most writers eg loser neurotypicals. I don't plan what I'm going to write, ever, and this enables me to keep everything I create fresh and surprising. Often times it feels like I'm tapping into some ethereal force that is laying down pure truth and knowledge on the reader.

I don't know why people buy books, but they do. I will be releasing a few dozen books over the next 48 months and then will never work a real job. This will establish enough passive income to do what I have always dreamed of: hard drugs non-stop. People buy any old trash, so once I have established a reputation as a classic writer (some would argue I already have but I am much harder on myself than most people) I will just put out complete trash. I'm working on a markov chain generator that will be able to create 500 page manuscripts in seconds. Soon, nothing I write will have to make sense, so I'm will be making sense for much longer.

An Introduction To Trading

The numbers are going up, the numbers are going down, the numbers are hovering around a certain average number. That is what is happening all day every day with trading. You want to buy the number before it goes up and sell the number before it goes down. Every time you do this, you make your money number go up.

If you mess up and sell after the number goes down, your money number will go down. This is really bad and makes all the decisions you make following that less advantageous as your money number is lessened and thus the magnitude of the effect of numbers going up and down are dampened.

There is a way to make all the numbers you're trading be magnified. This makes good trades even gooder, but bad trades even badder. Yep, higher stakes on the upside generally means higher stakes on the downside. Life usually works that way, it would seem.

Another important thing to trading is that you play the part of a trader. It's true that everything I just described pretty much sums up the fundamentals of all trading, but that is not very interesting and is even kind of stupid sounding. After all, no value is created and nothing beneficial is done. It is a zero sum game, so if you're getting rich you're taking money from somebody else who is hoping to take more money from somebody else other than them.

You should learn how to use MSPaint if you want to be a good trader. This will help you draw lines and triangles on charts. These lines and triangles are completely useless the majority of the time, but they give you confidence and trick you into thinking you're not gambling, so you feel good about spending all your time gambling.

Make sure to purchase multiple monitors so you can look at multiple graphs at the same time. This will help you make important decisions and show your IQ, because all good quality trading is done by humans looking at charts rather than insider information and algorithms. When people see that you have multiple monitors with charts and lines on them, they know you're the real deal.

Last but not least, set up a twitter account and tweet about everything you're doing. That's what professionals do. Encourage strangers to take out loans and risk their money on pure speculation. Use lots of mumbo jumbo terminology like fundamentals and fomo to show that you have done your research. Tell your friends and family about what you're doing with your finances non-stop.

With this primer, you have been introduced into the world of trading. This is not gambling. This is serious, logical, rational, and respectable. This is something that anybody can make money with easily, if they make all the right decisions repeatedly and don't get emotionally invested in their trades. This is something that you should spend lots of time thinking about and learning. You will be the next Wolf of Wall Street if you play your cards right, so go for it!

To get access to premium shapes to draw on screenshots and terms to drop into dinner conversation with other elite traders, sign up for my course for only $9.99 a month. You might be wondering why I am selling tricks and secrets rather than using them myself, but you really shouldn't worry about that. Don't think too hard about any of this, and just give me your money if you want to get rich. I want you to get rich, but you have to give me your money first.

White Nationalists
White nationalists online are essentially what they claim jews are in the real world. This is not an insult to either jews or white nationalists, since I am apolitical and

don't see race, skin color, gender, sex, height, weight, or any nuance in anything, so please do not get upset at me if you are a white nationalist, a jew, or both.

White nationalists get kicked out of every internet community they join, because they do not play well with others or look out for anybody but themselves. They come onto a social media platform and immediately make everything about what they like and dislike, and because digital evolutionary selection pressures, white nationalists generally have a much higher verbal IQ than everybody around them and take over any online community they are allowed to grow in.

White nationalists say jews are greedy and good with money and run the banks and media, but white nationalists make up most of the users of bitcoin and over 95% of youtube commentary channels. Once again, this seems to be due to the fact that they have been forced out other activities or simply don't want to do anything much besides talk and make money without doing physical work.

White nationalists are the minority on most internet platforms, but end up influencing the majority of online laws or moderation policy. Because of how they behave, certain things are allowed and disallowed that would never be brought up or considered otherwise. White nationalists and jews both have a lot in common in this respect, both punching well above their respective weights in the effect on both the online and the offline world. Once again, this analysis is not political or edgy in any manner and is not advocating or condemning anything or anybody, but rather giving a scientific and objective bird's eye philosopher's view of reality.

Mosquito Bites
I wish that it was possible to just cut open my wrist or leg when I'm outside on a summer night and let mosquitoes drink my blood. This isn't because I'm some weirdo sicko freak, but rather that I hate the itchy feeling

that comes from getting mosquito bites. I have absolutely no self control so whenever I get a mosquito bite I repeatedly scratch it it until it goes away.

Feeling itchy might be one of the worst things in the world. Having relatives die is less annoying/upsetting than the constant physical urge to scratch that comes from mosquito bites. I refuse to use bug spray because of the chemicals in it (plus I'm lazy) and I love to stargaze, so in the summer my only options are to overheat from wearing clothes that covers most of my skin but still leaves my face and hands exposed, or to let mosquitoes feast on my flesh.

Mosquitoes are such weird bugs. They're ugly. They're not fast. They're not strong. They aren't cool. They're just weirdos. They remind me a lot of a certain type of hyper critical underperforming bitter person I see in my day to day life. My haters remind me a lot of mosquitoes, to be quite honest. They are bloodsucking parasite bugs who I wish were dead but refuse to do anything to stop because I'm lazy.

Productivity

Lately, I have not been getting much done. I keep on having things to do but not finishing a satisfactory amount of them per day. Of course, I'm still getting much more done than most people (most people get practically nothing done ever) but I'm not operating at a level that is appropriate for what I desire of myself.

I was doing really well when I was working on getting my first book written, but now that the book has been published, I am completely off my groove. Watching people continue to pay money for something that I have already put work into is very surreal feeling, since I get satisfaction from seeing people consistently consuming it (and giving me money in the process) without me doing anything new to earn that satisfaction. It's a bit like watching porn or doing drugs where you are getting something for nothing, which of course means that you are giving something that you just don't realize. In this case, it is a lot of my motivation and drive and as a result my focus.

Another thing that is impeding me is cryptocurrency. I'm not somebody who cares about money on a fundamentally emotional level, but I do find patterns and sequences really mesmerizing, so during bull runs where certain cryptocurrencies are consistently going up, it's really easy for me to spend hours watching how they retrace their movements and trying to guess what is about to go up or down due to patterns/momentum I see repeating. Also, I am a big fan of watching people be unhappy, so I get pulled into reading social media sites and chans where I can enjoy people who made stupid trades get really upset or talk about how they want to kill themselves because they are now broke. Part of my enjoyment is the knowledge that I handle financial fluctuations much better than these people and that in their situations I wouldn't even care and that they are essentially helpless emotional retards.

Lastly, I recently got some organic cocao powder that I'm pretty sure is destroying my brain. It's just too good and mildly stimulating that I feel myself slipping down a dark path of addiction. It won't be long until I'm under a bridge offering to do unmentionable things for raw organic cocao powder that I can mix into cold water. My sleep schedule has been seriously disrupted by this cocao powder. Worst of all, I bought 2lbs of this stuff and can only reasonably go through two or three teaspoons of it a day so I'm going to be going through it for quite some time.

Still, I am not depressed. I do not despair. This dark time in my life will pass. I will emerge from this cloud of confusion with a new purpose. All it will take is time. Eventually, my book will stop selling or I will get bored of checking how many more it has sold each day. The cryptocurrency market will crash in a year or two, like it always does. I will run out of cocao powder or my brain will stop responding to it until I reach a baseline of a functional addict. Then, I will return to my former glory of full productivity. At least I'm not like the wage slaves I see all around me, they will never even reach the levels of productivity that I maintain when I am unproductive. I spit on the wage slaves. They are scum. They are subhuman.

In The Zone
So much of life comes down to not ignoring small impulses and then turning those small impulses into a small bit of forward momentum then turning that small bit of forward momentum into something a little bigger and a little bigger until you have something that is amazingly substantial. Everything little adds up to something big, not the other way around. For whatever reason, most people seem unable to grasp this, and so they never try to create anything because they are too demotivated by the scale of what they're attempting.

Everything that I've ever done has always started as something very small that I then combined with other small things. This applies to both good and bad things, of course, which is why it is so important to be specific in what you're paying attention to and ignoring on a day to day, hour to hour, minute to minute basis. This is a bit of a chore in the beginning, as you're essentially constantly tweaking things against your current natural habits (if something that you're already involved/not involved in is proper you won't tweak it so you won't notice it), but eventually you end up where you only need to make periodic tweaks and everything is generally in flowing a positive direction.

The biggest thing to realize is that, while there are authorities and experts in whatever it is you're trying to accomplish, those experts and authorities generally aren't the ones who are trying to teach people or spending their time selling guides. They're busy actually doing what it is that you're trying to do, and that's what makes them authorities and experts. The lesson you should take from them is that you should just start trying to do what you want to do and learn from experience. Book reading and instruction is a fine complement to actual life knowledge, but they're compliments, not guides. Your real understanding will come from repeated failures and successes in various types of activities.

You're not going to be "in the zone" if you spend all your time trying to figure out how to be "in the zone." You're not going to be a master painter if you spend all your time reading about master painters. You have to just do the things you want to do and know that you're most likely going to suck at them for a really long time until you get decent at them, then good at them, then great at them. Not much in life is really hard, it's just that things that seem hard are a complex combination of a lot of easy things that you can only properly map out and understand by interacting with. Go do things poorly until you can do them well.

Be Careful

Be careful, the feds are watching us. They are tracking our tweets, trust me. The government is worried about our network of e-book writers and podcast hosts leading an armed uprising that takes over the whole country. This means that we need to be on high alert for how we proceed. There is no doubt in my mind that there are hundreds of infiltrators trying to subvert our online forums and prevent us from reaching an actionable consensus.

For hundreds of years, there have been disenfranchised people like ourselves who talk angrily about the various abuses of power. For hundreds of years, nothing has fundamentally changed in human nature. Now, after hundreds of years of nothing really being different, we are on the cusp of actually achieving meaningful, lasting change. We are on the edge of a violent and bloody revolution which will lead to a glorious utopia, which is why we must be so very careful at this point in time.

I first noticed the prevalence of cointelpro agents when I was reading comments on the latest podcast. There were too many complaints and negative vibes to possibly have been normal, so I did a bit of digging and am now comfortable in concluding it is indeed the deep state trying their best to dissuade us of our important mission.

The government knows that the people are now one or two big events away from rising up and taking back power, so they are careful never to do anything explicit like kill any of us ever, but they are indeed worried. This is why they have to resort to psyops on the internet as well as infiltration of our meetups at local pubs. Believe me, we are all on government lists at this point.

What can be done? Never relax. Never take it easy. Never let your guard down. Always stay aware. Always keep your opsec secure, lest rogue government agents dox you on social media. Once that happens, you will be harassed on the internet, which is the worst thing in the world and is basically like literally being murdered and is super scary and dangerous.

We are winning the infowar, but we are now under serious attack by nefarious state agents. They hide around every corner, waiting for us to slip up. One little mistake by any of us and we will be set back years. Always be on edge. We need your support more than ever. Send us money, we have quit our jobs to better focus on the mission. We are in the final stages of the infowar. It's almost the endgame, be careful.

Human Sacrifice
The Mayans used to sacrifice humans on top of pyramids made of corn, or something like that anyway. This is something that I think we should bring back. I don't really have any great reason or delusions that it will solve

the problems in society, but I do think we should bring back human sacrifice for a variety of reasons.

Firstly, people get way too upset about minor inconveniences and trivial matters that are unimportant. If you had to worry about getting your heart cut out while everybody watches and cheers, then you would be less upset when there was traffic on your drive home from work or when the grocery stored didn't have the type of beer you wanted. By raising the stakes, people would just be grateful to be alive and learn to appreciate life.

Secondly, there would be a lot less edgelords emo edgelords running around. These are the types of people who are always talking about wishing they were dead but never killing themselves, even though killing yourself is fundamentally a very simple technical task that can be accomplished by anybody with half a brain and a genuine desire to be dead. This type of person would be the most visible worriers about human sacrifice and would thus not be in the position to posture towards being enthusiasts of dying.

Thirdly, it would be funny to see all the people who are pro death in other respects (abortion, unhealthy eating habits, unhealthy sexual behaviors) protesting against explicit human sacrifice. Everything is so phony and fake that talking with anybody about anything is almost always a waste of time. Nobody actually knows what they're talking about or what they believe, so bringing human sacrifice back would force a lot of people to unravel the tangled ball of string that is their worldview. This would most likely cause a large amount of amusing mental breakdowns.

Lastly, it would be funny to watch how nothing really changes fundamentally. Everybody will eventually accept any sustained law or practice, no matter how barbaric and cruel it is, as long as it is seen as legal and pushed. After the initial discomfort, this fact of human nature wouldn't change, and eventually everybody across both sides of the political spectrum would agree that human sacrifices are both moral and needed, when they obviously aren't.

What we have now is its own form of human sacrifice, except it is people being slaves until they die instead of being killed. This is crueler because everybody is constantly lying to themselves thinking that something is going to get better in their life and they're finally going to enjoy working for somebody else for fifty years when in reality they're just trading their time for shelter and will most likely end up in some nursing home being abused until they die of old age or smothered by a pillow by one of their relatives who hate them because they didn't leave them any inheritance. At least with human sacrifice we had some illusion of human decency.

Author Dom

You call that a book? That's not a book, that's a pamphlet. It's so small and tiny, aren't you embarrassed? You should be ashamed of yourself. I'm laughing at you right now. Everybody is laughing at how little your book is. It's not even three hundred pages long. You probably double spaced it and used extra line-breaks to pad your work. This is so pathetic. How embarrassing. You will never be a respected author. You should just quit now, before you get mocked in front of even more people.

By Thirty

By the time I'm thirty, some big things are going to have to happen or else I will end up extremely upset. This is not a list of requests, but rather a list of demands. If I do not see these demands met, I will be forced to take drastic measures and will also be quite angry and most likely depressed.

I demand that I will be a multi-millionaire by the time I'm thirty. This is not an unreasonable demand, and it will most likely not be that difficult. I will most likely be a multi-millionaire in the next two years at most, but if not then I will have to get increasingly desperate as I will be twenty six and only four years away from being thirty years old.

Another demand I have is that women continue to hit on me in a sexually aggressive manner. I am not really interested in sex, but I love how women are constantly trying to get me to fall in love with them and have sex with them. This is great for my ego and also makes other males around me both jealous and frustrated, and there is no feasible reason that it should stop, so if it does then that will mean that something has gone horribly wrong.

I also demand that people continue to respect me and look up to me and make excuses for my lack of maturity. I do not plan on becoming a functioning member of society any time soon, or ever for that matter, so it is not in my interests for people to change their standards for what is expected from me. Do not think that as I get older that I will become a good person, I can assure you that the exact opposite of that is happening. With every year, I become more selfish and less kind.

These are three reasonable and simple demands, and I will stop here with my demands for a while, because I have other things I need to do with my time. That said, I will make further demands clear as time progresses. If you do not like these demands, then feel free to go away and never speak to me again. I am an unreasonable individual who refuses to play nicely with others or change for the better, so you will just be wasting your time and mine. I will close this essay with yet another thank you to everybody who enables my horrible behavior, thank you.

Singlemindedness

For whatever reason, I'm only ever satisfied with how my life is going when I'm in the midst of some project. Sometimes the project is work related, relationship related, creative related, or some sort of experimentation with diet related, but there always has to be a project that I'm working on.

Whenever I'm not busy working on a project, I feel like I'm going crazy. I don't really know why, but I get urges to just do stupid stuff and pick fights with people in order for there to be some risk involved that requires my attention to manage. Maybe it's partly due to my young age and will get more bearable with time, but at the moment whenever I am free from working on a personal project, I seem to be drawn towards self-sabotage.

I've managed to work this to my advantage and use it as extra motivation to stay busy, but it is still frustrating whenever I finish a project and find that discontented and unsatisfied feeling popping back up. For example, I published my first book about a week ago. The book is not perfect, by any means, but it is to a higher standard of quality than most books as well as a hearty four hundred pages in length. Now that the book is finished and in general circulation, I don't really feel any sense of pride or satisfaction from it. In fact, I'm slightly perturbed by the fact that I keep on making money on it over time despite not doing any additional work for additional money. I am not complaining, as I'm very lucky to have an audience as well as be in the position to have enough free time to create something people are willing to pay me for, but it is simply a really weird feeling or rather absence of feeling that I am unsure of how to process properly.

I'm working on a second book now. This essay will be in the book. I am slightly disappointed with everything, because writing a book has been just like every other creative project I've ever done: not really that hard or complicated. I genuinely enjoy writing and it's really cool holding a physical book in my hand that I have created, but my search for some sort of magical or mystical process I can be involved in has once again failed. Much like programming or drawing, everything involved with writing a book can be broken down into extremely simple substructures. All that is needed to create extremely simple substructures: a bit of prolonged concentration and lateral thinking.

As of the time of writing this, I have at least two more years of being on probation. I plan on writing three books in total during this phase of my life, so two more books in the next two years. I'm already 25% done writing this second book, so I will most likely end up finished writing these next two books with around one year (at least) to go of probation. This means I will have to find other projects to fill my time in order to remain productive rather than self destructive. Most likely I will already be financially secure by that time, so money is not really an issue to me.

To address this upcoming free time, I will most likely work on multiple programming projects. I'm already working on a few, but they will most likely be finished by the time I have three books out. I may get back into playing guitar or spend time learning the piano. No matter what, I just need to be doing things. I am glad I have this weird problem of always doing things, but it is kind of isolating because I can never seem to lose myself in the moment like people around me can. I sometimes wonder if I'll ever be satisfied while at rest rather than just satisfied while busy and unsatisfied while not busy, but once I find out the answer, the answer won't matter.

Money For Drugs

Hey man, can you please give me eighty dollars? I'm out here in the streets at night and I'm just trying to get some money so I can have a roof over my head. You are so funny. I love you man. You and I are like brothers, so I would really appreciate it if you gave me money now. I just really need it or else I'll have to do horrible things in order to get shelter.

Man, I just really need some more money, please give me money again so I can get back on my feet. I'm really trying out here, friend. I'm trying so hard to turn my life around, but I just need twenty five dollars so I can get some food. I'm so hungry, I need twenty five dollars. No, I won't get a job to earn money.

I'm just down on my luck, as it were. Why are people making fun of me? Why do strangers not feel empathy for me when I am begging for change outside of a Wal Mart? Why do people I don't know make fun of me? What have I done wrong? Sure, I'm a drug addict who has repeatedly lied about needing money and used that money for drugs, but this time I'm really serious.

Stop making fun of me. Give me money. I need money to live. I'm going to kill myself soon, then you'll all see. Before I kill myself, however, I need you to give me your money. Please, give me your money. You don't want to have my blood on your hands, do you? Wouldn't you feel so much guilt if I ran in front of traffic or jumped off a bridge? I have so much potential that will be wasted, because of your actions. Just give me your money or I'll kill myself.

Pitting Countries Against Each Other

July Fourth is coming up, and with it comes the best holiday on earth. This holiday is not really great because America is great, but rather because the rest of the world sucks so much compared to America. Sure, America has a lot of problems, but it also has a lot of positive aspects that make it the best country on earth. The reason I enjoy this holiday so much is that I spend all of it being obnoxious to non Americans on the internet. I take on the role of a completely insane individual and play up every positive aspect to America while also pretending to love America's more nefarious proclivities, such as continuous destruction of foreign countries and cultures.

While July Fourth is a great holiday, it is only tangential to the topic of this essay, which is how to properly troll countries on the internet. What a lot of people do when they intend to insult a specific country is straightforward: they insult a specific country. This is the incorrect manner in which to go about things. This way leads to the residents of the targeted country having a direct rebuttal, which is to attack the country in which the attacker resides in.

The proper way to attack a country is by behaving in a disingenuous and roundabout manner, comparing the country you are attacking to a country that is a traditional rival to the country that you are attacking. When you compare these two countries, you must go out of your way to compliment the country you are attacking's rival country and then refrain from complimenting the country you are attacking. In this manner, you will have misdirected all the retaliatory energy from your country onto the rival country of the country you are attacking. What this then leads to is that you will also rally positive feelings from the rival country and they will then defend you as well as attack back when residents of the country you are attacking try to defend themselves.

This strategy can also be applied to interpersonal relationships, business deals, or really anything where you want to insult people without facing any risk. It is sneaky, uncharitable, and slimy, but that is how the real world works. Don't let failures like Cicero try to preach some weird form of virtue and sadomasochistic honor, the only important thing in life is winning. This means that sometimes you have to use third party countries as proxies for trolling countries you dislike on the internet. Learn how to properly pit people against each other to get what you want and you will become unstoppable, both on the internet as well as real life. This sort of warfare is why America is the best country in the world.

Selective Dishonesty

My life is a bit tricky. This is because I have some very noncomtemporary beliefs as well as a belief that it is important to not pander to people or lie to them if possible. I'm in a weird position where I am constantly surrounded by people living life in a way I find distasteful or shortsighted, but I know that if I said what I believed was proper, I would just be treated poorly or even face negative consequences for trying to be helpful. I end up lying by omission and allow people to do things I know are bad for themselves.

I know it's not my responsibility to lead people who should know better, but that doesn't change how if makes me feel. I've written about this before, but it is a kind of melancholy resignation that I'm helpless to really change much, especially any aspect of people who think they know better than me. My ability to let people do and say things I don't agree with doesn't seem to be mirrored by them, or else I would be able to express myself to them without negative consequences because of their irrationalities and projections of malice on myself.

I have decided that I don't really care on a serious level, because if I did then I would feel more than a slight discomfort and unease about the situation I'm in, and I don't feel more than a slight discomfort and unease about the situation I'm in. Chances are, when I am in a situation where I can afford to be completely honest with people around me and end up pushing them away, I will do that and never look back. I don't want these people to dislike me or not want to be around me, but I also don't want to continue to aid and abet their delusions.

Good Advice
A fact of reality is that there is a lot of really bad advice constantly being pushed everywhere. It doesn't matter how old you are or where you are, chances are you are being told very stupid things by very thoughtless or even malicious people. Remember that most "successful" people are "doing well" in life in spite of their habits not because of them, and they are oftentimes more miserable

than people who are less "successful", so just because somebody who has a nice job or a lot of money is giving you advice doesn't mean that they know what they're talking about.

The reason that most advice is horrible is that people who know what they're doing generally don't give advice. When you give advice to people, you open yourself up to negative outcomes and resentment if those people don't follow your advice properly or refuse to follow your advice and things turn out poorly for them. Because of this, it's more profitable to generally let people be stupid with how they progress in life and benefit off their stupidity.

One group of people who give advice are mediocre losers. These are the armchair generals who have never done anything that didn't immediately fail. These people generally did well in school or thought they were going to have some fulfilling corporate career and are insecure with the reality that they are an inconsequential cog that doesn't matter to anything or anyone, and so they try to exert control and establish a reputation as being the expert in something. By telling people what to do, they get to have some weird emotional satisfaction if the people listen to them as well as when people don't listen to them.

The other group of people who give advice are the people like Dave Ramsey and Jordan Peterson who make money off of insecure people who are lacking in any real life authority figure or ability to think for themselves. While the advice that they offer is not usually actively harmful, it is probably a bad sign if you need to be told to clean your room or not get into mountains of credit card debt to afford some new car when you're working a dead-end job. These types of people will not help you to be anything but slightly above average, and that is a really bad place to be. You're not going to succeed in life listening to these people, unless all you desire is to have a slightly above average life which will be kind of existentially depressing.

Who can you listen to if you want to get good advice? I would recommend reading things like Proverbs, Meditations by Marcus Aurelius, and Epictetus, but those writings aren't going to give you really good advice. All those things will do is kind of introduce you into a more logical, detached bird's eye view of how to process your surroundings as well as your perceptions of your surroundings. The only person who can really fix your life and give you good advice and make it so you don't end up some fat depressed slob drinking alcohol and smoking weed and watching TV in your thirties is you. You need to start being honest with yourself and think about literally everything you do and whether it benefits or harms you on a short term, mid term, and long term basis. Once you're over a certain age, you need to be your own boss of your personal life, not looking for a talk show host or youtuber or psychologist to be the sagely parent that you never had. The age where you should really start looking inward for advice varies by person, but I would say early twenties is probably the time to really start being introspective if you're not already. If you're in your early to late teens, the only applicable advice is just to stay busy in things that aren't mindless consumerism. As long as your busy doing things like reading, writing, art, exercise, hiking, etc, you're going to avoid a lot of the negative habits that will prevent you from developing mentally and emotionally into an efficient thinker when your brain is more finished growing. Drugs, especially drugs like weed or pills that make you feel good, are something to avoid if possible. Once you're older you will have plenty of time to do as much drugs as you want, and much better drugs, as long as you stay out of habits that destroy your mind and willpower when you're young.

Nobody is coming to order your life. Nobody really cares about you past a certain point. You could drop dead and I wouldn't care. The people who don't know you and pretend to care about you are people who most definitely don't care about you. Keep this in mind when somebody (especially public figures or strangers) is offering some paid service that appears to come with some good Samaritan message. There is good money in obscuring the fact that nobody but you can make your life positive and that it's also not really complicated, it just takes the ability to look honestly at your motives and your actions and stopping yourself from doing self-destructive behaviors. You are the only person who will ever help save yourself from becoming a failure. Stop looking for father figures.

Utter Disaster

My life is spiraling out of control. How could this sort of thing keep on happening to me? I don't deserve to be put through such mental turmoil constantly, but here we are yet again. Yep, the WiFi on my laptop stopped working again. This means that I'm going to have to restart my laptop in order to connect to the internet. This is a horrible situation to be in.

Restarting my laptop takes about thirty seconds, but it destroys my whole workflow for hours. I need to be listening to music non-stop in order to inspire me and keep me motivated. Not having internet access means I can't listen to music because I never download or pay for anything digital that I don't need to. Now there is just silence and the mental anguish that comes with the silence.

Another problem is that I have a whole bunch of various python scripts running that need to be restarted every time I restart the computer. I'm not smart enough to figure out how to set up a script to start up all these python scripts automatically, so that's another two minutes of things I have to set up whenever I restart the computer. This is also very emotionally taxing for me, since I don't handle slight inconveniences very well if I'm not the reason for them. I basically shut down emotionally and behave like an autistic eleven year old child. Many people have seen this sort of weird behavior from me and it's really beyond my control but that doesn't make it any less strange or preferable to avoid.

The worst part of all is that because my laptop has a solid state drive, the restarting is so quick. If there was a delay on the startup, then there could be a ritual of sorts that I could do in the meantime and it would just be an aspect to life that I could fit into other daily tasks. Instead, it's just short enough that I can't walk away and go do anything productive while I wait, but long enough that I feel existential angst and dread sitting around doing nothing. It is emotionally traumatizing every time I have to do this.

I'm going to have to bite the bullet and purchase a three thousand dollar gaming desktop workstation soon. There's really no other way to stop this deadly dark pattern of self destruction that I am willingly allowing myself to participate in. I'm probably going to set up a gofundme and beg for money to purchase the PC, not because I need the money but because it's kind of funny. Maybe I'll ask one of my doting sugar mommas to buy the computer for me and make up some weird lie about my current computer being out of date and now unable to process word documents and how I need 16 gigabytes of video memory to render text on a screen properly.

The time has come for me to restart my computer, and so I will end this essay here. This might be the last essay I ever write. Who knows if my computer will even start up again. If my laptop dies, I might just stop going on the internet forever. This sort of unpredictability is too taxing on my psyche to put up with for much longer. I fear I might snap or do something crazy.

Monetizing Schizoids

It is very easy to make a large amount of money: all you have to do is become a prostitute, have a white collar career, or sell drugs. What if you don't want to do any of those things and you still want to make a large amount of money? Is it possible? What if you don't have any work ethic and refuse to do anything hard, is it still possible? Yes, it is still very possible and still very easy to make a large amount of money. All you have to do is monetize schizoids.

Schizophrenia or schizophrenia-lite symptoms are extremely under-diagnosed. Most people you know suffer from some form of schizoid delusion. They are afraid about the economy, the republicans, the democrats, fascists, communists, Christians, gays, Catholics, men, women, eating, not eating, etc. Almost all people have some active form of paranoia and hypochondria that makes them behave irrationally in multiple ways. Still, they do not lash out or cause problems besides being annoying to deal with, so nobody really notices how mentally ill most people are. Because of this, no steps are taken to help these people and stop them from being mildly deranged idiots.

Take a look at the communities around any political party, podcast, television show, book, or individual. These are where the most visible schizoids are. It doesn't matter what the political angle they believe in is, ninety five percent of everybody involved is obviously mentally ill. Even the "anti-political" communities are inherently political, trying to usher in some schizophrenic utopia and blaming all the world's problems on the antithesis of their worldview. These people have jobs and make money doing work for other people, but do not forget that they are mentally ill schizoids.

A lot of people, as the get older, mellow out and try to grow up in how they behave and how they present themselves. This results in them distancing themselves from people who are passionate. While this might be more comfortable and surface level logical, what you want to do is the opposite. Lean into the insanity of the masses. Learn how to speak their language, even if you yourself aren't suffering from their sickness. These are the people who you can monetize. Sell them t-shirts of your "podcast" (four losers sitting around an apartment talking about things that don't matter), you book about your podcast, tickets for a meetup around your podcast.

Sure, you will have to be around a ton of deranged and disgusting schizoid slobs if you go this route, but that is the price you have to pay in order to avoid the fate of the frustrated white collar worker waiting to die. All you have to do is pretend you're not sane for about one decade or three and you will make millions of dollars and then be able to do whatever you want for the rest of your life. Make the mentally ill masses your cash cow. Become a cult figure in some obscure niche that doesn't matter, just like nothing matters.

Help Me

I'm not a very sexually minded person. Sure, I am attracted to women (female) and I enjoy a good flirt or two, but I am not somebody who spends time daydreaming of coitus or those sorts of things. This is partly because of my modest and down to earth upbringing and partly because of my neuroatypical brain. I am not asexual, far from it, but I am not some ruffian sex addict.

My fame has become something of a problem for me as of late. I continue to be sexually harassed by barely legal females. It is quite embarrassing for me, especially since I see most people my age struggling to get even mediocre women interested in them, being that I put absolutely no effort into making myself attractive. In fact, I often dress poorly and slouch as well as eat garlic in hopes of scaring away people from interacting with me, but this seems to only add to my appeal.

The strangest thing about all of this is how women keep on complimenting me about everything I do, even though I'm quite sure that most of them are not aware of more than maybe ten percent of what I do, and anybody with a functioning moral compass would be disgusted by me, were they aware of all the horrible things I have said and all the immoral things I have done. Still, I get constant flattery and scandalous looks from women of all ages and all social classes.

Beautiful women love me, and it is quite a problem. I'm not ready to settle down just yet, and I am not interested in mindless sex. I'm something of a sapiosexual, so all the nudes I get sent are quite honestly offputting, although I do genuinely appreciate the sentiments and bodily offers.

I'm kind of at a loss for what to do with all these women. I do not wish to hurt their feelings or damage their self confidence, being that I am a gentleman and most of them are model material, but I also do not wish to give them false hope. I am considering setting up an auction site for one day of my time per month, where during this time I will hang out with a female and allow them to make me food and kiss me if they meet my standards. I will grace them with my presence for as long as I deem fit and they will give me hundreds of thousands of dollars. I will most likely use the money to gamble or do philanthropy, but probably not philanthropy.

Women love me, and I love women on an intellectual level, but I need somebody to help me. I am at my wits end dealing with all these females constantly vying for my attention, begging me to take their fortunes and their virginity. Perhaps I will start having weekly girlfriends soas to be kind to all the beautiful young women who constantly try to win my heart. I do not know why, but I have become something of a sex symbol in Japan, so I have thousands of legal aged Japanese females hitting on me every month. I will see if any of them want to dress up in lewd maid cosplay and be my unpaid servants.

Ex

Men need to start coming together. If we just form teams, we will be able to be able to get unlimited sex and unlimited money with a little finagling. How? It's simple, all we have to do is trick women into doing what we want. How do we trick women into doing what we want? It's even simpler, we take turns breaking up with women.

Spend enough time in social circles and you will see a familiar pattern. When a relationship goes south for any reason, the female in the relationship will begin targeting the male's perceived insecurities and weaknesses. Women are able to switch from working with to working against their partner at the flip of a coin, and all of them do this, always. There are no exceptions, just women who don't see a good avenue for attack so they don't attack and remain on good terms with their male ex.

This pattern is exploitable, because often times a woman will start flirting with the male friends of male they are now attacking in order to try and drive them apart. What this means is that they will do seemingly insane things that are even self destructive, in an attempt to harm their ex. Knowing this, men should start trying to getting into relationships with women they do not care about but their friends do, and vice versa, and then slowly drive the women to hate them until the women cheat on them with their friends, and vice versa.

The financial manner in which this can be taken advantage of is also quite simple. The males should spread the rumor that their friends are degenerate gamblers with debt problems and that they have given money to those friends multiple times, but have stopped doing so in order to stop enabling their friends. This will then make the woman who hates her partner feel a compulsion to give her own money to the male friend in order to make her partner upset. The male and his friends can then split the money.

For whatever reason, women are essentially always doing things to try and get back at their ex. This can be a very harmful behavior for men, since it is a hassle and annoying when noticed. It is also very disturbing, because I personally do not think of any of the women I have been in relationships with and I have no desire to interact with them once the point of a functional relationship has passed. That said, this is how reality works, and we must not allow what we want (women not to obsess over their exes) with what is reality; because of this, we must learn to turn these negatives that try to harm us into positives that benefit us and those we care about: our male friends.

A Message To My Haters

This last year has been tough for you, I'm sure. I was losing my mind and imploding up until around then. It looked like I was going to lose it all, perhaps even end up dead. Then, a miracle happened, I recovered. Now, I'm back and I'm better than ever. I have a book out, I'm working on a second book, I'm going viral left and right, my net worth will soon be in the millions, and I'm going to have a series of movies made off my life and a famous actor will turn me into a cult figure known across the world. I'm fitter, smarter, faster, stronger, and better looking than ever.

Please know that I have no hard feelings towards you. I understand that I have not been a perfect person in all aspects all the time, and that I have often said cruel things or done stupid things that made people feel bad. I understand that I can be quite uncaring or selfish and make everything about me, like I'm doing right now. The world, to me, revolves around me and I have been rewarded for this outlook.

I understand why my success and ongoing ascension might have rubbed you the wrong way. I've hurt a lot of people emotionally to get where I am, that is true. Now that I have so much forward momentum, the time has come for me to extend an olive branch of sorts and say that I would be happy if you came along for the ride. No, this does not mean I want you to get in touch with me or interact with me. I don't want that and would probably call the police on you if you did. I merely mean that you should feel free to join in the growing movement of people who

IT IS THE SECOND - 140

are enthusiastic and positive about me, rather than dwelling on negative emotions.

Every minute you spend thinking about me is a minute that I have stolen from you, and I apologize for that. I really do feel sorry that I have taken up some weird space in your mind, and I don't want that to continue. I want you to be successful in life, like I am, and to really be able to thrive and become your own person. You can't do that if your time is spent hating on me. Please, for your sake and my heavy conscience, move on with your life and get over me.

You are so much more than your dislike for me. You have so much potential and value to give the world. All you need to do is flip all this negative energy into positive energy, and I promise you that you will be in the best place you have ever been in your life; mentally, physically, emotionally, and spiritually speaking.

I have been where you are right now, to a more limited extent. I have been frustrated. I have had problems with abusing substances and doing stupid things while under the influence. All the bad choices I made stacked up higher and higher until everything came crashing down and I was forced to face my own self destruction. I have done so many embarrassing and stupid things over the years that I would probably feel weird about if I had any shame or remorse. But none of that matters, because about a year ago I was fully honest with myself and made a conscious decision to cut out negative behaviors from my life and try to improve myself while not spending energy on people I thought I genuinely disliked. Now that I have some distance and am on the right path in life, I see that I don't really dislike anybody, not even people I might have "reason" to dislike.

I want you to be happy. I want you to be healthy. I want you to be successful. You can't do that if you care about me. Please, stop caring about me. If you can't do that, just know that I like you genuinely and dispel any

140 - IT IS THE SECOND

negative emotions you or I may have for each other. Please, go and live your life to the fullest. Go make your mark on the world for the better. Go, be free. Be happy. Be healthy. Be you to the fullest. Fly away, my child. Shoot for the stars. Embrace the light side of reality. Have a nice life.

Please Exercise

The biggest change I have made in the past year is that I have been exercising regularly. I don't go to they gym or take steroids or anything like that, I just do 120-200 pushups, 120-200 situps, and 40-60 pullups almost every day. I plan on increasing the average of each of these numbers over time, and started a bit lower than this, but the important thing is that I'm doing exercise.

Exercising for vanity or even health is kind of futile and I don't do it for those reasons, but rather for the fact that it puts me in an active and productive pattern. I stay busy and motivated on other things when I break up my time with a set of pushups, situps, or pullups. This gets my blood flowing and then when I return to whatever I'm working on, whether reading, writing, programming, or anything else, I'm more alert and able to focus.

Life is not about doing big all or nothing things, but rather repeatedly doing easy manageable things that build up momentum that can be transferred into other tasks. Exercising is something that will keep you honest with your time as well as make you more self aware about what you're putting in your body, because when you eat very poorly you'll realize that any exercise is much more exhausting.

Exercising also helps with sleep, which is an important thing to get. I sleep less than most people, but now that I am exercising regularly I find that the quality of my sleep has been a bit better and I have an easier time falling asleep. You need a balance of physical and mental strain throughout the day, and most people get one or the other.

There is so much time I waste and still waste with mindless browsing of the internet or reading stupidity or playing little games. Exercising takes less than thirty minutes of that time a day, and it's much better. It is a shame that people turn exercising into some weird freak sport where people get oiled up and wear speedos to be judged by old men, because in its normal form it provides a good form of mental and physical discipline as well as a healthy outlet for physical energy. Please, do a little exercise each day.

The Vault

I had done some work for him. He was a pretty nice old man. His problem was that he was an alcoholic and also had a loud mouth. I don't really care about either of those things, and I don't judge people for their vices generally, but he had screwed up when he had been bragging to me about how much money he had, and how he didn't keep any of it in the bank. I wasn't even trying to get him to tell me about it, because I knew what would happen if I knew, but one day when he was drunk he babbled to me about where he kept his safe, in the corner of his bedroom closet. It didn't take long before I had verified it, identified it, and how he got into it. Then, it was only a matter of time until what happened happened.

He had a dog which liked me a lot. I don't really care for animals either way, but they all seem to love me. It's probably because I'm generally a low stress individual and animals pick up on that sort of stuff and assume the best about people who radiate a lack of stress. I made a point of becoming good friends with the dog, because I didn't want to have to kill the dog if it started barking. This sort of forward thinking was something I had learned to do from past instances of not being forward thinking. Usually, you can do whatever you want to anybody without any plan and nothing will come of it, but you can always do whatever you want to anybody without anything coming of it as long as you plan ahead.

I remember the day like it was yesterday. Just like all of my other escapades, there was an amusing lack of excitement or anxiety that punctuated something that would traditionally be associated with excitement and anxiety. It was especially calm, because it was snowing. I needed it to be snowing and had been waiting for a good snowstorm so I could do what I needed to do, so I had waited for a good snowstorm until it came. Patience is a virtue, especially with these sorts of situations that shouldn't be forced until it is the perfect time for them to be forced.

As previously noted, the old man was an alcoholic. This wasn't casual alcoholism, this was life destroying alcoholism, or it would have been. I can't really get into the details of what this man did to get money, but it wasn't particularly impressive or honorable, but it also wasn't bad. I didn't really respect him, to be quite honest. He had lucked into a lot of good things and wasn't smart enough to put those things to use or keep his mouth shut, so somebody took everything from him. I was the thief in the night for him.

Anyway, when that fateful day arrived, I was prepared for it. I made sure nobody realized anything was out of the ordinary, because I had made not being around on a daily basis into a habit. The snow was falling heavily when I trudged up to the door and took the spare key out from under the rock where it was hidden, but not before I had verified from a nearby window that the old man was in a drunken snooze on the couch. I went in casually, and then petted the dog. The dog was quiet and wagged its tail, so I didn't have to kill it. There were liquor and beer bottles everywhere, the house smelled disgusting.

The old man remained asleep in his drunken manner on the couch. I walked into his bedroom and opened his safe using the proper implements. I took out half of his money and put it into my backpack. Then, I shut the safe. I was wearing gloves the whole time so I wasn't worried about fingerprints. I could have taken everything, but I didn't want to be greedy. This wasn't about greed, it was more about the challenge and life experience.

I was about to leave when the old man started to wake up. I froze in place for a second, hoping that he would fall back asleep so I wouldn't have to do anything unpleasant. It quickly became clear that he wasn't going back to sleep but was about to actually be conscious, so I made a choice. The dog was in the other room and wasn't worried, and it wasn't really a risk, so I quickly went over to the couch, took a pillow, and smothered the drunk old man until he died. I took the pillow with me and later destroyed it, but the old man didn't really put up a fight because he was old and decrepit from years of drinking, plus he was extremely drunk even when he was waking up.

After doing what needed to be done, I walked out of the house with the money and the pillow in my backpack. It was still snowing heavily, which was important to me because I knew that it would obfuscate my walk to and from the house. I walked for a little while until I got to my mode of transportation, then I left. I never looked into anything because I'm not stupid but as far as I can tell, people just thought the old man died from natural causes because there was no evidence of foul play or any break-in.

Being Nice To Girls

Sometimes, you should be nice to girls. This is not to get anything from them, but rather to keep them confused and on their toes. The last thing you want is a girl to have figured you out. Once that happens, then all hell will break lose. Then they will start to push your buttons and slowly make your life spiral out of control. They are destructive by nature, so you need to keep them guessing. Of course, it's imprudent to be nice to girls on a regular basis. You need to be productive and working on projects, and you can't do that if you're emotionally consoling a female or listening to her talk about inane stuff all the time. So, you should as a default be kind of distant and reserved, but every so often turn into the nicest person ever.

Every few days I roll a die and if it lands on six, then I am nice to at least one female for that day. This means that there is a one in six chance of being nice to a female. This is a pretty riskily high frequency of being nice, so if you want to be more realistic you can roll a die twice and if the total of the two rolls is eleven or twelve then you will be nice to them. This will happen at a lower rate than one in six rolls, but I'm too lazy to calculate the actual chance of this happen.

By deciding when to be nice and when to be mean on a semi-random mathematical basis, you will be steps ahead of ninety nine percent of all men already. You will be seen as "unpredictable" and "mysterious" even though you're just being pragmatic and thoughtful in how you proceed with your relationships. Women will start to pay you even more attention and treat you consistently well, because they are used to having people treat them certain ways when they act certain ways and will be thrown off by your more mindful behavior and wonder what your secret is. Of course, you should not tell them what you are doing, because this will remove the mystery from the equation and level the playing field.

You're not going to find this sort of actionable advice in pickup artist guides. Why? Because pickup artists are idiots who don't know what they're talking about and are constantly lying. They are not fucking women, they are fucking you by giving such poor tips and tricks. This sort of psychological deviation from the norm will pay dividends as long as you properly play your cards and stick to the plan.

Women get bored by constant nice guys and constant mean guys. They get bored by somebody who is constantly nice. They get bored by somebody who is constantly mean. Think of every interaction as a hand of poker. You want to be giving them enough of one sort of behavior that they think they can figure you out, then out of the blue behave in an opposite way without any real warning or signs. By doing so, you will become an alpha male chad woman seducer king.

Snorting Drywall

One time, during one of my many psychotic blackout mental breaks, I ended up snorting a ton of drywall. I don't really know why, but I was just gone mentally. I remember coming too realizing that I was chopping up lines of crushed up drywall and realizing what I was doing and being really horrified. I stopped snorting the drywall, of course.

The next forty-eight hours were the most uncomfortable and strange hours of my life. I had absolutely no appetite and my nose was clogged with drywall gunk, and everything tasted like drywall. It was almost impossible to get to sleep because of the taste of drywall in my mouth as well as the smell of drywall in my nose. It has a very distinctly chalky taste and smell.

I remember just laying down trying to sleep while my head was pounding and I felt like I wanted to die. I take full responsibility for what I did, but I don't really know why I did it. That period in my life was a really dark time, to be quite honest. It's important to eat healthy and get enough sleep and not deal with other mentally ill people or else you might end up blacking out and snorting drywall, which is something you should never do.

Alcohol

I have used and abused a fairly decent number of drugs. I have not done any specific drug in any large amount, and I have not ever gotten addicted to any drug or felt any real cravings for them, but I have a fair bit of experience and perspective on drug use, mostly uppers like cocaine, speed, and other similar things. With that said, the drug that has undoubtedly enabled the most stupid and idiotic behaviors by myself would have to be alcohol.

There is something about alcohol that just makes doing stupid stuff a lot easier. The stuff I've done while drunk hasn't been malicious, but it has been socially inappropriate or rude or dumb. With too much alcohol, I tend to get set on one course of action and am unable to consider different courses of actions and don't realize what I'm doing is strange or maladpted. For example, one time I drunk called somebody probably sixty or so times when they wouldn't pick up, because we were supposed to have scheduled something and they were being flaky. While this is funny in hindsight, I'm sure it was unsettling to the person on the other end at the time.

Another thing I've done while very drunk (I used to see how much vodka I could drink before passing out for a few months back when I was in my early twenties) was tell a girl that I would find it funny to have sex with her sister while she watched. Through a lot of whining and cajoling and lying, I managed to temporarily salvage that relationship, but I am pretty sure it was the start of a very unpleasant situation. Yes, what I had said was true and it still is true, but nobody in their right mind would admit that.

Yet another memorable very drunk moment was after I had walked a girl back to her apartment on a cold winter night. We were both drunk, but I had had the brilliant idea to finish the unfinished shots at the restaurant table before I walked her home, so I was in an unhealthy mental state by the time we had arrived at her place. We had a conversation and I gave her some money for the bus that she had taken earlier that day to see me. After she had gone inside, I realized that I had given her more money than I should have and did not have enough money on me to pay for a bus ticket, which I needed to get back to the place I was staying at the time. This resulted in my drunkenly banging on her door and repeatedly calling and texting her in the middle of the night until she slid enough money through the door for me to pay for the bus ticket.

None of these examples are particularly horrible, and they are mostly amusing to me now, but at the time they were quite distressing. The worst part is that they were all idiotic and completely avoidable if I had the common sense not to drink too much. I have a lot of other times where I have done or said stupid things while drunk, such as bursting out sobbing while talking to a friend and then doing donuts in their field in my car until I blew a tire and passed out after I turned off the car, cursing out an entire country publicly after hanging out with gracious people from that country, yelling slurs in a bar in NYC then falling down the stairs as I left, and many other things I'm sure I'm forgetting, but these particular examples I highlighted because they all played into serious interpersonal problems that didn't need to happen and were stupid on my part.

I'm sure that a lot of the stupid things I've done while drunk where for more reasons than just being drunk. When I was at the age of most of these examples, I was under a tremendous amount of stress and pressure as well as had a lot of attention that most people my age (or any age) never have to deal with. Still, without drinking, I'm quite sure none of these things would have happened. That alone is reason enough for me to be highly negative towards alcohol in general.

Those are some personal examples, and they aren't really addiction related, but alcohol is also a horrible drug for addiction. I've watched it slowly eat away at people who have frustrating life situations, and it's still doing so to many of my friends. It fixes the symptoms of problems temporarily, but ends up depressing my friends physically and mentally. Also, the same decision making issues that I have experienced seem to be at play with my friends when they are drinking. It's sad to watch, and the worst part is that I know that there's no good way to stop other people from using alcohol poorly, so I just have to kind of watch people I care about decline in various ways, waste time and money, and make poor decisions, much like I did whenever I would drink frequently or heavily.

I'm not completely against drinking, although the tone of this essay is quite negative. I am sure I will drink in the future. I don't have a problem with people who can casually drink without it causing a problem, as many people seem able to do. That said, I find how lightly alcohol is treated compared to other drugs, for example nicotine, to be completely inverted. Nobody is going to make stupid social mistakes from smoking a cigarette, but smoking is looked down on while casual alcoholism seems to be pushed and praised everywhere. Drugs aren't good to use, but speaking from personal experience, alcohol seems like the most dangerous drug that is easily accessible.

Uber Economy

Up until very recently, taxis were highly regulated affairs. Now, there are apps like Uber and Lyft that have made the taxi industry more of a free for all, and this has had a lot of cascading effects that most people are not aware of. Historically, being a taxi driver meant you had to work for a bigger company who paid for medallions in order to be allowed to operate in various cities. This meant that there were certain standards and expectations, but also better pay for the drivers. This is not the case with invention and success of apps like Uber and Lyft.

Being a taxi driver has now been turned into a high turnover business, because the payoff isn't good enough to support anybody who tries to do it full time. Uber and Lyft have outsourced the labor pool to a level of competition that makes it so only people who are unable to do cost benefit analysis are involved. This doesn't matter to the companies, because they get a cut of every drive without incurring any of the costs like spent time and wear and tear on vehicles.

Prior to the prevalence of smartphones, this sort of business model wasn't feasible. In order to succeed, Uber and Lyft have allegedly bent a lot of laws from the beginning of their operations, knowing that by the time anybody noticed what they were doing that would mean that they had a significant amount of people using their service, which would mean they would have a lot of revenue, which would mean that they could pay lawyers and lobbyists to make their alleged legal improprieties inconsequential. This strategy worked,

Most of the people who drive for Uber and Lyft are losers. These are the people who get involved in things like Cutco or other multi level marketing endevours, not understanding that it's almost impossible to run a profit for time invested. Traditional taxi drivers haven't been losers, but they are now being increasingly priced out of operating a cab, because cabs are getting less use because they are less competitive than Uber and Lyft.

This sort of setup sounds nice on the surface, but it is a race to the bottom in terms of service. Eventually, everybody who isn't a sucker will catch on that only suckers drive Uber and Lyft trying to make money, but that won't mean that Uber and Lyft will stop. They will continue to collect their cut of suckers, and the traditional taxi services with higher fees because they (need higher fees to pay drivers a living wage) will struggle and go out of business or cut costs and start using the same predatory tactics Uber and Lyft engage in.

This situation is not limited to taxi services. Hotels as well as apartments are other industries that being harmed by this behavior. Hotels get less traffic and have to shut down. Apartments cost more because people have figured out how to monetize apartments. This also causes problems for landlords because they are unable to control who is living in their apartments, which opens them up to problems and uncertainties that previously didn't exist.

I don't really think there is any proper manner to address these problems. They are essentially companies that have figured out how to exploit a tragedy of the commons and work around laws and regulations that have served to protect and sustain industries and thus the people involved in them. This will have a lot of negative side effects that can't be predicted, but it will also have positive aspects that can't be predicted. As always, industries and people will adjust to the shifting reality to better accommodate what is working, and what is now not working will die off.

A Proper Bathtub

There are a few things that I will never be able to forgive my parents for. One of those things is the fact that we never had a proper bathtub in any of our houses. Yes, we had a bathtub of sorts, if you could call it that, but this was worse than having no bathtub at all. You see, there is a correct minimum size to a bathtub and an incorrect minimum size to a bathtub, and we most definitely had the incorrect minimum size bathtub. Allow me to explain further.

There is a ritual aspect to sitting in a proper bathtub. The fact that you are in a proper bathtub fades to the background and everything is in its correct place, allowing you to focus on your thoughts, read, or relax. This is not the case with the bathtubs I have been forced to use my whole life, where the bathtub was too small for my legs and arms.

When a bathtub is too small, you are hyper aware of how you are positioning your legs, arms, and head. This is because there is no physical manner in which to properly submerge all of your legs or arm at once and you must cross your legs in order to fit in the bathtub itself as well as most of your midsection underneath water. Still, this will turn into a sick game of uncomfortable shifting back and forth constantly.

To make matters even worse, the bathtubs I endured were torture on the neck. There is no proper way to rest the head in these sorts of tubs. This is particularly noticeable when one is exhausted from a day of rigorous physical and mental exertion, as I often am, and simply wants to half pass out in some warm water. This is simply not possible. At best, you will feel like you are dying and hyper-confined in a cramped wartime nook bomb fallout shelter for midgets.

Another aspect that my parents seemed completely oblivious to is the fact that bathtubs need to be of a marble material. We had a sort of plastic shell material that I am quite sure was leaking microplastics into my developing body and destroying my mind as well as giving me long term terminal cancer that will kick in after they are gone so I cannot exact my revenge on them for poisoning me in this manner. I'm a very tactile person, most likely due to being on the autism spectrum, so feeling matters a lot to me. I am disgusted by the feeling of plastic in a bath. There is something so unhealthy, so radioactive, so stupid about it, that it is unacceptable.

People need to start paying attention to how they build their baths. If you own your own house, there is no excuse to put in a cheap bath. If you can't afford to get a full sized bath made of marble, you can't afford to own a house. Scrimping on necessities like proper bathtubs is psychological and physical self abuse as well as child abuse. There are certain things that should not be done cheaply, and bathtubs are one of them. There is no excuse to deprive your child of the human right that is a marble bathtub that is big enough that it allows them to stretch their legs and rest their head in a comfortable manner.

Idiot Privilege

Sometimes I take a step back from my day to day activities and look at reality in a semi-objective manner, and I am flabbergasted. I get paid an increasing amount of money monthly to produce deluded content that highlights the worst aspects of my imagination and personality. I do not do hard work, I do not try hard at anything, and I am not doing anything complicated or challenging, and yet I am being rewarded much more than the people who work hard at a real job and pursue a real career.

I am the beneficiary of idiot privilege. I have worn down everybody around me to the point where they have no expectations for me and I am not required to do anything or relied upon by anyone. As long as I am not actively burning down buildings or having psychotic breaks I am treated like I'm a good person. This is a very weird situation to be in, and it feels quite surreal, but I am not complaining.

Idiot privilege is the best. I will be a multi-millionaire before I'm thirty. Everything I do makes me money now. I am the most iconic idiot of the twenty first century, which means that I do not need to worry about people trying to ruin my reputation. In fact, the more people spread negative rumors about me, the more funny I find it and the more I benefit from it.

At this point I would keep quiet if I found the cure for cancer. First off, cancer is natural selection and just like all medicine and hospitals should be illegal, cancer should never be fixed. Secondly, I have too much to lose by gaining the respect of normal people by curing cancer. Once I cured cancer then people would not think of me as an idiot and I would have to deal with self important morons and deluded college types trying to talk to me. I hate those people because they are actual literal idiots and waste everybody's time.

I might pirate a movie tonight after I come back from getting wings with a friend. It's boneless wing night so the wings are discounted. The friend will pick me up and then drive me to the restaurant and then we will eat and then they will drive me back to my house. I have a car but I haven't used it in over a year. I like being driven around by friends and family members because they're like my slaves and servants. To be quite honest, I don't really like eating out with other people but I do it as an act of charity and personal amusement. I would much prefer to be eating alone in peace and quiet.

Stupid people have got it figured out. Nobody expects anything from us. We just relax all day every day. We suck the blood of the productive people who never do anything to make us do actual work because they're too tired from doing actual work. It's quite funny to watch and be apart of. The strangest thing is that I'm going to be much richer and successful as an idiot than all the non idiots. Life is just funny that way. Idiot privilege is really funny.

Years Left

I figure I have about five or six more years of genuine creativity left. After that, the mental rot will probably set in. This is why it's so important for me to be productive now. Most people think about life as a sort of constant progression where they work their way up the ladder of success as they get older, but it's quite the opposite.

You start life and you have no responsibilities. You don't have a job and you don't even have any school. The only responsibilities you really have are not drowning the dog in the bathtub and not wetting your bed or picking your nose. Besides that, you kind of have free reign to do as you please.

Then, you hit your teens and for the next decade you're in school. You have to deal with total morons around you and teaching you. You are tested on things that don't matter, like history, science, and mathematics. I cheated at everything I could easily cheat at in school, to be quite honest. It wasn't that I couldn't do it, even though I probably couldn't do it that well if I tried, it was more that it was so boring that I was looking for any excitement and actually interesting thing to do, so risking getting in trouble was what I started to do.

After school, you get a job and then you work for the rest of your life. Every year you cope a little more about how unhappy your life is making you, but you are earning money and have the respect of people around you for being "responsible" and a "functional member of society" so you suck up all your discontentedness and continue to work at a soul crushing job. Maybe you get a wife and kids, maybe not. It doesn't really matter, because you're going to be a wage slave until you are in your fifties.

Then, you retire and you have nothing to do and barely enough to get by, so you spend the rest of your life watching tv in the middle of the night and drinking beer. You take a lot of different medications for high blood pressure, low blood pressure, cholesterol, stress, depression, anxiety, and your quality of life continues to decline until you die or you end up in a nursing home. If you end up in a nursing home, then you are treated like a senile criminal and force-fed pudding by abusive urban females. Then you eventually die.

This is why making stuff now, in my prime, is so important. I will be getting dumber and dumber soon, but whatever I create now will live on and continue to benefit me long after I have become a dumb idiot, which I will definitely become sooner or later. In this way, I will have escaped the cycle that most people fall for. I will have transcended decay and as a result will be able to take advantage of lots of gold digging women in order to feed my ever expanding ego.

Epstein
Recently, the strange case of Jeffrey Epstein has resurfaced in the news. It has pretty much been accepted by most people that he was involved in some form of sex trafficking and underage prostitution rings. While this may or may not be the case, he is a billionaire and I don't feel

like being murdered or sued so I'm not saying whether any of this is true or untrue. Personally, Epstein never did anything wrong to me so I can't really make a character judgment.

What is kind of funny is not Epstein but rather everybody in the media who covers Epstein. It doesn't matter if you're "right wing" or "left wing", if you're mildly successful in traditional media in any manner, you are aware of people who are actively involved in underage sex trafficking.

Most conservatives you know by name are not even one degree removed from people who manage underage prostitution rings/sex slavery. Basically, here is how reality works: at any political events, there will be some older gentleman who have ties back to a certain country in the middle east. These people will give money and advice to people in the media as well as sponsoring events, then when they are in a semi-private situation with the people in the media (or politicians or entertainers), they will offer their target a "barely legal" female (or male) up for sex. Most media people, like most people, are not very good at resisting surprise temptations, so they take them up on the offer. Later, it turns out the female (or male) was underage and the whole situation was recorded. From that point on, individual is then enlisted into pushing whatever agenda is desired to be pushed.

This is not a rare occurrence. This is not a hypothetical situation. This is what happens. If you see young adults being pushed by older people and established organizations, on the left or on the right, this is because they have blackmail on them and are able to be controlled. This is why you see a lot of seemingly smart media people constantly say and do stuff that makes them look stupid in order to push an agenda. They have lost their ability to speak their mind and are basically corporate puppets.

This same situation applies to politicians and entertainers. This sort of thing is partly why I have gone out of my way to establish a negative reputation. Not because I am going to have sex with any underage females (or males), but because I don't even want to be approached by the types of people who engage in that sort of stuff, and by being unapproachable and seen as non-family friendly I remove myself from the pool of viable mouthpieces. I'd rather be seen as scummy and not have the opportunity to be blackmailed by disgusting people than end up as what most people in conservative media are, which are pervert drug addict pedophiles desperately trying to come across as genuine and kindhearted so they can make money for their handlers and not end up with their life and reputation ruined.

The media is such a sick place filled with incestuous weirdos being funded by literal pedophiles and rapists. That's the reality of the situation and that has probably always been the reality of the situation and will probably always be the reality of the situation. Epstein will not get in serious trouble unless somebody who is in charge of him is now using somebody else to do the same thing Epstein allegedly did. Nobody in power gets in trouble for these sorts of things because they have the money and power and connections to deal with things legally and illegally. The media doesn't actually care about this because everybody in the media personally knows multiple sexual predators. Nothing will actually change and it's sad watching people spend so much time and energy giving attention to people who are no different than Epstein, just lower level, because they're pretending to not be like Epstein because somebody higher up gave an order to make an example out of Epstein in order to make room for somebody else or distract from something else.

Wooden Doors
Oh no, the air is escaping through the cracks! AAAAAA we are so stupid, we didn't even make the doors air-proof! What were we going to do with all the bodies

anyway, after we dug through their entrails looking for diamonds and cut their hair to make mattresses? We are so stupid and autistic, time to take meth.

Therapy

Therapy has got to be the funniest thing on the planet. The only people who could possibly benefit from it (besides the people making money from being therapists) are people who don't have any real friends that they can talk to. These people have no real friends to talk to because they are miserable weirdos who don't know how to be introspective, so they go to a therapist. Ninety-nine out of one hundred therapists are horrible. They make more money the longer you stay with them, so they are incentivized to keep you feeling like you're making personal progress without actually making any personal progress.

I have to go to therapy for court mandated reasons. I do not mind this, because it breaks up some of my time and allows me to talk with a stranger and that helps me adjust how I talk with other people when I'm trying to get a particular response or reaction, but it is essentially a waste of time. There has been nothing that has been said that I am not aware of already. I know more than the person who I am talking to and have most likely read much more psychological studies and theory, as well as having a real life track record of being highly successful with understanding what makes people tick.

What happens in therapy is essentially emotional coddling. Some stranger is being paid to hear you speak and tell you that you aren't the cause of your problems (you usually are) and that you are a good person (nobody is a good person). They might give fairly good suggestions about how to deal with symptoms of your neurosis and insecurities and flaws, but none of them will ever be able to address actual problems like an individual needs to if they want to become self actualized or gain a cohesive understanding of what makes themselves (and others) tick.

Therapy is an outsourcing of personal responsibility. It is another sort of indulgence similar to the one the Catholic church used to employ, where you give some stranger your money in order to feel better about yourself instead of improving yourself. There have been studies that show that therapy actually makes people worse.

If you think you need therapy, just talk to friends and family members about problems you have instead of trusting a stranger who will probably try to push pills and mumbo jumbo on you. If you don't have friends and family to talk about your problems with, then open up a word document or get out a pen and pad of paper and start writing down all the negative things about yourself that you would say to yourself if you hated yourself and were trying to hurt your feelings. Write down all your failures and flaws and insecurities and be brutal with yourself. Then study those things, especially the interpersonal things you have written down. Work on fixing those problems so you can have real friends to talk to about your problems.

Some stranger is not going to fix the fact that you think you suck. Your friends and family are not going to fix the fact that you think you suck. Only you are going to fix the fact that you think you suck. Don't be a sucker and don't give strangers money to talk to you. Don't look outward for some mommy or daddy with a worthless degree to decide things for you. Chances are that you're smarter than anybody who is a therapist or psychologist or therapist.

Therapy is a scam. It's just a pipeline to co-dependence on pharmaceuticals and the state. It should be considered child abuse to send your kid to a therapist, but it isn't considered child abuse because the government and people connected to the government make a ton of money off of parents letting strangers destroy the brains of people who are vulnerable with trash theories and stupid ideas that just lead to a lifetime of mediocrity at best. Don't go to therapy unless you're being forced to by law. It is literally "the rapy" with a space removed.

A Switch Will Flip

Fairly soon, a switch will flip. It will be subtle, especially at first, so I doubt that many people will notice what has happened. You will probably pick up on what has changed, being that you are so intelligent, but I think most people will not be able to see or understand the reality of what the "new deal" is.

Just what is the thing that will be modified in its form? I can't tell you, at least not yet. This has to happen without its happening being explained or anticipated, or else it won't function as smoothly. I can speak from experience when I say the most valuable things in life are those that you don't plan for.

You will see. It's only a matter of time and desire. That's just a fact, even though it may seem more like a riddle than a statement of truth at the time. That is another aspect to all of this that you don't realize until you fully understand what it is. Then you will understand it and I will be happy that you understand it.

Watching PBS

Something myself and a friend would do when growing up is watch the Charlie Rose program on PBS. Charlie Rose is/was an old white or jewish (I'm not sure which to be honest but it's television so chances are he wasn't white or was anglo which is essentially the same thing as being jewish since they basically do the same stuff) and would interview random people that generally had no business being interviewed.

The interviews sucked, but we watched them anyway. We played a funny little game where we tried to find a way to make every statement some weird form of sexual innuendo. This is something I did not come up with, as I do not have a naturally crass mind and am a respectable individual, but I did find it quite funny.

I'm pretty sure this is what caused me to start reading into what everybody says in a schizotypal manner. Now, whenever somebody says anything, I'm always picking apart word choice, pauses between words, and deviations in presentation from the plain form of the statement. I see patterns everywhere, and it's all because of watching old people talk when I was a child.

There really is no point to any of this essay, I just thought it was amusing enough to write about. I'm sure other people have done stuff similar to this, but I've never heard anybody describe doing this. Me and my friend were probably the only people under sixty years old willingly watching Charlie Rose and PBS.

Going Bald

I think I'm slowly going bald. This probably isn't the case because every day I look in the mirror and pull on my hair to see if it's falling out and I don't really see any problem, but I'm pretty sure it's just happening so gradually that I won't be able to notice it until it's too late to stop. This is my main impetus for for working out and getting kind of fit, or else when I finally do go totally bald I'll look like a jewish prisoner in Auschwitz.

I have ledge in the back of my head that will be awkward to see if I go bald. It kind of looks like that crystal alien skull in *Indiana Jones and The Kingdom of the Crystal Skull*. This is called the occipital bun, and it's because I have Neanderthal DNA. Most people don't have the bump on the back of their head or Neanderthal DNA, so there is a good chance that I will face discrimination for the bump as well as for looking like an emaciated jew in the prison camp at Auschwitz.

Did you know that when the allied forces reached Auschwitz, they forgot to take any cameras and had to do a re-enactment of fake prisoners at a later date? This is true, it's a re-enactment of the concentration camp. This doesn't really mean anything or infer anything but it is very amazing that nobody ever teaches any of it in school. Sometimes an army forgets to take cameras to places where war crimes are being committed.

Going bald doesn't really make me feel insecure. There's no good reason to hate myself for things I can't really change. Worst comes to worst, I'll just end up wearing a baseball cap everywhere. I have already started doing that, mostly because I'm a schizoid and don't want facial recognition cameras to see my face, so nobody will even notice that I'm coping for my lack of hair.

Political Correctness

As of the past hundred years, there has been a gradual uptick in how people are punished for expressing illiberal or conservative positions on a wide variety of social issues. This is not really up for debate, and so it is not really the subject of the essay. Rather, I will be examining some potential reasonings for this as well as some possible effects this may have on various aspects of life as well as people as a whole.

We live not in a post scarcity world (which is impossible) but a world where there is an unprecedented amount of excess available for most people. This is not a paradise, as poorly used excess is worse than being constrained to the bare necessities and allows people to get into all sorts of trouble, both physical and mental. What has resulted is that there are a lot more fundamentally unsatisfied and unhappy people who also have a lot of free time.

Another aspect is that the rate of communication had increased by several orders of magnitude, and the friction between having an idea and sharing it with strangers has decreased by several orders of magnitude. This means that people who disagree with each other are now exposed to each other at a much higher frequency and the interactions are more vivid than they used to be without resulting in some physical resolutions/dispersion of negative energy.

Media gatekeeping is also always in play. Successful industries are generally run by people who know what they're doing to some degree, and this applies to radio, television, newspapers, books, and now the internet. What is pushed on platforms will generally be pushed because the people who manage those platforms know they won't face some extreme backlash that they can't handle. Of course, people in charge of these things make mistakes about what they think will be good to push, but most of the time (not always, but usually) even the negative publicity is generated on purpose in order to increase audience engagement and buzz.

With regards to media and opinions, only certain views are ever allowed to be pushed in the mainstream. In the past, because the vectors for public outcry didn't exist as they do now, their wasn't really a way to make money off of this sort of public outcry, which meant that there weren't many incentives for public outcry, which meant that there wasn't as much public outcry as there is currently.

Now with the internet and social media and rapid global communication, there is a perfect storm of sorts. Being pro political correctness or anti political correctness can be monetized, and public outcry can be monetized by both of these groups, no matter which way the public outcry is directed, because there is virtually always some push-back public outcry in response to the initial public outcry. There is also a way to monetize commentary on all political correctness and public outcry without taking sides, which then magnifies everything on both sides for everybody. It is essentially a new feedback loop which is combined with the excess of free time and restless discontentedness that seems so common in our current reality.

That is some partial analysis of why political correctness/general drama and gossip culture has become more prevalent over the recent years and decades. What will happen because of this? Nobody can really know for sure, being that there are a seemingly infinite amount of variables at play that we can't really account for, but the following is a very limited and surface level appraisal that makes logical sense.

The people who will be successful in life now are the people who can move with the way reality works, rather than moving how they wish reality works. Honesty is almost always only rewarded when the honesty lines up with popular sentiment or is worded in a way that it is not directly obvious that it runs counter to popular sentiment. This winning group of people can be broken into two groups: people who know how to hide that they don't agree with popular sentiment while still acting how they want but in a camouflaged context and people who just happen to agree with popular sentiment and don't realize that they're not having problems speaking their mind and being transparent because they happen to live in a time where their values are the norm.

The group that will always be punished is the group that is objectively correct and behaves in an objectively correct way and believes objectively correct way, but does so in a way that runs counter to popular sentiment and thus incurs some social or physical cost that puts them at an disadvantage, evolutionary speaking. If you're in a room where everybody says one plus one equals three and that anybody who says one plus one equals two is a demon who needs to be killed, the prudent thing to do is just not mention that you know one plus one equals two, because you gain nothing from doing so and will most likely be severely punished.

This is where I think we are heading, to a reality where the people who can pretend to be politically correct or give off an aura that doesn't make people concerned with them while still being aware of things that aren't popularly understood will win out long term, while people who are less capable of being nuanced or clever will be punished and eventually lose the evolutionary battle due to deprivation of resources that comes from being a social outcast. The other group of people who by default go along with the flow of reality will just remain in the middle of the pack, and as a result, not really win or lose.

Is this a good or a bad thing? I don't really think in those terms outside of a very narrow range of things I find morally disturbing (incest, rape, pedophilia, destruction of innocence, etc), so I don't think this situation is good or bad. It's more a fundamentally new configuration of incentives and rules where resources are more linked to agility rather than stability, which has been enabled by increased velocity of resources along with the decreased friction of communication. Because the rules to the game of success and failure have changed, the winners and losers will change. It is what it is, and that's that.

Targeted Individual
As of late, I have become paranoid. Things are going so well that it seems unreal. I have money coming in even when I'm sleeping. I am getting a ton of positive feedback at a constant rate. Women are trying to get my attention. I am working on multiple projects that are all coming along well. Follower counts and all positive metrics are consistently heading in an upward trajectory. Life couldn't be better, but there is a nagging thought that keeps on tugging at the back of my head.

This can't continue unabated. Soon there has to be some sort of tragedy or loose end that I didn't properly take care of that comes back to bite me and bring everything tumbling down. Everything is too easy. Everybody is treating me too well. I've entered another time of unreality where nothing even seems real because of how little discomfort I am in. Now, it's just a constant stream of success.

It won't be long until people start gunning for me once they realize that I am successful and they are not. Soon, people who want something from me will start to suck up to me. Soon, the deranged individuals who have become personally invested in my destruction will grow desperate. I feel the walls closing in on me. I fear that I may not escape from the next flurry of parasites and predators unharmed.

Still, I will persevere. These are the final days of tribulation. Like Jesus in the garden, I shed a tear for the near future and await my betrayal. Then I will go up on a proverbial cross and suffer some illusionary defeat, and then and only then will I be able to come back to life and triumph over my detractors. Then again, perhaps that has already happened.

The way I have set everything up, once I have left the orbit of struggling, I will be free of gravity completely. I will then be able to do whatever I want, whenever I want. Until then, however, I have to be on guard against the haters and the losers. I need to stay focused. I need to ignore the weirdos and the deviants and the burnout alcoholics. I am doing this quite well now, but I am still cautious. I will overcome.

Goo Goo Gaa Gaa Baby

Make sure you drink some water every day. You don't want to die of dehydration, right? Drinking water is good for you. Drinking soda is bad for you. Did you know that? Most people are not aware that water is healthy and soda is unhealthy.

Also make sure that you know how to use the toilet. You don't want to soil your clothes. That is bad and unhealthy. You want to be a big boy and use the toilet, OK? I am so proud of you for taking the time to learn these very confusing topics.

Lastly, make sure you go outside sometimes. There is a little thing I like to call "fresh outside air" that you won't get inside your mom's house. Open the door and walk outside, then you will get "fresh outside air" and it will be good. Then you will see how outside air is different than inside air.

It is important to adult properly, which is why I have decided to remind you of these important things to know. Also, don't pick your nose, read old books, listen to old music, learn how to count, take showers, eat food, and when you want to sleep then you should close your eyes. If these tips helped you, feel free to purchase my e-book and give me a follow on twitter.

Chopsticks

I was probably six or seven years old, about to walk down some stairs with some chopsticks in my left hand. Then somebody told me to be careful or else I might trip down the stairs. I assured them I wouldn't trip down the stairs, then I tripped down the stairs, about ten steps in total, and slammed my chin into the floor and split it open. I had to go to the hospital to get it all stitched up, and the surgeon remarked how well I stayed still for somebody my age. The truth is that I don't really remember all that much pain. I probably permanently damaged my brain when I split my chin open, but the thing that I'll always remember is being warned, laughing off the warning, then the warning turning out suspiciously prescient. It was like something out of a movie.

Hanger

When I was probably ten or eleven, I remember playing alone in my room. I had a lot of free time in my childhood, mostly because my family members were busy doing their schoolwork and helping each other with schoolwork and chores while I hid from what I was supposed to be doing and read, listened to the radio, or drew. It was probably around two or three in the afternoon on a school day.

I was really bored on this particular day, and had been daydreaming for at least an hour, when I suddenly got the urge to see what would happen if I took apart a metal hanger and stuck it into the wall socket. I thought about it for a little bit, aware that I would end up shocked. I had shocked myself quite a few times with friends using an electric fence as well as licking one of those 9 volt batteries for a mild to dull buzz, depending on how strong the battery was, so I knew what would happen if I stuck the hanger in the wall socket. I was just curious to see what the extent of the shock would be.

Not thinking of any possible reasons why this might be a stupid or dangerous idea, I decided to go through with my experiment. I unwound the hanger until it was just one thick metal wire that could be bent. I bent the thick wire in half. Then, with one hand on each side of the bent wire, I sat down directly in front of the electrical outlet in my room and took a few excited breaths. I vividly remember the moments immediately before sticking the hanger in, the insertion and momentary delay, when the final connection was made, the loud pop, the jolt of electricity, the spark, being electrified, the circuit breaker blowing, and what happened after that.

When I was electrified, I jumped back from one side of the room to the other, around seven or eight feet. It wasn't a conscious decision, but rather something like when the doctor hits your kneecap and your knee shoots forward. The adrenaline rush I felt from being shocked like that was one of the best adrenaline rushes I have ever felt, mostly because I was not expecting it. I remember staying still sitting on the floor, looking at the slightly charred plastic on the front of the outlet where the spark had occurred, and feeling genuinely in a good mood. It was a great amount of excitement.

I probably fried part of my brain by doing this, so I don't recommend anybody try it. Ever since then, I'll get a slight pain in my chest once or twice every few years. Maybe I took a decade or two off my life. Maybe my mental situation is in part due to electrical self lobotomy. It doesn't really matter to me, because I had fun. That's what life is all about. Imagine if I hadn't done this, where would I be right now? Probably making mid six figures a year doing some sort of computer science related consulting for a government (domestic or foreign), but I'd be miserable. Now, I'm unemployable and not miserable. All in all, I'd say things are working out pretty well for me.

Playing Tag

I was probably fourteen or fifteen years old. I was playing some form of tag with neighborhood friends outside. It was dark out. This wasn't normal tag, this was some weird version that was a hybrid of hide and seek along with tag. My childhood was very charmed, and so I spent most of it in wholesome activities like fishing, playing games outside, reading, and anything else you would find in a nineteen-sixties family sitcom.

Anyway, I was running away from somebody, and ran into an area with fairly high grass. Everything was going fine, I was (and am) the fastest runner in the neighborhood so I wasn't going to be tagged. Then, some grass wrapped around my left ankle, which ended up pulling against me and slamming me to the ground. I flew headfirst into the grass and dirt, then my eyes started to water.

It was then that I got a nosebleed. A lot of people in my family get nosebleeds. It's not from drug abuse or anything like that, just poor genetics. It's kind of funny, because I'm the only person in my family who has ever put drugs up my nose and yet I'm one of the only people in my family who never gets nosebleeds. I can't remember getting a nosebleed other than this one time in my life. I also got an immediate headache.

This incident most likely gave me a concussion and further damaged my brain, because I had a splitting headache for hours after it. It also deviated my septum and made the tip of my nose crooked, which is kind of funny because ever since I can remember I always have had the sniffles, so people probably think I'm a drug addict, although I am most definitely not a drug addict.

What did I learn from this incident? Nothing. I will still run in tall grass if I feel like it. I do not care if I trip and slam my head into the ground at this point in my life, because my brain is pretty much fully developed and I also don't really care if I get brain damage. Sometimes, there's really no point to bad things that happen. When this is the case, there's no reason to be upset or search for some deeper meaning, you just move on and go do something else. After this happened I think I went inside, ate some food, played some video games, drank some tea, and went to bed.

The First Twenty-Five

The first twenty-five years of life are absurdly charmed. You start out as a baby and get everything given to you, then you get a little older and you're a cute little child. Everybody is nice to you and calls you cute. You get a little older and now you're in middle school. Everybody is still nice to you and compliments you on your appearance. You get even older and people continue to be nice to you. You are now in high school and people your age continue to be kind to you and lots of people are always complimenting you.

You're at college now, and everybody tells you how smart and impressive you are. You have done so well in tests and are getting good grades. When you have questions, you are pleased to find that there are a lot of people who are eager to help you. People are even willing to do a lot of your work for you, and although you like to do things yourself, sometimes you let them do your work for you. College is pretty great. Best of all, you're working towards a career you are sure will be fulfilling.

You are almost done with college and you are surprised to find how easy it is to find work. You apply, you go for an interview, and you get a job! It's that simple, which makes you wonder why you see other people complaining about not being able to find work. They just must not have what it takes, unlike you. You don't worry about other people though, because they're not you and you're killing it. Somehow, getting a job isn't really as enjoyable as you fantasized it would be, but you know this is what you want to do, and everybody is encouraging you to pursue your dreams.

You're twenty-four years old now and done with college. People are still really nice to you and you have a steady job, but for some reason you feel like something is kind of *off* in an indescribable way. You have also picked up a bit of an alcoholism habit, although everybody around you makes lighthearted jokes about it and you don't really see it as that harmful, it's definitely taking a bit of a toll to be drinking on an almost nightly basis.

Then, twenty-five hits and some weird switch flips. For some reason, people aren't really being all that nice to you anymore. They're not rude or outright mean (usually), but they're kind of cold to you. Young women start treating you strangely and most men ignore you. It didn't used to be like this, but now it is. Guys at work don't really seem all that eager to talk to you now.

The years go by and you get older. You continue to drink and dabble with other drugs. People get progressively more indifferent towards you. You get fired from your job and a younger girl that reminds you of yourself in your early twenties gets hired in your place. You now realize that you had the world in your hands when you were younger, but nobody ever told you. Now, you have no influence, no power, no sex appeal, and you realize just how shallow reality really is. Most of those men who were nice to you were nice to you because they wanted to have sex with you. You weren't particularly competent or talented in anything, and you never will be.

Every year gets worse and worse. You grow more and more bitter. You'll probably end up settling down with some infertile middle class non-white who has a good job and an inferiority complex about being non-white which leads him to fetishize white women. Everybody in your family will be thrilled that you're getting married, but you'll be bitter about reality until the day you die. You screwed up, but it's genuinely not your fault. Nobody told you that the constant party until you're twenty-five was going to end. You weren't even aware that life was a constant party. You probably hate your father for not doing a proper job raising you, and you're right to do so. He screwed up and now you're paying the price.

Boring Boring Boring

Reality is so boring when there is nothing going wrong. When bad things are happening, I can find humor and entertainment in the disproportionate and absurd reactions of people around me. Right now, however, everything is perfect. There have been no insane terror attacks. There is no horrible drama. There is nobody who got killed in a car crash or diagnosed with terminal cancer. All that seems to be is a lukewarm pool of serenity.

I am so bored at the moment. I might do something stupid in the near future just to feel some excitement. There is no weight to actions or risk to anything right now. I'm pretty much just going day to day in a productive manner and getting a lot of tasks completed in a consistent fashion. I hate this feeling.

I need to see panic. I need to see stress and feel uncertainty. I need risk. I need to be alive and active and on guard against some external variable that might potentially ruin my life, or else I will go crazy. People who live in this habitual predictable reality of safety in which I currently reside are not really living. They are people who take no risks and are happy to take no risks because that means they will never feel pain or defeat.

The sort of doldrums I'm experiencing right now must be what makes people enjoy browsing facebook and watching TV. Cutting myself would be more enjoyable than what is going on right now, which is nothing.

I'm thinking of buying a dual sport bike to ease my suffering. With a dual sport bike I'll always be very close to dying. One little mistake while driving/riding, by myself or people around me, and I might suffer a life altering or ending injury. This will give me the kicks I need to feel alive. This will make reality tolerable.

Flash Games

When I was in high-school, I spent a fair bit of time doing some flash game development. For the younger audience, flash games were essentially arcade games that could be played in the web browser. At a certain point, different groups decided that flash was not profitable enough to continue to support it, so they made up an excuse about it being insecure compared to regular html websites (a lie), and so flash was discontinued. While all of this is interesting and worth discussing at a later date, this is not what the main thrust of this essay is about.

What I learned from programming flash games was how to properly structure software. There is a certain level of engineering that you arrive at after making enough human computer interfaces, which is what games are. After a bit of practice, you learn how to pass information and format data as well as other specific techniques. There is a surprising amount of nuance and detail that needs to happen when designing anything software related, and every little decision ends up impacting a lot of decisions down the line. This means that you become very particular with how you're setting things up.

What surprised me about flash games is how much more complicated they were to make than anything else I have ever done. They weren't hard to make, they were just extremely complicated. If I had to guess, this is very similar to how people who make traditional watches operate. Nothing is *hard* about making a watch with a few hundred gears, it is a matter of following simple rules and understanding how everything is interacting with everything else, then spending a lot of time being careful about how the watch is put together.

Writing is so much easier than programming simple flash games, and programming simple flash games is not hard. With writing, it's a one way street. I am putting something on paper and then I'm done with it. There is no need to properly structure anything. There are no bugs or compatibility requirements. Once it's done, it's done. This is not the case with flash games I made in high school, where I had to come up with an idea, mechanics around the idea, build the mechanics, test the mechanics, adjust the mechanics, imagine how people who don't have my understanding of the inner workings of the program would interface with the program, then adjust what my ideal was to be compatible with external input.

People who write for a living need to get over themselves. This is not hard work. This is not complicated. This is not something that requires all the much intelligence. In fact, most non-writers could easily be better writers than most writers, it's just that the non-writers are busy doing extra talented things.

It's so funny watching the complexes people get because they pay attention to the praise of people who are very eager to praise. No, you're not a genius because you know how to put together a vaguely coherent pdf of a few hundred pages (at most) and use amazon to self publish. You're not going to change the world, at all. You're not helping anybody. You're not a suffering artist. You're not anybody special and once you are dead nobody will care.

Creative people are some of the most deluded people on earth. Yes, it's objectively better to be a creative person. That's because most people are too busy being productive and working hard to get into a mindset that is needed to be creative. Because successful creative people managed to get around the rat race and take advantage of economic inequalities that allow them to make way more money than they would in an objective economy, they feel like they're worth the money they make. They are not worth the money they make. They are generally worth much less than the people making minimum wage scraping grease off the grease machine in the back of a fast food restaurant.

Did I Make You Mad?

Did I just make you mad? Are you fuming right now? Do you hate me? Do you despise me? Do you want to kill me? Murder me? Hit me? Frame me for some horrific crime? Wound me emotionally? Physically Spiritually? End my life? Torture my loved ones? Kill my pets? Burn down my house? Tear out my hair? Poke out my eyes? Blow me up with a grenade? That's understandable.

Instead of being upset at me, why not just not be upset at me? Take a deep breath, calm down, and smile. There is no need to be upset. There is no need to not like me. Just realize that everything I say and do can be taken in a negative way or a positive way. It's up to you to be mature and take it in a positive way.

Once you stop getting angry about things I say and do, you will start to see how I'm not that bad of a person. Once you start complimenting me and treating me well and laughing at all the horrible things I've been involved in, you will realize that perceptions are only perceptions and perceptions are up to the one who perceives them.

I do not have the power to make you upset. Only you have the power to get upset at me. If you get upset at me, then you are really getting upset at yourself. It's up to you to be the bigger person, so don't let me drag you down. I am just an innocent carefree individual having a laugh here and there, not some evil that you need to lash out against.

Just relax and enjoy your life. Stop getting bent out of shape at words. Realize that sticks and stones may break your bones but words will never hurt you. Be a shining example of self control and emotional fortitude to everybody around you. Demonstrate that I am harmless by not caring when I am a horrible person. Then, you will achieve inner peace and nirvana.

Armchair Generals

The following is fairly straightforward, but for whatever reason I hadn't really internalized it or understood it until the past year. Most people who talk about things don't really know what they're talking about. This especially applies to people who do a lot of talking. When you actually do stuff that has fail conditions, like engineering projects or something that requires planning and execution in order to be completed successfully, you are bound to fail a lot of the time. After a while of failing, you gain an appreciation for doing things without being over confident or talking about them until you know they're a sure thing.

When you are experienced with doing things and failing at things, you also tend to get humbled with regard to how you judge people who are doing things you have done, because you can understand how they might be overlooking some aspect that they have to fail at before they can properly do whatever they're trying to do. This has been the case with me. Even though I'm not really a proud or humble individual, I have definitely gotten less verbally caustic or rude to people I see making mistakes, because I've made more mistakes than anybody I know of.

Generally, the people who seem to be the most into the business of other people fall into a few categories. There are the people who haven't really ever attempted anything and so have no frame of reference for how things should be done. They generally aren't really malicious, just kind of deluded and naive. Another group are the people who have tried and failed and then given up or settled. They are miserable because they have compromised on their dreams and have to live with the fact that they didn't stick with whatever it is they were trying, so now they are bitter and sometimes malicious towards people they see who are attempting to do the things they failed at doing. The last group might be well meaning, but they are generally haughty. These people tried something and it worked the first time, so they have no experience with what is the norm for most people, and thus can't really relate. As such, they are usually overconfident until they eventually fail, which most (but not all) do. When they fail, some will give up, some will implode, and some will push through.

None of these people are really evil or bad, although some of them do have very negative motives and will be a negative impact on your life if you let them. That said, it's very important to not worry too much about what any of these people say. They don't really matter in the grand scheme of things unless you involve them, and there is no good reason to involve people who don't know what they're talking about. It's much better to just do your own thing and try your best and put your best foot forward, knowing that you're going to fail and have a lot of hiccups on the road to success, a road that you might never get to even if you try your hardest. Then, if somebody who seems to be in a better place than you who has gone through similar problems and struggles offers advice, you should listen to that person and take their advice seriously.

Most importantly, try not to directly spite armchair generals. Most won't stalk you or harass you, but they will be generally negative about you to others and root for your failure, which is something that you shouldn't want to encourage people to do. If you set up that environment, then people will be watching every little thing you do and little problems might be magnified and get you into a bigger funk than is warranted. Also, there's no benefit from wasting time and energy on people who don't matter. They won't do anything with their life besides talk and critique, so you should just distance yourself from them lest they rub off on you. All in all, armchair generals are mostly harmless but worth avoiding because they don't really know how anything works or else they wouldn't be armchair generals.

Public Service Announcement

We like to joke around here, that much is clear. With that in mind, I feel it is my responsibility to take a moment and remind everybody of the fact that while we may sometime say things that are offensive, crass, and downright demented, we are not bad people. In fact, we are not only not bad people but we are good people. That's right, we are morally superior people who care about important things. We would like to go over some of the things we believe, just in case some people are unaware.

Rape is bad. It can happen to men and it can happen to women, but it's bad. There's nothing good about rape. We do not support or condone rape nor do we participate in rape, either on the victim or criminal side of the equation. If you think rape is good, please do not continue to read anything I create.

Another thing that is bad is decapitation of women. This is something that needs to be said, because I have a suspicion that women being decapitated is becoming a socially acceptable hobby for violent men. No matter the public sentiment of the time, we disavow all decapitations of women. It's simply not right. Do not decapitate women, and if you do, do not read the rest of this book or contact me. I am not friends with anybody who decapitates women.

We do not support bad things. We support good things. If you support bad things, you're a bad person. If you support good things, you're a good person. Do the math. Think about whether you want to be a good person or a bad person. Personally, we want to be good people. If you want to be a bad person, you're not welcome here.

Hopefully this important and needed Public Service Announcement has made the reality that Paul Town is a good person/organization/project with strong moral characteristics. Hopefully you will join me/us/they/them in being good people who do not support bad things like rape or the decapitation of women. Take a stand and let people know that you do not think bad things are good things, even though it may be popular to say that bad things are good things.

Frankly, we find these sorts of things important to distance ourselves from. By doing so, we are sure that we will prevent further rapes and decapitations, because lots of potential rapists and decapitators will be dissuaded from raping and decapitating by reading this public service announcement. Our estimates show that approximately eighty percent of our readership are potential rapists and decapitators, so by this essay alone we have essentially done more humanitarian work than most people could do in ten lifetimes, and we're just getting started. You're welcome.

5G

We got fiber internet at my house recently. It's great, except for one thing: the router that they set up uses 5G technology. This is driving me insane. I am no longer in control of anything I do or say, legally speaking. It's not even me in control anymore, it's the 5G. I might do anything, and I mean anything, to anybody or anything at any time and I couldn't stop myself.

I can feel the radio or micro waves or whatever they are burring into my skull. I'm pretty sure that the government is using me for testing. That would explain why nobody but myself seems to be negatively influenced by the 5G. I'm being poisoned and everybody around me acts like there is something wrong with me. Nothing is wrong with me, everybody is just delusional.

I'm getting dumber with every minute. My IQ has most likely dropped several points since the start of writing this essay. Me so dumb dumb. Me no like 5G. Now me getting cancer. Now me being killed by invisible waves. Now me dying. Urrrgh. Uggggh. Urrrrrrgh.

Being Performatively Explicit

There is a very interesting subset of people who feel the need to state certain obvious truths repeatedly. There is a small portion of them that are people who seem to have some form of OCD or social anxiety, but the majority of the people who engage in this sort of behavior tend to be deeply screwed up in some way or another.

Everybody who isn't brain-dead knows certain things are wrong. Even most people who do horrible things are aware that those things are wrong, they just don't really care (or are out of control in some manner) and do those things anyway. Because certain things are intuitively bad and taboo, this creates a sort of opportunity for people to make jokes that run counter to the common understanding regarding whatever they're joking about. Normal people either able to laugh along with the joke or ignore it, but this conspicuously loud type of person feels compelled to tell people that they do not agree with obvious jokes.

Generally, I have seen a pattern where people who engage in this sort of behavior tend to be hiding some serious habit of wrongdoing that they know is wrongdoing. The vocal virtue they espouse is a weird attempt at misdirection in order to establish the fact that they are not people who do bad things, but people who don't do bad things generally don't worry all that much about making sure people know they don't do bad things, because doing or not doing bad things isn't generally on their mind and they focus on more healthy, productive things.

While there are definitely people who are very serious about being virtuous and moral and make it clear to people that they are very serious about these things, they are a very rare type of person and they generally don't spend their time issuing condemnations of people who aren't also attempting to live a virtuous and moral life.

This bizarre behavior likely stems from the insecurity and guilt that comes from being engaged in activity that the person finds shameful but can't bring themselves to stop engaging in. Instead of working on their own problems, they insist on trying to drag everybody down to their level of feeling bad all the times.

While I wouldn't recommend being around the inverse of these sorts of people (those who take a perverse amount of pleasure being crass, reveling in, and encouraging clearly wrong behavior), I try to stay away from performatively explicit people. These types are not loyal and they do not have strong backbones. They constantly initiate weird moral tests and are incapable of being direct or honest. They spend their time gossiping and complaining and are generally a waste of time and energy when they're not being an active detriment to everybody around them.

Group Project

A lot of people think that *Paul Town* is a group of people. They think there is some distributed effort that is underway; some bigger, grander purpose. This is understandable. After all, Paul Town has created a disproportionate amount of varied content as well as influence and knows a disproportionate amount of abnormal individuals in different corners of the internet and in real life. What is the truth? Well, that's something that people just aren't ready for yet. Even if they were, it's just not time for the big reveal. Believe me/us, there is a big reveal coming.

Anybody paying attention can tell that there is more than just boredom, anti-social personality disorder, and a ton of free time at play. Anybody connecting the dots can feel the shift in the air that has happened over the past few years. This is bigger than you, than me, than us. Can you feel it? I can feel it. This isn't just a singular person making stuff that amuses and interests them. This couldn't be the work of only one person. There is too much going on for it to be the work of one person.

Do you want a little hint? Do you think you deserve one? You deserve nothing, least of all a hint, but you will get one now. Throughout all of Paul Town's writings, there has been a persistent code which pertains to certain facts and future events. This has also been hidden in all of Paul Town's videos and other media he has created, as well as the source code to all of his software projects. Each genre of Paul Town creation has different keys and ciphers, so don't think that learning the proper way to parse something written will help you understand how to parse video material. It won't. If anything, it will simply make everything more confusing, as there are also counter-cyphers embedded into every medium to throw people off.

Is it possible that all of this was just made up off of the top of my head? That I'm just kind of messing with a lot of people for my own personal amusement? That I have connections to hundreds of well known people and an ability to create anything out of anything and I'm just a singular person? That I'm just the exception that proves the rule of human mediocrity and lack of vision? Yes, that is possibility, but is it the most likely situation? No, more likely you have stumbled upon a multi-decade psyop in its infant stages. Most likely this essay was formed in a laboratory with a chalkboard and multiple people conversing over the course of multiple days. Most likely there is a coherent secret code that is worth spending days and weeks trying to find that is hidden in everything the elite conglomerate that makes up *Paul Town* has created.

Good luck unraveling this group project. Most likely, you will never find out what it's all about. Most likely, you will end up giving up after a few months or a year of earnest searching, or go crazy and lose everything in a schizophrenic breakdown. Then again, maybe you'll figure it out. Maybe you'll put the puzzle together. Maybe you'll win a very valuable prize. Then again, maybe all of this is made up. Maybe I'm just sadistic. Maybe there is not meaning, no group project, no secret code, no benefit to spending time filling your head with fantasies and hypotheticals. Maybe you're already well on your way to a schizophrenic breakdown. Maybe you'll be committed to a psych ward in the near future, and it will all be because I made up this funny little joke of an essay. Then again, maybe there is something to everything that is being created. Who really knows?

The Tightrope Of Depravity

There is a certain line you have to walk when you're doing things for other people. On one hand, you have to be unpredictable and deranged enough to warrant attention, and on the other you don't want to remain too long in that territory or you will scare away people who you need to not be scared if you ever want to have commercial success. Of course, I don't care about commercial success, but I do care about doing what I do to the best of my ability, so I walk the tightrope of depravity.

You need to emotionally abuse your audience. You need to make sure they think you love them one day and that you might kill them and their loved ones the next. This fear is very important, otherwise you deal with strange people who feel like it's OK to get in your personal space and hassle you. If somebody did that to me, I would kill their family members. Maybe I wouldn't, but I could. I could easily kill all of the people they cared about and make them watch without thinking twice. Of course, I wouldn't. I'm a nice guy. But I could.

The minute you show that you can be controlled, that you can be predicted, that you can be replicated, you lose all of your mojo. Once you're predictable, nobody cares what you're doing. Nobody cares if they know what you're going to say before you say it. You have to be unpredictably predictable but only part of the time. The rest of the time you need to be a loose cannon.

If you are too destructive, of yourself or other people, eventually people will just pity or fear you, and neither of those things are sustainable. Both push people away to a level that you'll never get back. Keeping attention is a catch and release situation, not a scare away or disgust away constantly situation. Pull them in then push them away then pull them in and push them away again. Keep on doing that to more and more people, and eventually you will achieve success. Do it poorly and your life is ruined.

People like to watch bad people do the things they dream about. The things they imagine, they like to see done by people who get away with it. This acts as a substitute for them, without risk, because they project their delusional self image on your actions. If you're losing at life and doing horrible things, you're just disgusting and somebody to make fun of. If you're doing well while you're living out their stifled anti-social impulses, you're their hero.

You have to be worse than the normal person but also better than the normal person. You need to have some sort of social proof that shows that the things that you're not supposed to be doing but you're doing anyway aren't destroying you. This will show that the rules of the average Joe don't apply to you, and you will become an aspirational figure. Do this correctly and you'll be a living god. Do this incorrectly and you'll be the homeless heroin junkie begging for change and being spit on by people who used to be his friend when he's not being sodomized by people with grids.

Wireless Earbuds

It's going to be really funny when a few decades pass and everybody realizes that wireless earbuds have destroyed billions of brains. Basically, the brain is being fried. That's just science. How do I know about this? It's just common sense. No, I have not done any research on this and I have no experience on anything scientific and I don't even have any education past the tenth grade, but I'm really sure about this sort of stuff.

Things are getting really bad. The elite, consumer electronics companies, are now destroying their market with things like wireless earbuds. Once again, don't ask for sources because I don't have any, but you can trust me. They are lobotomizing you a little bit more with every song you listen to, and you love it, because you're already a mindless sheep.

They won't get me, I haven't used earbuds or headphones since 2017. I stopped shortly before I was placed in a mental institution after being found roaming outside in a nearby neighborhood in below freezing weather with a case of near hypothermia. I learned a lot of forbidden knowledge during that psychotic episode that lasted about a year. Now, I'm completely sane and completely back to normal, but I know deep secrets, like the fact that wireless earbuds are frying your brain. Don't ask me how I know this stuff. Let's just say that I have seen beyond the veil. Stick with me, you might just learn something.

Old People

It's time to face reality. You're old. You're not young, fifty is not the new thirty, you're old. You have one foot in the grave. If you had a heart attack and died tomorrow, it wouldn't really be that out of the ordinary. Did you have a good life? No? Well, too bad. That sucks for you, but unless you were born with some disease or condition that made your life impossible to do well at, after the age of around twenty five if your life sucks it's your fault. You wasted your life, your life is over, you'll never get that time back, and that's that.

There's no reason to go out in an embarrassing manner. You don't need to spend the last few decades (at most) of your now consistently declining life running around like a chicken with its head chopped off. It's time to grow up and take responsibility for the mediocre waste of life that your life has been. It's time to cut your losses and do something for somebody else instead of being a drag on everybody and everyone around you.

Give all your money to young people. Give your property to young people. Hopefully you have children and grandchildren to give it to, but there's a good chance you lived your miserable failure of a life in a completely selfish way and never had kids. If you didn't have kids, hire some young people to help with your computer or mow your lawn and overpay them for their work. Give them all that money you aren't ever going to use instead of spending it on some retarded car your eyes are too bad to drive properly or a disgusting cruise filled with other spoiled idiotic old people who are throwing away their wealth in order to avoid doing anything decent with it.

Look, I get it. It sucks when you realize you have done stuff that has no value. I did that for a few years until I realized that I was doing stuff that had no value, and then I stopped. There's still time for you to stop being a parasite. There's not much more time, and even if you are one of the rare old people who actually does anything nice for anybody else, chances are that it won't outweigh the sheer magnitude of your life of being a loser, but at least you ended well and you might be able to trick some people into thinking you aren't a piece of trash.

It's really not your fault that you wasted your whole life. If your parents were smart, they would have beat you with a belt when they saw you acting like a mentally ill self obsessed delusional brat. They would have told you how reality works. You would have realized that strangers are not your friend, that you have a responsibility to create offspring, and to equip those offspring to go into the world in a better state, both financially and mentally. But, like you, your parents were idiotic morons who neglected passing on knowledge and a mindset that are both necessary for generational success. As a result, you're a disgusting blight upon the earth.

You'll be dead soon. No amount of bargaining or giving money to doctors will stop that. Even if doctors could help you live longer, you couldn't afford those doctors because those doctors are for actually rich people who have done things of note. You have never done anything of note. The only time you'll ever make the news is when you're in the obituaries. That's sad. You're sad. Life is sad, when you're you. Watching people like you exist is sad. If I had my way, you and all the people - young and old - would already be dead.

Traveling

Traveling, for most people, is essentially a weird ritual that is engaged in when the rest of life sucks. Reality is not fun for most people. It consists of eating unhealthily, reading and watching things that are unpleasant, talking with people who are unenjoyable to talk to, working a job that is soul crushing, and then drinking alcohol to cope with all of this on a daily basis. Look around you whenever you're in public and most of the people you'll see look unhealthy and kind of dead inside.

When you are one of these people, travel is a little break from what is real. All of the sudden, the facts that you're going nowhere in life and you hate waking up and dread going to sleep and have nightmares while your asleep disappear. All the money you have saved up and worked for gets thrown away in order to support your delusion for a few days to a week. During that time, you can lie to yourself that you're a winner. During that time, you can pretend you are somebody who matters.

The truth is that traveling is a meme unless you're me. If you're me, you don't have responsibilities that are connected to geography or time. I can disappear off the face of the earth for a month or a year and come back and I'll be getting paid the whole time. In fact, disappearing for a while just makes me earn more money, because people wonder what I'm up to. I can travel and live like I live at home. I can just do whatever I want, whenever I want. I don't have to pretend.

Because I don't have to pretend, I don't really fantasize about traveling. There are a few things I want to do in various places around the globe, but it's not travel for the sake of travel. America is big enough and varied enough that I can see any climate and get any experience I want without leaving. Traveling is a large waste of time. Days spent in the air or on a train or boat quickly add up.

The people who think traveling makes them interesting are so pathetic. They are tourists, and nobody likes tourists besides people who take advantage of tourists; and they hate tourists. Here's an idea, instead of coping by wasting money, how about people who spend their time traveling and running away from their self created hell on earth instead focusing on making their existence not so horrible. How about they do things that give themselves a leg up in the real world instead of buying seven days in some beach-front resort knowing that in two weeks they'll be back in a cubicle wishing they were dead.

Oooh. Wow. A sandy beach. Wow. The mountains. Wow. Some third worlder servant at a hotel serving cheap liquor. Wow. So exciting. This is what life is all about. This is what makes suffering for decades worth it. This is why I am willing to sit in an office building rotting away. This is why I'll never be anything and when I die nobody will care. I will never do anything of value for anybody, but at least I'll be able to take pictures of myself at some *exotic* location to share with people I'm trying to impress. This is life. This is living.

Stop Calling Me A Troll

A lot of people really make me angry. Why? Because they're idiots. They don't understand what words mean. They misuse words and they say things that aren't accurate and that makes me really mad, especially when it's about me. This sort of behavior applies to the people who insist on calling me a troll.

I'm not a troll. Trolls are lowly creatures, existing only to make other people uncomfortable or upset. Trolls aren't thinkers, philosophers, or artists. I am a thinker, an artist, and a philosopher. I am not a troll. I am not somebody who lives to mess with other people. I am not a worthless nobody who spews a ton of confrontational communication at strangers, delighting when they take my bait and give me attention. If anything, I am conflict adverse.

My work is too important to be classified by trolling what I think of and create will change the world forever. When I am gone, millions will mourn. There will be statues of me erected across the globe. Women will sob uncontrollably, both those I have had sex with and those who wish they could have had sex with me. These are not predictions, these are just common sense conclusions.

Stop calling me a troll, it is really hurtful. Would you call Einstein a troll? Would you call Woody Allen a troll? Would you call Bill Cosby a troll? Would you call the guy who played President Underwood in House of Cards a troll? No, all of these people were geniuses. I see different aspects of myself, my actions, and my work reflected in each of these people. If they are not trolls, then I am not a troll. They are not trolls.

I don't have anything against trolls. Some of my best friends are trolls. I used to do a bit of trolling when I was younger. Sometimes, I would give random homeless people large sums of money just to see how they would react. Other times, I would volunteer to give blood. I've donated one of my kidneys and one of my lungs. That is the trolling I used to do. You could have called me a troll back then, but not anymore. Now, I'm busy writing books and creating software that empowers trillions of people. Now, I'm a thinker, an author, a philosopher, a philanthropist, a genius, and an important person.

When you call people trolls who aren't trolls, you besmirch the actual trolls. You degrade their profession, their calling. You say to them, "Anybody can do what you do. I don't know what you do and I don't really care. I am an ignoramus who spits upon trolling. I am an idiot and I look down upon what you do. Do not try to educate me, for I will just scoff at you." Do you want trolls to feel bad? Do you want to harm strangers with these untoward words? Do you want to hurt them? Why? Are you a sadist?

The same thing goes for calling me somebody who practices irony. I do not engage in irony. I have trouble distinguishing between coughs and sneezes, so I am not really capable of irony, to be quite honest. I have never been ironic in my life. I have been sarcastic and passive aggressive in certain weaker moments, but that is not the same thing as irony. In fact, it is an insult to the actual ironists to label what I do as irony.

People need to learn the definitions to words and terms before they use them. That's not true, they don't need to or else they would, and they don't, so they don't need to. I would prefer that they learn what words and terms mean, but that is more a flaw with me than with anybody who does these things. I really need to get over myself. I am so pathetic. I am so lowly, so demanding. I am the scum of the earth. I shouldn't even be alive. Somebody should gun me down in the street. I wish the person who emailed me saying they were going to rape me to death with dogs in the middle of the street had actually done it. I am the worst person who has ever lived.

Isolation

I'm always alone. No matter who I'm with, I'm with one person: myself. That's it. When I'm talking with somebody, I'm really just listening to them. They run the conversation. What they want is what they get, unless I'm trying to cause a problem. I'm not really there. I was never really there. I'll never really be there. I'm only here, somewhere on the inside of my head, watching myself react to other people.

Oh poor me, nobody relates to me. Nobody can understand me. Nobody gets where I'm coming from. Nobody will ever really be able to connect to me. I am such a victim. I feel so sorry for myself that I'm never actually honest to anybody around me. I never actually let down my guard and everything I do is a highly calculated wager of percentages balanced against other percentages.

Everything is about me, even the things that aren't about me are about me, because I am constantly thinking about how they might interact with me now or at a later date or how they might interact with other things which might interact with me now or at a later date and so on and so forth. Yeah, I'm a real deep thinker.

I'm dishonest, disingenuous, conniving, and loved by everybody, which just makes me even less of a good person. If people are fond of a bad person, do those people deserve a good person? Do those people even deserve to live? Why? It doesn't make any sense to me.

I will hang out with most people, if the situation allows. I will go almost anywhere and do almost anything, and in the moment I will almost always enjoy whatever it is I'm engaged in. I'll even trick myself into feeling like I'm best friends with whoever I'm with. But before I do something and I hang out with somebody and after I do something and after I hang out with somebody, I have no love or enthusiasm in my heart. I don't care.

This isn't my problem. Everybody else is at fault, not me. I'm perfect. I couldn't find a flaw with myself and I can find constant flaws with everybody else. I'm the best person alive, probably in all of history. That's just reality. Am I lying about all of this? Is it fiction? Is it true? Does it matter? Does anybody care? Who cares? Not me. I don't really care. I'll never really care. It might not be a joke, but it is really funny.

Zoloft

I've never had the displeasure of trying Zoloft, and I never will have the displeasure of trying Zoloft because I'm not stupid enough to let people make me take Zoloft or any anti-depressant, but I know a few people who take Zoloft. It's quite funny, in a kind of sick way, how that stuff eats away at the brain and the soul.

Are you hungry all the time? Do you like to make excuses? Are you fat, unmotivated, lazy, stupid, and bad at reasoning as well as being anxious all the time? If not, take some Zoloft to fix that. You'll never get anything that isn't a requirement for somebody else done, because you'll lose the ability to think in any manner that is not dictated by an external force.

Parents put their kids on these medications all the time. These people bring little children into the world, then because of their own mediocrity and neurosis (usually caused by drug abuse) they make innocent little creatures destroy their brains and their body so they don't have to be good parents who provide good outlets. It's so funny, if I was a kid and somebody did that to me, I would murder them.

What type of person is happy to ruin the lives of people who rely on them? Most people are that type of person. This is just the reality of the situation and it most likely is the reality of the situation. So few people exist outside of being the slave for somebody cutting them a paycheck that barely anybody has any idea of how anything works. Everybody just does what they're told and what makes them feel good, even if that is turning their child into a moron.

Most parents are actively harmful towards their children and their children grow up to be actively harmful towards their children and so on and so forth. It has been this way for a long time, except that until recently, people didn't have as much ability to screw up a child's brain with a pharmaceutical and psychological cocktail of drugs, psychiatrists, therapists, and 24/7 media exposure. Now, it's just more evident. Now, I get to watch genetic lines that succeeded by pure luck for hundreds of years be destroyed by neurotic mothers and morbidly obese absentee fathers.

Is your kid depressed? Is your kid suicidal? Does your kid misbehave? Has your kid expressed concern about liveleak beheadings he saw or the cable news you pump into the home and the talk radio you play in the car when you drive him anywhere? Don't adjust how you treat your kid. Don't tell them everything is alright. Don't explain to them that you didn't realize they were paying attention to the trash you expose them to and then stop exposing them to trash. No, google anxiety and other vague terms, schedule an appointment with a fraud getting cruises and dinners from pharmaceutical companies, and get your kid on drugs that will destroy everything about them.

What To Do Today?
There isn't much for me to do today. I have a lot of free time that hasn't been sectioned off for some greater purpose, so I'm able to decide what I get up to. This is amazing, because usually I am busy doing work for other people non-stop. Usually, I am unable to be productive and benefit myself. What will I do? Will I do some exercise,

some writing, some drawing, play guitar or piano, some reading, relax outside, go on a hike, go on a drive, ride a bike, talk to a friend, watch a movie, or take a nap? No, I will do none of those things.

Today, I will spend getting into arguments with strangers. I will find people doing things that I don't agree with, then I will place myself in vocal opposition to what they're doing. I will keep on doing this for hours, getting in arguments with random people. I will gain nothing from it except for the excitement of making other people get in arguments with me.

Sometimes, when I do this sort of stuff, it causes problems for me. I can't get a good sleep because people are actively harassing and spreading rumors about me. Over the years, I have built up hundreds of people who dislike me and actively root for me to do poorly in life. This is not really a great situation to be in, but it's unavoidable. It's not like I could just not get random people mad at me.

When I'm old and gray, if I live that long, I will look back at all of this fondly. I am sure I will be surrounded by friends and loved ones who will all laugh at the numerous stalkers I provoked repeatedly. It will all be a laughing matter. Still, even at that age, I will most likely still be spending my time antagonizing random people. I don't know what else to do with my time.

There's nothing I could be doing that's productive with this time. I'm built for tearing things down and making people feel bad. I don't care if it's kind of a waste of time. I don't care if it's taking years off my life. I don't care if I drive people away and I have no real friends. I don't care if I'm stuck in constant negative thought loops that I can't escape, that my only reputation is that of a trouble maker.

While people make stuff, I make fun of people. While people work towards goals, I scoff at them. While people are forming relationships that will last decades, I'm surrounding myself with mentally ill misanthropes. I may not love my life, in fact I hate it, but that's the price I pay for being myself, I guess. I hate every waking moment, and I don't see that changing any time soon.

There's no joy in my life. There's no happiness in my life. There is no hope for a better future in my life. There are no positive outlets or hobbies that I am involved. All that exists for me is people abusing me and me abusing other people. That's the cycle that exists, and I will probably never leave that cycle until I find some relationship that miraculously lasts which provides some incentive for me to act positively and not engage with other negative antisocial individuals on a constant basis. Then, and only then, will I stop spending all my time in this manner. Until that happens, I'm just going to be constantly miserable.

Going Out

The best thing about being older is "going out." You can go out at any time. You can go out anywhere. You can do anything. You can go out. This is amazing, and one of the reasons why it is so important to live in a city area.

In a country area, you can't go out. There are no nightclubs. There are no bars open past 10PM. There are no bright lights and places to get drunk and dance late at night. The restaurants aren't up to par with the restaurants in the city. That is where the real fun happens, when you go out and enjoy eating food. What a thrill.

Being at home is boring. Going for walks is boring. Sitting outside is boring. Being alone is boring. You need noise, lights, and drugs to make the night-time interesting. There needs to be something that stimulates your brain. There needs to be places to go out to.

Only losers like being by themselves and not spending their money at recreational businesses. These people do not have fun. These people are boring and don't understand the joy of going out. What fools they are, doing whatever it is they do with their free time while we get drunk and drink and have alcohol. We hang out with girls at restaurants sometimes. Sure, we might not ever get anything tangible out of our experiences, but at least we have good experiences.

We adults work hard, so that's why we need to play hard. We deserve to go out and have fun at night. How else would life be bearable. We hate our normal life. We have nothing to look forward to. Our jobs are unenjoyable. Our friends are unbearable in a normal state of mind. We have watched all the shows on netflix and blockbuster films in the theater, so what is left to do? All that springs to mind is drink alcohol, buy clothes and electronics, and have sex. That's all there is to do.

Going out is so much fun. It's so fulfilling. It makes everything we do worth it. It makes us feel good about life, at least for the moment. Sure, there are the psychological, spiritual, physical, and financial costs of drinking and spending a ton of money on unhealthy food in unsanitary environments, but that is the price you have to pay in order to enjoy life. It's not like there is any other way to live, and live we must, until we are dead.

Disrespectful Wheelchair People

Lately, I've been seeing a new clique of disrespectful punks. These people blow my mind with how poorly they behave. They have no patriotism. They hate their country. They spit on the sacrifices that thousands of brave men and women in our armed forces have made. None of them are particularly impressive, which is most likely why they are so rude towards everybody. This little gang of miscreants are people in wheelchairs.

People in wheelchairs don't stand for the pledge of allegiance. This is unacceptable. They live in America, they most likely get disability benefits, and do not contribute to the safety of America, and yet they still feel they have the right to disrespect this great country. If my child refused to stand for the pledge of allegiance, I would put them up for adoption that very day. What is wrong with people in wheelchairs? What is their problem?

Another issue I've noticed with wheelchair people is that they complain about stairs. They refuse to walk down stairs. It's amazing. They demand people build ramps, then they demand people push them up and down these ramps. If there are stairs and no ramps, they won't just suck it up and be mature and use the stairs. No, what they do instead is whine and whine until somebody else picks them up in the wheelchair and carries them up and down the stairs like they are in some throne.

These people are delusional. They are lazy. They refuse to walk anywhere. They show know work ethic. I have never seen any person in a wheelchair working any job that required a modicum of physical effort. Why is this? Why do they refuse to do construction work? Why are none of them plumbers? Why are none of them telephone repairmen? All they do is sit on their rear end. That's all they do.

Wheelchairers are not athletic. This is most likely due to their lack of exercise. I have never seen any of them win a racing competition. They sicken me. They are worthless. Ask any of them to go for a jog or run and you'll get the most absurd excuses. What is wrong with these people? Quite a lot, it would seem.

We need to put wheelchair people in re-education camps. In these camps, they will not be allowed to use wheelchairs. They will be forced to walk. No longer will we allow them to be babies. Now, they must face the world like the rest of us. No more delusional fantasy land where they get taken care of. I think we would see a lot of these people turn into functional citizens were these re-education camps to be created. Society would return to normalcy without the wheelchair parasites.

Oh, how I hate these miscreants. They are not human. They are not functional. They do not work for their supper nor labor for their lunch. They simply lounge about all day. I can't believe that my hard earned tax dollars from writing important essays such as this one go to enabling these parasite freaks. We have gotten soft as a society, allowing these worms to gain leverage and social authority over those of us who are productive and well meaning. I hate these people so much. They drive me mad with rage. I don't know how much longer I can take it. Hopefully somebody will punish these people in wheelchairs before I finally snap.

Unaccountability

There is a certain point for some people where there will always be yes-men readily available. For most of these people, the existence of yes-men is because of wealth or celebrity. Once you have a large enough audience or a large enough amount of capital, you'll never have nobody willing to be around you. Another sort of person who has this situation who might not yet have celebrity or wealth is somebody who is extremely charming or good looking. Usually, charming and good looking people get rich, famous, or both.

This situation is a problem when people begin to do self destructive things. For most people, when they do self destructive things, they will lose friends or have financial problems. This will be enough negative feedback to stop most people from continuing to engage in self destructive behavior for too long. This is not how it works for rich/famous/charming people, however, because if people seeking to use them will happily fill the vacuum left by well meaning people who dislike what is going on.

Personally, I am not traditionally wealthy or famous, but I am charming enough that I very rarely face consequences for anything I do that's bad, even if I go out of my way to let people know I have done those things. This is obviously beneficial in a lot of ways, and I am not bemoaning or lamenting the situation I find myself in, but

I can honestly say that it has had many downsides. There have been a lot of self destructive tendencies that I have been enabled to indulge in far past a reasonable point. Perhaps I would have still continued with these bad behaviors as long as I did (and do), but it would have been nice to have people telling me that what I was doing was stupid. That never happened, so I did a lot of stuff without even considering the long term negative effects that they might (and sometimes did) end up having.

What can you do if you are the friend of somebody who falls into the categories mentioned? First of all, realize that your friend is not your responsibility, although it is a nice thing to try to look out for them. This means that if you think they might lash out at you or cause you harm if you try to stop them from engaging in bad behavior, you aren't in the wrong if you act in a manner of self preservation and don't confront them. You are more important than them. That said, you should err on the side of tough love (in private) when possible, while making it clear that you're not looking down on them or being envious. Chances are, if they are new to being unaccountable, they will ignore your advice. That's fine, don't get emotionally distraught. Just distance yourselves from them slightly but be available and make sure you know you don't have any hard feelings towards them, you just think what they're doing is a bad idea. Chances are, they will eventually come to their senses. Whether it's before or after serious problems arise is irrelevant, because they will eventually remember that you were the one who nudged them against going in the wrong direction. This might result in them feeling negative towards you, depending on the internal character of the individual, or it might result in them getting back in touch with you and trusting you more. At that point, it's important to make it clear that you don't have any bad feelings or superiority towards them and you just want what's best for them, and that you are happy for them and their new direction.

If you're in the situation of unaccountability, what can you do? The most important thing to do is keep good friends around you who are good people. These are people who liked you before you became whatever put you in this new position, which means the chances that they're now trying to use you are much lower than new friends you make because of your new position in life. Another thing you can do is consider who is encouraging you to do or say certain things. Are these functional or dysfunctional people? Are they happy or unhappy? Are they accomplished or unaccomplished? Are they healthy or unhealthy? If the people telling you it's OK to behave in a manner that seems to run counter to common sense are degenerate drug addicts who are depressed and mentally ill and have no real family or friends, chances are they're just bad people who aren't really looking out for your best interest. They may be fun to hang around for a day or a week, but there is generally a reason why some people have no long term friends.

You are not the exception. I am not the exception. Neither of us may have to really follow social norms to survive or even do well, and we may both be in a position where we can pretty much do whatever we want, but that doesn't mean that we should do whatever we want. There are things that cause long term problems, and those are things which are illogical, self-destructive, and run counter to nature for no real reason. If you can't logically justify whatever you're doing for some positive functional purpose, chances are that it's neutral at best, and usually will impact you negatively.

This Is Directed At You

Yes, you're reading this right. I am talking about you right now. I am talking to you. You know who you are. You really screwed up. I don't forget things. You know what you did. In reality, I don't really care what you did. It doesn't really matter, in the grand scheme of things. That's not quite true, is it? No, it's not. It doesn't really matter to me. It doesn't matter to me because I am bigger than you and I don't need you.

What you did matters to you, because it's the biggest mistake of your life. Without me, you're nothing. You will never be anything but what you are now, which is an embarrassment. You probably wake up every day and think about how to make things right with me, and I never explicitly tell you that you have no shot on purpose, that way you stay in a sort of limbo, unsure of what to do.

It's really funny watching you fail at life. I check a few times each year and every time I check you're doing worse and worse. You had your shot to be a good person and not abuse my connection with you and you screwed up. You had the golden goose in your hands and you let it get away. You're never getting the golden goose back, ever.

As time goes on, it's just going to get more depressing for you. Everybody who is anybody or will be anybody knows what you are at this point, even though only a few people know what you did to me. I'm going to keep on doing well and getting better and better and you're going to keep on a depressing downward glide until you're dead.

Oh well, better luck next time. That's not quite right, there is no next time. There is no second chance. There is no redemption. There is no restarts. You are done. You are finished. You bungled something that I made absurdly easy for you. I want to thank you for showing me what to avoid in the future. With your example, I won't involve myself with anybody who fits your profile. You are so below par. You got given so much in life and you wasted it all.

You have never earned anything in life and you'll never earn anything and you're quickly realizing that people aren't going to keep on giving you stuff, but it's too late to fix anything. You have no talent, nothing that sets you apart, and no discipline. You will flounder about for the rest of your life in increasing desperation. You will continue to try to "team up" with naive people until you teach them why nobody wants anything to do with you.

I would say I feel sorry for you, but I don't. I can't wait until I find out you're dead. I can't wait until something really bad happens to you. You deserve really bad things to happen to you. You don't deserve anything but misery and pain. You have nothing positive about you. Once you are gone, nobody will be upset. Everybody will be happy when you are dead. Please, kill yourself.

Mask Off

Sometimes, I cry. I'm genuinely a very emotional man. I'm a big softie. I'm a romantic at heart. The truth is, I pretend to be edgy or callous to cover up my insecurities. This is the real me. I just want to hug people and listen to John Denver music in a circle around a campfire. This is the real me.

Violence and hatred scare me. I don't know how people can have negative feelings towards others, that stuff just eats away at the soul. I am deeply spiritual, being a lifelong nondenominational Christian. I'm not some hard-hearted cynic who doesn't care about anybody else.

This who act has gone on too far. It started as a joke between friends, making fun of how sensitive I am. I care so much about what people think about me that it has caused multiple mental breakdowns. I just want people to like me like I like people. I just want love and peace.

So please, don't say mean things about me. Now that you have read this confession, you have seen the real me. I am very sensitive, so soon I will retreat back to my shell and play pretend. Soon, I will say hurtful things, but this is all misdirection. Just know that everything I do is from the perspective of a genuinely kind, genuinely nice, genuinely good person who you should relate to, sympathize with, support financially, and defend wholeheartedly. I love you.

Things You Can't Say

There are quite a few things that I want to say, or rather write, that I simply can't. These things are hilarious to me for various reasons, but the current climate makes them impossible to say without facing backlash that might put my sterling reputation at risk. This is just the nature of the game I'm playing; I'd be a fool to ignore the rules. That said, I will now present a few of the different essays I would write if I could write whatever I wanted, but since I can't write whatever I write, I won't write these essays. Everything from this point on is stuff that I do not endorse or support or find funny.

The first essay I would want to write is just the n word. This isn't very complicated. It would be about six hundred words in length, around three fifths of the usual thousand word essay format that I operate in. All the words would be the n word. This isn't the n word with a soft "a". I'm talking the n word with a hard "r". I'd like to say that this would in the service of some sort of cultural message, but it's more the idea of a whole page of that word with no context or explanation that would be hilarious to me, since I know a lot of people would get upset about it for no real reason beyond wanting to get upset at stupid things, like n words.

Another essay that I can't really put out is a how to guide about what not to do with women. This wouldn't be a weird creepy snuff piece, I'm not that sort of person. It would be more of a slapstick *Three Stooges*-esque work of art. In it, a cardboard box would serve in the place of a woman, then a narrator would explain what not to do to women with a bat. Then, the rest of the essay would describe hitting the cardboard box with a baseball bat repeatedly, angrily, and with malice. In the end, the box would be completely obliterated. It would be a massacre, the box being incapable of defending itself, being much weaker than the sadistic violent man with the bat. The ending of the essay would reiterate that it's never appropriate to hit women and that one should never take a baseball bat to a woman's delicate frame, but even joking about it was simply too far for somebody like myself.

There are things you just can't say, if you want to be taken seriously by serious and valuable individuals. I need to be accepted and respected by the mainstream if I'm to be successful. I have movie deals and book contracts I'm working towards. I dream of getting that spot on night-time television. I want to be the next Disney star. I can't afford to make stupid mistakes making stupid jokes. Everything I write will be poured over by lawyers and public relations experts who will either offer me million dollar deals or not. I need to be on my best behavior. I need to act like the respectable intellectual I am. I am not a racist. I am not a sexist. I am not a bigot. I am not a violent or unhinged individual.

Bad Characteristics

There is a weird aspect to playing up genuinely negative traits I have. What happens is that, in an effort to not make excuses for or justify certain objectively bad things I have done, I can come off as flippant or glorifying of things I am not trying to be flippant about or glorify.

For example, a lot of my poor decisions and misadventures are gone over in a very matter of fact manner. This is because I don't feel bad for things I've done, so I'm not going to pretend to have remorse or shame. With that said, this purposefully honest omission of regretful emotions tends to lead people to think I am bragging about bad things. I'm not, I'm just not pretending in the opposite direction.

I admit that there is a lack of nuance and closure that I engage in purposely. This is mostly to keep the more linear and concrete people unsure of what's going on, because I find those sorts of people kind of dull and stupid and would prefer they don't make up the bulk of people who enjoy what I do, but also because it's amusing to watch what sorts of wacky conclusions people draw from inferring justifications or condemnations that aren't really there.

There is a certain level of uncertainty on my own part, with regards to how I present myself and my work. Most likely, as I get older I will have more clarity as to what is appropriate and inappropriate, but I cannot afford to wait until I know exactly what I am doing, so I am just doing as best I can. If the past is any indicator of the future, which I believe it is, then my mistakes now will be forgiven and overlooked just like my mistakes in the past have been. Then again, perhaps people will become fed up with me soon and nobody will pay attention to anything I do, though I doubt that will happen.

This isn't some weird justification or discussion about a "conflicted" character. I'm not conflicted about much, if anything. I'm aware that I don't have all the information or perspective needed to behave in the most optimal manner, but I'm doing the best I can with the information and perspective I have.

Creative people seem to try to push anything but an honest perspective. Even the either they highlight only the good or bad or perverted or pure, rather than an honest or direct mix that resembles something human. Everything seems either whitewashed or demented at the end of the day, rather than things just allowed to be what they are without some sort of praise or damnation. I really want to avoid that, so I err on the side of putting the more despicable elements to myself on display without spending time preaching for or against those elements.

A Matter Of Friction

The following essay mostly applies to a certain type of person who is similar to me. Basically, whatever I'm doing I stay doing not because I'm enjoying it, but rather because it is more of a hassle to do something else rather than keep doing whatever I'm doing. There are a lot of times where I enjoy whatever it is that I'm doing, but that is just a benefit to what I do, not a driving force. I'll often do things that I'm not really enjoying, simply because I'm already doing that thing. I'm fairly certain that everybody behaves in this manner, to some extent, but I am a bit abnormal in how I process certain costs and rewards to activities so it is worth mentioning that your mileage may vary with regard to how well the following strategy works.

By far, the biggest reason that I have been so productive as of late is that I have made unproductive things more of a hassle than productive things. What I mean by this is that I don't have easy access to much entertainment and am limited in the places I can spend my time. I do not have easy access to video games or other forms of entertainment that most people my age have.

I don't go out past 8PM or travel or even have my car on the road, so I don't have many easy outlets for the excess energy that I have stored up. I could afford to buy a powerful gaming PC and a decent car as well as pay for its insurance and other things, but going through the process of setting those things up is also a hassle, enough of one that it stops me from spending time initiating the process. With that said, taking away easy ways to spend my time does not mean I do not spend my time doing things, it just means that I spend my time doing more productive things that serve me now and are building up my future.

I still waste time, but it's wasted more in daydreaming and thinking about wasting my time (and money) in other ways that I never actually go through the process of doing. I'm not getting the reward from easy entertainment, and I still seek out rewards, so I end up building various systems and patterns that are beneficial, such as spending time writing or programming. It's easier to open up a text or code editor and spend an hour or two on something that will pay dividends in the future and engage my mind now than to open up a browser, do a bunch of research on what PC parts are best to buy, order the parts, wait for the parts to get here, set up the PC, then play video games. If I had the PC already set up and functional, it would be easier to download and play video games (and get a hollow positive emotional reward) than to exercise, write, draw, read, or do programming (and get a genuine positive emotional reward.)

Like I stated in the opening paragraph, most likely I'm wired in a manner that is abnormal. Probably, I'm less motivated by rewards and more motivated by restlessness and excess energy than most people. Regardless, this sort of mindset to understanding what causes you to do whatever you do or don't do is very useful. Figure out why you make once choice over another and figure this out multiple times, then put yourself in situations where you know your personal psychology will set you up to prefer the optimal choice rather than the suboptimal choice. I do not have a good work ethic or more determination than most people, and yet I get way more done than anybody I know of. This is not because of any magic, but rather because I've gotten better at structuring my environment to operate in a long term positive loop rather than a short term positive loop that is negative in the long term.

Lots of Mistakes

I have made so many mistakes of varying degrees and done so many things which should, on paper, result in me having a bad reputation and walking around in shame. This outcome has not been the case for a multitude of reasons, but mostly because I understand how cycles of drama or gossip work.

What is important to realize is that most people respond to responses, rather than forming genuine opinions. What this means is that if you freak out or react poorly to people bringing up your flaws or errors, then whoever sees how you have reacted will view the thing you are reacting to as something that is very serious.   the other hand, if you do not react poorly (or even respond at all) to people bringing up things that are objectively serious, most observers will assume that whatever is being brought up is unimportant.

Another thing to take note of is that people are constantly doing stupid things and making mistakes. What this means is that no matter what you do, within a few weeks or a month (at most) somebody will do something as bad or worse as whatever it is you have done. While this shouldn't really matter, people are comparative and unable to focus on the same thing for a long time, so it does matter. Especially if you go out of your way not to react poorly to people bringing up your mistakes or misdeeds, you'll quickly find that people move on to other things which are more recent and aren't being handled as well as you are handling your mishap.

Lastly, it's important to keep perspective about who you are. Chances are, you won't be remembered after you're dead and nobody outside maybe a few hundred or a few thousand people will ever know how you are. Also, unless you're something like a rapist or pedophile, whatever stupid stuff you have done is most likely not that bad. Realize that you don't really matter, the people who will try to make you feel bad for stupid stuff don't matter, and that soon there will be somebody else who gets embarrassed, as long as you make sure people don't get what they want out of trying to embarrass you, which is some sort of emotional response or meltdown.

I will continue to make stuff that I want to make, and I will definitely do many more things that I look back at and scratch my head in confusion. Mistakes really don't matter unless they kill you or stop you from doing what you're trying to do. Even then, who really cares? When you're gone, you're gone. You won't be around to see what people think about you, if they even do think about you. None of this stuff really matters. Just do what you want and realize that only suckers let mistakes and potential mistakes determine how they behave. Other people can figure out how they want to emotionally react to things I've done, I'm too busy doing things to really care.

Oy Bruv

Oy bruv, that's wild, innit. For shizzle, ittain't bidness-like, it reallytaint. Ittin't right ittaint. It'z a traversty lurv, itis. Thistain't Dickenz ittaint, no sirree. Whata nonce, innit, bruv. For shizzle. Nowtaint dat a shame, on me mum. Yees bruv, if I do sayzo meself, I do. Time to sippa muh tea and God save the queen, that bastahd. Go fack yah mothah.

I'm Not Gay

You're not gay? What do you mean you're not gay? Son, don't disappoint me like this. *SMACK*

You bring shame upon this family with your heterosexuality. *WHACK* *WHACK* *WHACK* *WHACK* *WHACK* *WHACK* *WHACK* *WHACK* *WHACK* *WHACK* *WHACK* I can't believe my own child would do this to me. *SLAMS HEAD INTO TABLE*

What is wrong with you? Why are you so mentally ill? You don't like boys? You don't kiss boys? You disgust me. Get out of my sight. Leave my field of vision. *HITS THE CHILD ON THE SIDE OF THE HEAD WITH A CLOSED FIST* Get out of here, before I shoot you in the face with this shotgun I carry around. *POINTS SHOTGUN AT THE CHILD* You know what? I can't take it any more. *BANG* *BANG* *BANG* *BANG* *BANG* You're dead now, disgusting freak, but you are the one who has killed the joy inside me.

Paul Joseph Watson

Paul Joseph Watson was raised in a very small town in Texas. The population was somewhere in the ten thousand range. He grew up running packages for the post office on his bike, being unable to pass the driver's test. Young life passed pretty uneventfully for Watson, being that he had dropped out of school in the sixth grade due to being held back for four years and getting frustrated at the lack of progress.

This free time from lack of schooling affording him the ability to research municipal politics. Due to this, he quickly became the most politically active young adult in his small Texas town. The local people in the town loved Paul, because he was so precious. He had a speech impediment that covered up part of his heavy Texan drawl, but you could still tell that he was a red blooded American male. He was particularly fond of eating BBQ and wearing cowboy hats.

When he was just twenty three, still a bicycle delivery boy, he got officially involved in local politics. There is footage of him at a rally for a local candidate for mayor. In the video, Watson is seen in a small crowd, face red and mouth slightly agape in a special kind of slight shocked ecstasy, bouncing up and down rapidly, his hands resting on his cheeks in an open palmed fashion. He was so excited to be a part of local politics, and everybody around him loved his enthusiasm.

This footage was when Alex Jones noticed the young and impressionable Watson. Jones got in touch with Paul, and began to employ him and groom him for his media company, Infowars. This wasn't some bottom of the barrel internship that was designed to go nowhere, Alex Jones was thinking long term. Jones had dreams for the young Watson, and the first was to rebrand Paul Joseph Watson as a political analyst.

In order to do this, Watson would need to be perceived as intelligent and cultured. His speech impediment was a big obstacle, one that only a man as genius as Alex Jones could have overcome. Thinking on a level of cognition that is rarely found in humans, Jones came up with the idea of relocating Watson to the UK, since nobody who is British is capable of talking in a coherent fashion. The plan worked, and soon nobody could tell that Watson was originally a disabled individual from a small town in Texas. The rest, as we say, is history.

Geography And Resources

It is pretty clear that certain geographical regions tend to have large groups of people who are better or worse at various things. For example, most innovation and inventions in the past few hundred years have come out of America, places in Eastern Europe have a higher rate of fraud and crime than places in Western Europe, the rate of rape is higher in South Africa or any African or Semitic country is much higher than the rate of rape in Iceland, etc.

Of course, there are a lot of different factors that are always changing that push different population groups in different directions. Immigration gets more and less lax as time goes on and voting blocks as well as economic and social trends shift. Different crops rise and fall in price as demand rises and falls depending on wars, the environment, disasters, and other tangential connected industries changing their standards and requirements.

With this understanding, predicting general shifts in how large population groups will perform is possible, with a lot of caveats. The farther out you predict, the more unknown variables and unpredictable events you are betting against, and those things compound in their impact as time increases. With that said, I think people are overlooking a general shift that is starting to happen with regards to what countries do increasingly well and what countries do increasingly poorly.

The industrial revolution and technology have reconfigured how capital is stored and transfered; in both form and physical location. With the industrial revolution came ease of travel and mass production, and with those two things came much less friction with regards to the transfer of both people and goods. At first, this greatly benefited a lot of traditionally industrious areas, since they were already doing well and had capital to put into bigger endeavors. The problem with this is that things got too easy for these people. They were already in geographical locations that were good for trade and finance (coastal cities are a good example) but difficult enough to survive in that a lot of lower quality people were pushed to the outskirts and kept out. With the vast increase of wealth and comfort that hit virtually everywhere (that isn't a completely dysfunctional third world country), a lot of leeway and room to grow for negative influences sprung up, and with those opportunities (combined with the newfound ease of travel) came negative influences which ruined those areas for good. Basically, people didn't realize what they had or why life worked the way it did, so they failed to protect against the downside of excess. It remains to be seen if there is even a proper way to protect against easy excess, but that is a topic for a different essay.

With this framework, it would follow that places like the UK, coastal cities in the US, and the affluent non-fringe areas of Europe should be steadily getting worse, and I think reality bears this out. Things have gotten too easy for too many people, and now a lesser caliber of people are gradually immigrating to and succeeding in those areas. The losers of our new global paradigm are traditionally successful areas and groups of people who have suddenly become more attractive than challenging and will remain so until their attractiveness is lowered to meet the lack of challenge. If I had to guess, the difficulty of reality in those environments has been lowered to a level similar to what it used to be in warm climates like India,

Mexico, South America, etc, and will slowly come to resemble people of that traditional geographical caliber.

We have discussed the negative aspects to this shift in travel and velocity of resources, but who will be benefited? I am biased, due to my personal proclivities and avoidant anti-social proclivities, but I would predict that over time, isolated and uninviting places such as Alaska, Russia, and colder Eastern European will be shown to be on a consistent upswing. The reason for this is the same reason for why the places I have previously mentioned seem to be getting consistently worse: the difficulty of living has been lowered from its previous level. Up until recently, you had to be very dysfunctional and/or uncooperative/pushy/aggressive to survive in the places I mentioned. You can't really trust or rely on many other people. Now, with ease of travel as well as other factors linked to ease of travel, people can be more cohesive and things can be more reliable.

Technology is another big factor as to why cold and isolated areas will greatly benefit. With the internet and more specifically cryptocurrency, the global economy is now easily accessed from these places. People in these places tend to be much more clever than equally dysfunctional environments that are hotter, probably because colder environments reward long term thinking more than hot environments and punish short term thinking much harsher than warm environments, so in order to survive you have to pass a certain threshold of ingenuity (which is not the same as intelligence but is definitely a helpful ancillary trait.)

Having been aware of and involved in bitcoin and cryptocurrency ever since early 2013, I remember that a large portion of all the developers working on various encryption and other technologies related to cryptocurrency were mostly Russian or Eastern European. A lot of them were scammers, but not all were. Digital crime is also another Russian and Eastern European dominated field.

Why the prevalence of Russians and Eastern Europeans in technology, specifically cryptocurrency and security, is so important is that it is indicative that their minds are wired in a way that is set up to take advantage of the world that is coming. What that means is that over time, capital will drift in their direction and they will be more successful financially and materially, which will raise the quality of their mates which will raise the quality of their group which will result in improved areas.

While these described areas have been greatly benefited - and will continue to be greatly benefited - by technology as well as travel, their climates are still inhospitable to people who generally make countries less functional. As such, they are not really penalized in the same way as warmer climates, which means that they now have net positive evolutionary pressures, while previous powers now have a lot of net negative evolutionary pressures. What this would indicate is that a shift is occurring and will continue to occur until there is some fundamental change in climates or some other base variable which serves as a filter for low quality individuals.

Surviving: A Web Video Series

Lately I've been concocting a reality TV sort of video series. The main premise is that I'm the individual at the center of the show and I go to different places and people video me as I do my best to thrive in those environments. It would be a bit similar to what Bear Gryll's did in his TV shows but more laid back and no tense objectives or high stress situations.

It's important that the places I go do not put me in danger or upset me, because my mental health is extremely fragile. A positive aspect to the show would be the little monologues I would do talking about how I am feeling mentally, if I am depressed, sad, or anxious. That way, people who are dealing with mental illnesses like the one I survived without help or guidance wouldn't feel so alone.

The setting of each episode in the series would vary, but the common theme is that all the places I go to would be luxury resorts or beach houses. Basically, I would be relaxing near a pool or jacuzzi for most of each episode, or drinking gin and tonics at the resort bar. These won't be some fake struggle sessions, these will be montages of me living my best life. I will have beautiful legal aged young women in each episode, doting on me, blushing when I make jokes, and complimenting me. This will serve to show the viewer that it is possible to mess up and overcome adversities and challenges and end up on top of the world.

Some other ideas for video series are me breaking expensive items, me driving expensive cars, me drinking expensive alcohol and eating expensive food, and many other activities that would be fun to film and fun to experience as well as being educational to the viewer. The main thing that is holding me back from making my video series a reality are my legal and writing responsibilities. Once those are finished, I will be ready to start work on this exciting creative project.

Of course, I'm going to need somebody to fund all of this. I am not made of money and I would never spend money on resorts until I was a multi-millionaire in an above the table on the books manner. This means that I am seeking a rich philanthropist or visionary to help make this work of art come true.

I have a few requirements for the person giving me the needed funds. They must understand that there are no requirements on my end by accepting the money. I do not dance to the tune of anybody but my inner voice. I will not owe anybody anything and I do not have a time frame in which this project may be completed. I go with the flow. That means I need a veritable blank check and unlimited time. The individual funding this will not get any of the profits made from this production, as I will be releasing it for free to the masses for their enrichment and enjoyment. I will put the rich patron's name in the credits of my production, provided I do not find them morally reprehensible or associated with organizations or values that I disagree with or dislike. I will run and distribute the show, I just need somebody to pay for the show.

Famine Fridge

Mother, there is a problem. I just took a gander in the fridge, and was met with a shocking sight. It would seem that father neglected to restock the egg supply. You both know how I eat one dozen raw eggs a day, what made you think this negligence was acceptable? Now, I have no raw eggs to eat. Now, I am hungry and I have no raw eggs.

Do you think that this sort of behavior will have no consequences? I need these eggs in order to mentally function on the level that my high stress vague internet job requires. Without the choline found in raw eggs, my brain is in a constant. There's no telling what I might do now that my tumtum is not properly satiated. What happens today is all your fault, you know that right.

I feel so sick, being betrayed in this manner. Here I was, thinking that you cared about me. That you weren't neglectful, abusive, hateful parents, and you proved me wrong. You took my expectations and spat on them. You looked me in the eyes and cursed me out with your actions or rather lack of actions. You have betrayed me. It's all so clear to me now, that I must not mean anything to you. You do not care about me at all, or else there would be raw eggs in the fridge. Here I am, once again suffering due to your negligence and emotional abuse.

When you're too old to take care of yourself, you'll wish you hadn't forgotten to buy your son raw eggs. You'll wish you had put me in a position to win in life, unlike what actually happened, which is me having to fend off starvation and mental illness without the proper resources or financial and emotional support. You'll wish you had treated me better. Let's just say that, OK? Yeah, let's just leave it at that. I'm too exhausted from lack of fresh raw eggs to go into more detail. I need to conserve my energy.

Medicine Is Dysgenic

Doctors are immoral creatures. Healthcare is disgusting and should be illegal. Medicine? Evil. Why do I say all of this? Because when you actually think about what helping sick and diseased people does to a population group, you will realize that we are screwing up natural processes and destroying thousands of years of biological progress.

When people get sick, that means that they were either engaging in stupid behavior, have genetics, or got unlucky. None of these traits are traits that should be encouraged or hidden. People who get sick should suffer and die or overcome their illnesses with their own strength and fortitude. With medicine, people who are too weak to survive are allowed to survive. They blend in with the healthy and spread their seed, weakening the gene pool.

Maybe if everybody who got cancer died from it, then eventually people would stop eating unhealthy food and polluting the environment. Instead, what we have now are people who put disgusting things in their body and don't care about smog or plastics, because they know that when they get cancer and other maladies, all they have to do is head on over to a doctor's office for radiation and a cocktail of drugs designed to allow them to escape the punishment they deserve.

Vaccines are another aspect of medicine that should not exist. Basically, if we didn't have vaccines, then we would be much more aware of who we let into our communities. We would understand that people from foreign places bring foreign bacterias and diseases, and we would be cautious. We would be very specific in the environments in which we raise our kids. This is not the case. People do not even understand how biology or diseases or migration of life-forms works anymore because we have vaccines which minimize the symptoms of unhealthy and unclean surroundings which makes people comfortable living in filth and squalor because the most visible results from living in filth and squalor have been removed.

Perhaps, if you can't fight off a sickness or disease with your body, you deserve to die? Maybe it is God punishing you for your sins? Maybe you are not a good fit for the herd and are being culled? We are all so coddled now that we think it's a horrible thing when some aunt or uncle or sibling dies. We do not understand our relationship to external things beyond our control because we insist on revolting against the natural order and propping up the disordered and preserving it well past its expiration date. This needs to stop, before it is too late and we are submerged beneath an ocean of biological and literal trash.

September Eleven

It is September Eleven, Two Thousand And One. What a day. What a beautiful day. I kiss my trophy wife on the cheek and take the subway into work. I'm a financial guru, so I work in one of the twin towers in New York City. That's right, I do finances. Today is going to be a big day for me. Today is the day my life will change forever.

I plan on killing multiple people at my job today. I can't take the stress and responsibilities that being a high powered finance individual entails, so I'm bringing a gun into work and getting straight to business. I am filled with anticipation at the thought of putting buckshot into the annoying faces I have to deal with every day. I want to watch their terror as I mow them down.

I plan on torturing a few of the victims on my floor before I blow them away. Their crimes: being straight up whack. These people are not bros or chill, they're idiots who annoy me with their small talk. I got a finance degree to do blow and hookers, and I'm all out of hookers and blow. I'm here to murder people, not do a stupid job in a stupid cubicle for stupid people. I'm going to enjoy watching these losers die.

I get into my job with my sawed off shotgun just fine. Security in this place is so lax if you know what you're doing, and I know what I'm doing. I'm going to make Columbine look like a joke. I'm going to murder so many people. The building is so big and I work on one of the top floors, that by just disabling all the elevators I will have an hour or two to slaughter as many loser office drones as possible before cops get to me.

The cellphone jammers are in place and the plastic explosives are rigged to go to to stop the elevators. I'm about to start the final act of my life. It's going to be a banger. I'm going to go out with a bang. I'm going to bang so many of the slutty female sluts in this building, with my shotgun.

It's about to be go time, this September Eleven, Two Thousand And One, when disaster strikes in the form of a plane. Yep, just my luck, some crazy deranged jewish people seem to have flown a commercial airline plane into my place of work. Oh God, there is smoke and fire everywhere. This can't be happening to me. I'm a good citizen. I pay my taxes. I have a wife and kids. Am I going to die today? Yes, I'm going to burn to death in this stupid building, for no good reason. Worst of all, I am aware that ragheads will most likely be blamed for this Mossad operation. They will be framed and I will die knowing the truth, that many more patriotic American males will die in the Middle East over the next decade and a half in order to protect opium fields and oil interests. I am dying now. I am burning to death. This is the end. I can't even use my cellphone to say goodbye to my wife and kids. I am crying. Goodbye, cruel world.

I'm Not A Loser

I'm not a loser. Do you want to know why I am not a loser? Well, it doesn't really matter if you want to know why I am not a loser, because I'm about to tell you why I am not a loser. In fact, not only am I *not* a loser, I am a winner. That's right, I'm probably the biggest winner you will ever have the good fortune to be exposed to. I am a genius. I am the best. I am a winner.

Why am I a winner? It's quite simple: I have a lot of opinions. I have so many opinions that I've even written multiple books and spent lots of time talking about what my opinions are. Opinions are really hard to have, and it's really hard to write, so that means I'm a winner. Have you written a book? I didn't think so. You don't look smart enough to write a book.

It takes a lot of hard work to write down what your opinions are. This is just a fact. It's not something as simple as taking whatever is in your head and putting it down on paper that somebody else prints and distributes. No, it's a lot more than that. There is so much more to the process of writing, that I can't even begin to explain any of it.

Writing is a mystical process. Writing is a mysterious process. Not anybody can do it, and almost nobody does it well. I am the exception, of course, because I am a winner. Writing makes me better than you. I have written more words on paper than you. I have stated my opinions in a more lengthy format than you, which makes me smarter than you.

What else have I accomplished in my life besides reading, writing, and talking? Well, nothing. I don't need to actually *do* anything. I am the idea guy. I am the general. I have the plans and the dreams. It's up to the little people around me to execute on my vision. If my ideas don't pan out, that's not my fault, but rather the fault of the people who try to put my plans into practice. Most of my ideas can't even be tried or falsified or even tested in any manner beyond talking, so there's really no reason to dwell on this boring minutia any longer.

It's hard to think; to come up with ideas. I am a philosopher; an aristocrat. I use semi-colons when I write to demonstrate my high IQ. You most likely do not even know what an incomplete clause or a run-on sentence are or how they function. You are so embarrassing. Know your place, knave, the gentlemen (me, myself, and I) are speaking. I am above you, because I can see the threads that pull at the fabric of history. I know how the pied piper plays his flute. I set the tempo and the drum beats. What does any of this mean? Even if I told you, you lack the cerebral power to understand. Just know this: I am not a loser.

A Lack Of Contractions And Hating Anime

Animals can often be appraised by their visual appearance. What this means is that you can predict how certain types of animals will behave by their size relative to similar animals, the color of the fur on their coat, if they look emaciated, sleek, or bloated, and a number of other factors. Most people intuitively understand this to some degree, but very few people understand that this sort of observational technique can be applied to humans.

There is a very strange linguistic habit that is easily observable in the online postings of autistic individuals. They tend to err on the side of not using contractions when most people would use contractions. What this means is that they will often write "cannot" in the place of "can't" or "will not" in the place of "won't". For whatever reason, this is something that autistic people do a lot. What is the use of this knowledge? It really depends on the situation, but can be helpful if you're trying to figure out how to best communicate with a stranger and see them not using contractions, because then you can adjust your communication style to a more autistic communication style.

Anime is very popular with autistic individuals. Being generally below average in social interactions and ability to fit in with others, as well as other reasons, autistic individuals love to watch and share anime related content.

While this is interesting, there is an even more interesting subgroup of maladjusted individuals who are not autistic, who hate anime. These people don't just ignore anime because they don't find it interesting, they hate anime and make sure people know it. These sorts of people are generally pedophiles or sexual predators or torture small animals are are overcompensating for their abnormalities by targeting what they see as vulnerable individuals: people who enjoy anime.

Another visual indicator that something is *off* with an individual is if they are hyper-cutesy or childish past a certain age. As of late, I've noticed that a lot of creepy adult men are using pikachu avatars on twitter. This is not a coincidence, and is probably something similar to why so many adults with cartoon drawings of themselves as avatars tend to have sex dungeons or be sexual degenerates engaged in illegal and creepy behaviors. As far as I can tell, when people are trying to signal that they are not harmful and that they are playful, they are usually harmful and not playful.

Once you start looking for common attributes across how different people of the same archetype present themselves, you will start to see similarities. Once you see enough similarities, you will develop a sixth sense of sorts with regards to what is a good sign, bad sign, or informative sign. Of course, a lot of this stuff is highly subjective and only works in the context of a bunch of other information, but you get the gist. With time, practice, and age, you'll get better and better at judging people and learning how to avoid weirdos and invest time into valuable people who might not be the best at presenting themselves in a flattering light.

We Are The Best

There are certain television shows that give me the heebie jeebies. The strange show where they repeatedly yell "we are the best" is one of them. I have never watched the show, because I had parents who cared about me growing up, but I have seen clips of this show and its disgusting main actor. The reason I have seen these clips is that I browse internet forums and communities, and for some reason a lot of people seem to have some strange emotional attachment to this show.

I suspect most of the people who like this show were abused or raped as children, are pedophiles, or fall into both of those categories. There is something disgusting about this show, something unnerving. This is not to mention the fact that all the females seem to be dressed up in a strange manner that is too adult for a child's show, hence why pedophiles and sexual abuse victims seem to be the people who like to watch this show.

Beauty and ugliness are very distinct. While it is not important to show children constant beauty, and the people who seem to harp on the virtues of beauty and purity also seem to fall into the grouping of people who shouldn't be allowed near children or vulnerable individuals, it is very important not to push ugliness and deformities on children. When individuals are very young, their disgust response and ability for rational discernment of worth are barely, if at all, developed. What this means is that they are soaking up their surroundings, learning from cues, relying on the judgment of those who are responsible for them.

To have kids see this "Robbie Rotten" character is child abuse, plain and simple. This man looks evil. He looks disgusting. He looks deformed. His facial proportions are all out of whack. Emotionally vulnerable individuals should not be repeatedly exposed to this strange individual because it normalizes this strange individual. It doesn't matter that he is supposedly a negative character, he is too disgusting to be shown to children.

This whole TV show reminds me of the childcatcher character from *Chitty Chitty Bang Bang,* another facially deformed freak that just so happened to be inserted into media for children. I'm not saying this is all some weird MK-Ultra plot to corrupt and disorder the minds of the youth, but that would not surprise me. Most likely there are weird individuals in the entertainment industry who have nosed their way into positions where they have easy access to kids, and that is why there seems to be such a disgusting amount of trash aimed at children.

It's not a good idea to let children have unfettered access to any form of media at this point. There is no gatekeeping or sensible values. Nobody at youtube or in Hollywood or at television studios care about your kids in a positive sense. They either see them as people who will buy junk or see them in a weird way, which is why they work in children's entertainment in the first place. Roald Dahl's poem about television is accurate, but it should be applied to the internet, the radio, social media, and even social interaction.

There's really no good way to raise children anymore. If I wasn't a strong-willed schizo with a tendency for anti-social behavior, I most likely would be spouting the same deranged freak opinions and values that I see everybody my age engaging in. These people are no different than most people were in the 1950s, it's just that standards of what is created have been lowered drastically due to environmental and technological factors. This isn't to say not to raise children, but perhaps the only good way to raise children is to bring them up in some weird cult like Mormonism or in the woods or something.

The people who made the We Are The Best television show are evil. I hate them. I am filled with disgust and rage every time I see what they made in front of me. How dare they propagate such filth on the general populace. Who do they think they are that they feel comfortable doing what they did? I wouldn't be surprised if they were involved in some weird pizzagate tier stuff. There is no justice in the world, or else everybody who made this television show would be in prison doing hard labor.

Databases

People are stupid and delusional. People also want to obfuscate reality in a desperate bid for self enrichment and self preservation. If you read Aristotle and you have a cursory understanding of how databases function and do not function, you will quickly realize that most of philosophy is either trash (illogical and deluded) or people talking about very basic database structure. Nobody seems to understand this simple fact.

You can spend weeks reading Aristotle discuss how certain things can be subsets of other certain things, but certain other things cannot at once be the subset of one thing while the subset of another thing, or that certain things can be the subset of multiple larger things at the same time, or you can spend an hour learning about how primary keys and foreign keys in databases work and don't work.

Here is the thing about philosophy, either things are logically sound, logically unsound, or the scope of them is too large and thus too vague to know if they're sound or unsound. The last grouping means you need to break whatever it is you're thinking about or discussing down into smaller parts until each of the parts is logically sound or there are some logically unsound parts found, which means that the larger "thing" is incorrect.

If claims can be broken down into logically sound or logically unsound, then they can be graphed. If they can be graphed, then to use words to a ridiculous degree when trying to be logical is an absurd waste of time and thus either the work of idiots or malicious individuals who are trying to draw out some simple point. Of course, this claim can be levied against me, but it falls short since I am not a philosopher or thinker and don't claim to be.

Don't get me wrong, most people who "know" how databases work are idiots. A lot of people who are well versed in philosophy are probably smarter than most people who use databases in some form of employment, but most smart people are idiots who don't know how to put their potential to anything that is useful or functional.

As far as I can tell, computer people have autism and a very narrow focus which makes them useless outside of whatever niche they are mildly capable in. They are essentially little cogs in a hive intelligence that is pulling together resources, they are not really autonomous individuals capable of rational holistic thought. Most people involved in philosophy are weird perverts with rich parents. They might be smart but they never really have had to work for anything and they are obsessed with their reputation. Because they are not really in a results oriented field and don't really need to have any coherent worldview and it's easier to just wallow in moronic delusions of importance rather than get a grip on entry level wikipedia pages, they don't understand how actually functional logic or a holistic testable worldview works.

What is the deal with people being so stupid? I am not smart, but I am smarter than almost everybody. I can think laterally, but somehow people who have a higher IQ than me seem locked into retarded meme careers like computer science or philosophy. Is everybody just a stupid automaton incapable of engaging me on an intellectual level. Am I destined to be the only person who has any idea of how anything actually works, able to draw conclusions based on structural similarities in a variety of seemingly unconnected fields? This would seem to be the case.

I am so lonely. I cannot connect with anybody on an emotional level because I am so much wiser than everybody. I draw conclusions that blow the onlooker's mind. The people around me never do anything impressive besides rote memorization. I am looking into ways to make myself dumber so I can finally have people who are on the same level as me. This is my sad reality, being a genius thinker philosopher sage.

Things Are

It's important to realize that everything has some logical reason as to why it is happening. This is not a moral justification of everything, since there are obviously bad things that are constantly happening, but rather an understanding that, on the macro level, stuff isn't disorded or chaotic. What this means is that if something doesn't make sense or seems illogical, there is some factor or variable (or many factors and variables) that you aren't aware of.

On the micro/individual level, things can be pushed or pulled in certain directions, caused or prevented, encouraged or discouraged, but on a larger level, chances are that you or I are not really going to have any long lasting change on anything. To paraphrase a different author, you can bend a river but not change the direction in which it flows. We can adjust tiny details (our lives and the people and objects we interact with), but not much more.

This outlook may seem a little nihilistic or depressing, especially since most people have grown up in environments that encouraged the harmful delusion that every individual has the power to change the world or "leave their mark" or be a hero in some way, but it's really not negative or constraining when fully understood.

Once you realize you don't get to pick how the machine we are all in functions, you start to focus on what you can change, which is what metaphorical gears you can reasonably apply pressure and resistance to. Instead of flailing about worrying about how reality "should" be or "shouldn't" be, you start to assess how things are. Once you get into this default state of analysis instead of panicked hyperactivity, you'll find that there is coherent and consistent logic to everything, and the more you study any puzzling situation or behavior, the more you'll suss out patterns that can be generalized and used to understand many other situation.

At the core of this understanding is a shift from trying to move things, to moving *with* things. Of course, nobody should be apathetic, so one can influence their surroundings (on a fairly inconsequential level as stated previously, but still on a non-zero level which justifies it) by moving *with* things in a premature or slightly lagging manner. Picture yourself as a gear in a watch with millions of tiny gears. If you try to go against the rest of the gears, you'll eventually break and be destroyed. If you apply slight resistance or enthusiasm, you'll stress yourself relationally to how much energy you expend compared to the default amount, but as long as you don't stress yourself too much you won't destroy yourself. You are a cog in millions of different watches at the same time. Some of the watches are big, small, positive, negative, beneficial, harmful, etc, but you are a part of them all. The more you understand how each watch works, the better you'll be able to adjust your behavior to whatever fits with your values and/or goals.

Things are the way they are and things will always be the way they are. Even trends (of all sorts, financial, social, interpersonal, natural, technological) are what they are, which is a sort of momentum that is growing or decreasing and that growth or reduction is also its own thing that is happening for logical reasons. This sort of analysis can keep on being done to a near infinite level, since everything is interlocking, but past a certain point it's not really practical or a judicious use of time.

There seems to be a large contingent of people who to draw unwarranted extensions of arguments or implications from discussions that do not try to make moral claims. This closing paragraph is an attempt to stop any of that before it occurs. None of this essay is an attempt to justify or make excuses for bad behavior. Just because there is a logical reason that rape or pedophilia occurs (people with mental problems and environments that encourage and enable those people) doesn't justify rape or pedophilia. To the contrary, understanding that there are logical reasons to objectively bad actions leads to an understanding that there are also ways to discourage and make bad actions less likely to occur.

Psychosis

There is nothing quite as enjoyable as psychosis. Drugs are enjoyable, sex is probably enjoyable, making out is enjoyable, lying is enjoyable, eating is enjoyable, stealing is enjoyable, breaking the law is enjoyable, taking risks is enjoyable, making people laugh is enjoyable, genuinely helping people is enjoyable, but none of these are as enjoyable as psychosis. There's just something about how everything becomes slightly off or absolutely insane that makes life worth living.

When you're psychotic, the rules of logic and reason don't apply to you. Things that would normally hold you back and make you cautious don't anymore, and things that you wouldn't even pay attention to or notice are suddenly freak you out or send you on these spiraling adventures and misadventures that make absolutely no sense outside of the context of the moment.

Psychosis is like taking some pent up beast that lives in the back of your mind (or stomach, depending on the person and the type of psychosis) and having it roam free. You're completely in control, but it's a different, more animal, less human form of you. Sure, it's not pleasant to the people around you and you may or may not become a danger to everyone around you, but it's life is a journey and along journeys there are times where it becomes necessary to risk your wellbeing and the wellbeing of those around you if you want to have any interesting journeys.

Once you gain the knowledge and experience of various forms of psychosis, you become further elevated from the boring people around you. They live all their lives in a rather mundane state of mind, so they don't understand what motivates unhinged people. They don't know how to react to people who are off-kilter, or how to see the signs of off-kilter people. They lack the perspective that psychosis gives. They cannot put themselves in the shoes of people who are not completely boring and inexperiences, so they are at risk for all sorts of problems when dealing with people who have more experience and wisdom than they do.

Psychosis is what losing your virginity is like, but for the mind and useful. I don't know much about sex, because I've never had it. This does not hold me back, because sex is a waste of time outside of procreation or psychological games, but I cannot describe certain actions and interactions that anybody who has had sex can describe. I could have sex really easily, of course, and it should be noted that I am simply too busy for sex but know I will be great at it, but I have not had sex with anybody yet. My understanding of psychology and human actions and interpersonal relationships has been permanently buffed by my various experiences of psychosis. People who never had serious psychosis are essential virgins of the mind.

Am I recommending people induce psychosis? No, I'm not a doctor and do not want anybody to harm anybody else or go down the path of mental illness. It is very easy to induce psychosis through psychological stimulation/trauma combined sleep deprivation. Sleep deprivation is really the key to everything. Most people are not able to stay awake long enough to induce psychosis without the use of drugs like cocaine, amphetamine, ritalin, modafinil, or things like that. Another path to psychosis is weed, but I think that's more retard psychosis than useful psychosis, so I do not recommend the use of weed, ever. Of course, you should not use any drugs illegally or behave in any unhealthy manner. It's better to be safe then sorry.

Dopamine And Serotonin

Dopamine and Serotonin are two words that should be illegal to say. Especially in online communities, people who want to sound much smarter and educated than they really are seem to be infatuated by those two words. Why? Because they are morons who are obsessed with feeling happy and feeling sad. They need to grow up and focus on not feeling anything at all.

Here is the reality of the situation: Yes, Dopamine and Serotonin are involved in how you feel and how you behave, and yes, social media does influence Dopamine and Serotonin levels in individuals, but that's like focusing on "Calcium Levels" instead of just focusing on positive eating and living habits.

Here's an idea: stop spending twelve hours a day on social media. Stop eating junk food. Go on walks. Go on runs. Eat healthy food. Do push-ups, pull-ups, and sit-ups. Make sure you're getting sunlight. Talk to people you aspire to be like instead of miserable losers. Then, your Dopamine and Serotonin levels will most likely be healthier than being neurotic and pretentious online thinking you're going to cheat the system of life by reading medical studies and circlejerking with other neurotic mediocre individuals who have never done anything but consume and regurgitate what they have consumed.

People think they're going to get something for nothing, that by understanding the names of things and hyper-specific chemical interactions in closed systems, they're going to be able to live forever without ever feeling sad or depressed. They want to feel satisfied and accomplished without doing anything satisfactory or accomplishing anything.

We need to ban medical terminology from books and the internet, stop teaching any form of biology or science in schools, and kill anybody with glasses. Make schools and universities illegal. It's time to stop pretending that humans are smart or that people with "smart opinions" are useful. They're worse than not useful, they're annoying.

Stop talking about things you don't really understand. You think you understand how Dopamine and Serotonin work, and yet you're still a miserable loser? That's weird, if I knew how something worked and I could improve my life, I would improve my life. You don't seem to be able to put your "knowledge" to any positive use, so either you're a weird self-destructive masochist and I don't want to take advice from you or you don't really know what you're talking about and I don't want to take advice from you.

All of this makes me wonder if language was a good or a bad thing. It would probably be better if we were all illiterate apes forced to murder each other to survive. I know for a fact that I could murder most of the people who talk about Dopamine and Serotonin, but unfortunately murder is illegal and I refuse to break the law. If they could shut up about Dopamine and Serotonin and whatever other meme-words are in vogue, then the world would be a much better place.

The Problem With CRISPR

For a while now, CRISPR has been in the news and has been touted as a very important technology that will have huge effects in the coming years and decades. Firstly, I am very skeptical of the whole situation, because most CRISPR related or adjacent news is coming out of China. China is not trustworthy or particularly innovative or original in anything they do, so until there is hard and fast proof that is reproducible, anything that comes out of that region of the world is most likely exaggerated, stolen, or completely made up. With that said, gene editing is something that should hypothetically be possible if it's not already being done, but it's not really all that interesting, and I am fairly certain it will never have much of an impact -- at least a functional one -- on the world.

Most of a person's genetics is related to the choices of generations before them. Lifestyle, health, and who is picked to mate with all influence how an individual will look and behave, and thus how their offspring will look and behave, and so on and so forth. What this means is that every person gives clues and hints about their upbringing, their lifestyle, their parents, and their future by their physical appearance (height, eye color, hair color, weight, teeth, hair length, choice of fashion, etc.) These clues are generally ignored by most people, because most people are not really taught how to read their surroundings since we have reached a point where danger is very minimal and excess makes mistakes seem not to matter on a time-frame that most people comprehend.

With gene editing, positive and negative consequences to actions will become less immediately clear. Poor people and rich people alike will be able to be more visually appealing, which will remove incentives to compete and perform well in order to marry or mate with an attractive member of the opposite sex. Because of this, over time the positive reputation that people have associated with being handsome/beautiful, tall, and healthy will be removed, because now success and failure won't lead to having better looking or worse looking offspring, which will remove the connection between positive personal characteristics like self-discipline and the positive outcome. You can already see this sort of confusion with trustfund children and people who get access to resources on a generational basis without earning them. The cause and effect has been removed, so the incentive to aspire in a positive direction becomes too vague for people to work towards, resulting in lazy, stupid, foolish, and embarrassingly poor mannered individuals.

Offspring is the car dashboard indicator light of the human race. If your kids are healthy, smart, and good looking, then you most likely are living in a productive manner and making good choices, and your children will be more likely to make good choices and succeed than people in similar circumstances who made bad choices and have unhealthy, dumb, and ugly children. This is very basic evolutionary theory, and it's not always the case, but that is the general way in which things operate, and it is a very good feedback loop which informs people how to behave on a lot of different levels (and this causes a cascading effect of functional values not directly pertaining to having children.) With gene editing, you will see a sort of excess that we have seen in America with regards to food, where a majority of the people involved are deluded into making stupid decisions repeatedly that end up harming them for a few hundred years until it becomes clear who has the common sense not to eat junk and who just didn't eat junk because it wasn't easily accessible.

Like I stated in the opening paragraph, I seriously doubt the legitimacy of gene editing on any real scale. I suspect this is similar to the "cloning" of sheep that was going on in the 1980s, where you had scientists and dishonest individuals exaggerating and flat out lying and being enabled by the press in a symbiotic relationship of deception. If it is all true and in a few decades we have designer babies, chances are that these "designer babies" will be completely uninspiring and not accomplish anymore than the genetically mediocre people they come from, since aspirational physical attributes are generally symptomatic of positive personal characteristics rather than causal.

The Reality Of Reality

People have no idea what's going on. They don't understand what they're doing, why they're doing it, what's working or not working, where they are headed, or really much about anything. Virtually nobody seems to understand the nuances of cyclical cycles and the wheels within wheels within those cycles. Everybody is just running around with various flavors of psychosis and delusion, and nobody will ever stop this from being the case.

There's so much profit to be made from muddying the water and making people panic or get angry or sad or happy or scared, that there will never be any change to the status quo. Everywhere you look, you'll see the same people engaging in different variants of the same thing people their age were doing fifty, one hundred, or five hundred years ago. Even what I'm doing is not unique and isn't something special, and I'm not special for realizing what's going on.

What is to be done about all of this? Nothing. Nothing can be done. Nothing will ever be done. People will try to change things, but if things were going to be changed then they would have already been changed. You can't reverse a river's direction without changing the whole world, and nobody will ever change the whole world. The names and the dates and the places will change, but nothing is really changing except for variable names. The system stays the same and will always stay the same.

The fact of the matter is that life is not hard for anybody besides people with serious disabilities. Life is not hard or complicated, but most people are stupid lazy idiots with emotional problems who grow up with lies and delusions being shoveled on top of them by the other idiots around them. Then there are the gurus and the "self-help" experts and cult leaders who offer an inverted version of the idiocy, and some portion of the idiots in circulation embrace it and perpetuate it. It doesn't really change anything, except that money, time, and energy get transfered from the unwitting to the malicious, which means that there is a constant pull towards things getting more exploitative and there will always be a constant pull towards things getting more exploitative.

The only thing that can really disrupt this momentum is something like a mass disease or catastrophic natural disaster or famine or ecological collapse. We had the black plague, which was great, but didn't fix anything. Now we have problems that stem from excess hedonism, like grids and other STDs, but we have medicine to help mitigate and conceal the symptoms of illogical and unhealthy lifestyles.

Even if 99% of everybody alive were somehow eliminated, the 1% that survived would just interact with the system of reality until the new 100% behaved in the same way that the old 100% behaved in. There is no escape from reality. There is no saving anything, preserving anything, helping anything, hurting anything. Everything gets ground down to the lowest common denominator and basest impulses eventually, which is not even to mention that most of the people with "lofty" ideals or goals have no better idea of how anything works or how to protect anything than the most degenerate self destructive drug addict prostitute.

Look at all the people around you and you'll see a medley of sloth, psychosis, neurosis, insecurity, inadequacy, instability, inexperience, and mindless directionless self sabotage. These people will never amount to anything of any worth. They do not have value. They do not matter. They are merely little cushions of suffering that you should do your best to arrange between you and other people who are similar to you. They are meatbags, sandbags, fertilizer for people who have actual goals, dreams, motivations, thoughts, hopes, desires, plans, and vision. You can be them, you can be delusional and try to save or condemn them, or you can not care about them beyond realizing that they're sometimes needed to benefit yourself and the people who are worth caring about.

Insulting Smart People And Authors
There is nothing I love to do more than insult smart people and authors. Being a smart person and an author, I can't be accused of being bitter or jealous, so I can be as negative and uncharitable as I feel without any proper

comeback. Even better, I hint that the things I'm saying about other people apply to me (they don't apply to me), so I come off as humble and self-effacing. I'm not humble or self-effacing, I'm haughty and conceited and vain and rude, but I'm charming more clever than everybody so it's OK.

The thing about smart people is that they have usually been able to coast along in life in a lot of different respects, because they are busy being productive and working hard and are thus not exposed to low quality or stupid people on any real level. This leads to them being unable to defend themselves from smart people like me who know how to engage smart people while not coming off like a traditionally smart person. Smart people have big brains for stuff like mathematics and engineering and various forms of science in very limited scopes, and assume that their expertise transfers to other aspects of the world. When they are confronted with somebody who actually knows how reality works (me), they get thrown off their footing as they quickly realize that all the years they put into understanding some narrow field is worse than useless, and actually an active detriment.

The reason that authors are fun to insult is slightly different than why it is fun to insult smart people, because authors are generally not that smart. There is a small amount of overlap between smart people and authors (me), but that sort of person is the black sheep of those two communities. Authors are really good at filling up pages with words, because most of them lack the ability to self moderate or understand when they should shut up. Their egos are huge because it's easier for people to pretend that they like whatever the author has written instead of wasting time actually reading it, but authors are too stupid to realize that most people who buy books barely even know how to read.

Authors and smart people should really be forced to do hard labor for a few years. They should not be allowed near the internet or in public spaces. They should not be allowed to speak or write. They should be beasts of burden who actually have to do work. Especially the bespectacled freaks. Those people are the worst and should have their glasses taken away and forced to pick apples while immigrants watch them laugh. Most smart people and authors would die after the first month or two of work, a good portion of the surviving smart people and authors would kill themselves after the first year or two of real work, and we could kill the rest of the authors and smart people after they finish their time working.

What percentage of smart people do anything worthwhile? What portion of authors will ever write anything that makes a positive difference? Statistically speaking, none of either group has any value. We have already gone to the moon and made *War and Peace* into a movie, what more is there to do? Nothing of value. Are trash poems and novels written by people who have never had any life experience worth the trees chopped down? Is there any genuine non-sadomasochistic justification for the creation of more meandering philosophy by pederasts who have never had an honest job or financial insecurities? Do we want more vaccines so we can live in increasing filth and squalor without catching diseases? Do we really desire increasingly exotic concoctions and remedies to avoid dying from orgies with the detritus found on dating apps? None of these things are needed. Smart people and authors are not needed.

Self Reflection

Do you ever look at yourself in the bathroom mirror? Do you ever ask yourself what you're doing and why you're doing it? Do you ever take a second when you're adjusting your car's rear-view mirror and look yourself in your eyes to see what you're seeing yourself see? Do you smile to yourself and feel the lips of your mouth press up against the constraints of your skin, feeling the pressure of the tension and the contraction of the muscles, and wonder why you can feel yourself in a better mood just by forcing yourself to grin?

Do you ever think about honestly answering people when they ask how you're doing? Do you wonder what they'd say if you told them that you're not doing at all, that you don't care about anybody or anything except yourself, that you're bored with life? Do you ever think about how they wouldn't care? They wouldn't care at all. They might get concerned or disturbed, but they wouldn't care about you. You know that, but do you really know why you lie to them when they ask you how you're doing?

Do you ever sit in the quiet and just think? Do you wonder why you're living the life the way you're living your life? Why you eat what you eat, drink what you drink, watch what you watch, read what you read? Do you have moments of self reflection at all? Does it matter? Has anybody without self reflection ever fixed everything? Has anybody with self reflection ever fixed anything? Does it matter if things are fixed? Are things even broken? Who knows? Who cares?

Do you ever look at what you have written and wonder when any of it is going to come back to haunt you? Do you ever wonder what the hell you're even doing or what you're trying to achieve? No, you know that nobody really pays attention to anything even if they're "paying attention" to you. Nobody is really making note of anything you say, write, or do. Sure, there is a record of your worst behavior, your worst thoughts, your most uncharitable ideas and statements, but nobody is ever going to pull those things up unless your life already perfect or already ruined. Until you have it made or you have been broken to pieces beyond repair, nothing about you matters.

Nobody important is keeping score of anything. Some people keep track, but they don't matter because people who are doing things and making decisions don't pay attention to people keeping track. People keeping track should take a hike, or take a walk, or run on a track and die of a heart attack. That will at least make the obituaries, unlike everything else they do. Life is just constant shoveling of fertilizer onto a huge rotting stinking ever-growing pile of fertilizer.

There's no use in stopping to wonder if you're doing the right thing, because nobody is. Even if you were, it wouldn't matter. You could be a saint and once you're dead things will go back to what they were before you were. Just do whatever you're going to do. Be a bad person. Be a selfish person. Don't stick your neck out for anybody. Don't get a career. Don't worry about anything, because it doesn't really matter.

Just be yourself. Drink alcohol regularly. Watch filth. Fill your mind with trash. Eat garbage. Hang out with bad influences. Try hard drugs. Don't exercise. Don't help strangers or work on charities. It's easier this way. In less than a hundred years you'll be dead and everybody will forget about you, unless you're a really bad person.

Animal Abuse

I love watching ISIS beheading videos. I make jokes about murder, rape, terror, and pretty much anything. I'm a big fan of gore videos. Yeah, I'm a bit of a sicko, I admit it. There's nothing that I won't make jokes about. I'm a tough guy. I'm cool. You probably can't relate because you're a whiny liberal. You're weak. You're not a real man. You aren't tough.

Did you just kick that dog? You are disgusting! I can't believe I just saw you kick that dog. You're lucky I don't have a gun on me right now, or else I would kill you on the spot for kicking that dog. Dogs have feelings. Dogs get hurt when you kick them. When you hurt animals it's very upsetting. I can't stomach animal abuse like that. What is wrong with you? You are a disgusting monster. Do you have no empathy? I'm not going to be able to sleep after seeing you kick that dog.

ONE (1) HOT/ PRETTY/ BEAUTIFUL LEGAL AGED <u>DISEASE FREE</u> <u>FEMALE</u> KISS COUPON

This coupon entitles a hot/pretty/beautiful legal aged disease free female to one (1) kiss with Paul Town, free of charge. The kiss may be on the lips, cheek, or forehead, at Paul Town's discretion. This coupon does not expire but is only valid if presented in a copy of the book it was printed in. Upon the use of this coupon, it will be marked by Paul Town in order to ensure it is not used multiple times. Multiple kisses may be redeemed by purchasing multiple copies of the book in which the coupon is printed, and thus multiple copies of this coupon obtained. Please note that

> Paul Town can also refuse your advances for any reason and you should respect his wishes.

Legal Requirements

There are a few legal requirements that pertain to anybody who purchases any Paul Town books. Unfortunately, most people seem to be ignorant of the responsibilities they are signing up for when acquiring these books. They seem to think that there is no job that they are legally obligated to work when in the possession of my writings, which is frustratingly naive and incorrect. I will now outline some of the tasks that have been agreed to by anybody reading, or familiar with, Paul Town literature.

Firstly, you must convince, trick, or coerce three strangers into purchasing at least one Paul Town book. This must occur within the first five years of your attainment of a Paul Town book or essay, or else a harsh financial fine will be levied against you, and your wages will be garnished by the coming Paul Town regime until you have died. Due to the fact that this guideline is going to be enforced strictly, it is only a matter of time until every single person on earth will already have purchased Paul Town books. This will lead to people having children just so they can have somebody to purchase Paul Town books for. This means that it is in the interest of self preservation that you fulfill this duty as soon as possible, before Paul Town becomes a household name and market penetration reaches the complete saturation point.

Secondly, you must yell "Paul Town" in a public area at least once every financial quarter. This action will serve to toughen you up and make you more resistant to social shame, and thus you will become a more successful and outgoing individual, which will then result in increased performance in your career as well as dating life. Over time, you will become and alpha male or female and learn to get your way in everything. People will fear you. The opposite sex will desire you, sexually. Your financial situation will be amazing. You'll be large and in charge. The penalty for not fulfilling this legal requirement is public execution, being shot in the back of the head and uploaded in video form to liveleak, ISIS propaganda style.

The third legal requirement is not a legal requirement, legally speaking, but rather an idea. Graffiti is pretty cool, but it's illegal. Don't do graffiti. That said, it would be cool if I saw "Paul Town" written in bathroom stalls, sprayed on the back of trucks, the sides of bridges, and under overpasses. This doesn't really serve any useful purpose, it's more for my ego than anything. It would also be funny to see "Paul Town" literally everywhere, taunting people who actually have real jobs and careers who are functional members of society, working hard, being good citizens. Once again, don't do this, but it's something that I would find hilarious.

Most authors or intellectuals do not have any requirements for the people who consume what they create. This is because they are appealing only to the lowest common denominator of individual, the idiot with too much free time and no good use for their money. This is not the case with me, as everybody who consumes what I create is a genius, savant, or psychotic. I appeal to the fringes of humanity, because I create only the best. It would be a waste of a platform if I were not to demand the very best from my audience. How could you respect me if I did not have these requirements? You couldn't. I wouldn't. I don't. That's a fact.

Alternating Content Strategy

My plan for life is multi-staged. I have modeled it after psychologically abusive women (and I suppose psychologically abusive men, but most of the psychologically abusive people I'm aware of are women), just on a different time-frame than these people and on a different scale. When you're dealing with this sort of person, you will see how they alternate between being mindfully on great behavior and then mindfully rotten. Most normal people are mindlessly mediocre people who are never great nor rotten.

How this sort of functional/dysfunctional behavior applies to my writing is that I am currently in the stage of being rotten. I'm producing filth and highly caustic material that is designed to be negative and rude and mean. I will create this sort of material for a few more years until it gets too predictable and nobody wants to be around me, then I'll switch to a more uplifting and positive sort of output for a few years.

By being mindful about what sort of content I am creating, I will be able to play the different types of material against each other in order to demonstrate supposed personal growth. Of course I have not grown as a person at all and if anything am regressing into a rotten manipulative cretin, but normal and good hearted people like to believe they are being made a part of some redemption story. There is no redemption here, just cold and calculating alpha brain high IQ four dimensional chess at play.

All of this can be summed up in how it mirrors bi-polar disorder, which is just a made up term like autism or schizophrenia that people use to justify and enable horrible behavior. Human nature is far too forgiving and optimistic, so people like me not only survive but thrive. There is no justice. I will never be forced to pay for my content crimes against humanity. I will never give an account of most of the harmful and hurtful things I have said and done. That's just reality.

Real Jobs
Working a real job sounds like hell. There's something so deranged and torturous about being around

normal people on any level where you're not telling them what to do or entertaining them. I would hate to have to work a real job with real responsibilities. It would be untenable.

Imagine going into work and getting bossed around by somebody who is ten years your senior and ten IQ points your inferior. Imagine taking a thirty to fourty minute lunch break and eating some trash food that you pre-packed or purchased from a local business, knowing that you're expected back in your office or cubicle in a few dozen minutes, and if you don't show up then you will get a stern warning by that same inferior elderly individual. Now imagine doing that every weekday for decades. Tens of thousands of days of dread spread out across the prime of your life. It would drive me crazy.

There's no good reason to work a real job. If you need money, just do something like selling drugs or stealing or fraud. Worst comes to worst and you get caught, you'll go to jail or prison and get free food and rent and be able to spend your time playing board games or reading books or talking to interesting people or exercising or sleeping or anything other than wasting away under fluorescent lights being babysat by other frustrated deranged middle class freaks.

Women who get married to workers are so much smarter than males who work. They get to relax and watch television and browse social media, then spend the money their husbands make. It's so great. I really respect women who get men like this to marry them. Most marriages are men signing up to be a legal slave for a woman, and the men are thankful.

Slavery never left America (or any country), it just got called employment. With enough little "employee of the month" charts and thousand dollar watches after thirty years of employment, the slave is now convinced it is not a slave, but it is still a slave. It's just one that isn't in the field picking cotton and being whipped. At least with slavery, the slaves didn't have the delusion of autonomy hinted at. They knew what they were in for, and if they didn't like it then they could risk everything and run away. Employees don't know what they're doing or what they're becoming, so they never run away. They are the frogs in the slowly boiling pots.

There are certain things that just take too much time for anybody who is trying to be productive and in control of life. Those things are cooking, cleaning, yardwork, changing diapers, commuting, traveling long distances, and a bunch of other things. Because of this, employees are needed. I am going to get my own employees/slaves/maids/ servants (all the same thing) to do these when I am financially well off. I couldn't imagine handling my child's feces, so I will wait until I am rich to get married.

Do you want to be a slave? Do you want to be bossed around by people who you dislike? Do you want to waste away and be satisfied with no real ability to do what you want unless it fits into the weekend? If you do, then go work towards a real job. Go get that degree. Get good grades. Work hard to impress strangers so you can work for them. Stop wasting your time imagining that you will ever have a good life or be happy. Stop pretending that you will relate to people who take risks and live life to its fullest. Go sit in class and sit in training and sit in the cubicle and sit in the nursing home and die. You're already dead.

Generational Upper Limits

The first thirty-five years of life should generally form the basis of knowledge that is used to live the rest of life well. Of course, as you get older you should continue to learn odds and ends, but the first third to half of life is really where the foundation and base on top of the foundation needs to be built. A majority of individuals seem to fail at this task and spend the entirety of their life attempting (and failing) to make up for lost time and a lack of forward momentum. With that said, a large portion of these people succeed in life to some degree, securing some form of employment, finding a partner, and passing on their genes.

What becomes of the people who follow a pretty productive path in life? These are the people who receive more beneficial than harmful advice growing up, as well as a stable environment that allows them room to make mistakes but also nudges them in an ordered and logical direction. A solid percentage of these people seem to succeed in the same sense as the other group, and create children.

What seems interesting to me is that following this logic, a clear gap between the productive and unproductive should continue to grow at an exponential rate in intervals of generations. This is clearly not the case. Yes, capital (wealth, property, opportunities) disparities tend to grow, but knowledge does not, and it's definitely not at an exponential rate. It would seem that certain things need to be re-learned by trial and error by each generation, no matter who is tutoring and guiding them. What this means is that there is enough "slippage" of knowledge passed on that it only matters very minimally how properly one is raised.

There seems to be an upper limit to efficiency/orderliness/productivity in a human that really can't be transcended by any knowledge or instruction. Some of this is most definitely environmental, but it would seem that most of it is due to the fact that for X number of decades from birth, a human being is going to be making poor decisions, wasting time, energy, opportunities, and wealth, and generally acting in a manner below their potential.

What can be inferred from this? Most things are accessible to anybody who has enough of a mind to pursue them. It's not that hard to succeed on a very large level. Of course, certain private clubs and hierarchies might be closed off, but they do not seem very eugenic or necessary to anything except on a very shallow level. This is not to discount shallow level things, since shallow things are very useful when interacting with people who value shallow things, but rather to say there is not all that much of a difference in quality between extremely rich aristocrats and an average citizen in a developed country. Sure, there is a difference in opportunities and capital, but there really isn't some higher quality of character. Often times, a level headed non-aristocrat or somebody outside of an aged hierarchy is of better quality and has more common sense than somebody isolated from the cares and worries of normal individuals.

There are inter-generational inefficiencies that thousands of years of advantages and education have not been able to remove, so chances are that these inefficiencies will never be removed. There is not transcendence of any group or tribe on any horizon. For the foreseeable future, reality will continue in the way it has always continued, with the most delusional and unhinged individuals vying for power and influence, then wasting their power and influence until somebody else who is delusional and unhinged takes the power away from them.

Charity Work

Have we really thought through charity? Yes, it's a nice concept and the people engaged in it are mostly well-meaning, but is it really, genuinely, sincerely, good? Does it benefit humanity, or drag us down? Should poor people be helped, or hurt? Should we give food to the hungry, or watch them starve? Should we open the door for old people, or slam the door shut on them so hard that they stand back in stupefaction?

Yes, some people get down on their luck. Some people have times when they are poor or mentally ill, which makes them homeless and behave in a suboptimal manner. These people are not to be mocked or laughed at, generally, but that is not to say that they should receive help. It does not follow that suffering should be assuaged from an external source. To fix somebody else's problem is to harm them, as they are not forced to confront whatever the issue is and overcome it or perish.

I have been poor and mentally ill. Some even say I am still poor and still mentally ill. That may or may not be the case, and may or may not continue to be the case, but I know that when things were bad and the chips were down, nobody helped me. Nobody gave me the solutions to my problems. Nobody stopped me from causing problems for myself and getting into trouble. Because of that, now I do not rely on or trust anybody but myself to have my best interest in mind. I am thankful that everybody around me was a detriment to me, because I learned various cause and effect relationships that I would otherwise be ignorant of.

Without being abandoned and treated poorly by everybody around me, I would still be like the people around me: miserable, wasteful, deluded, boring, lazy, idiotic messes who will never accomplish anything in life. Now I am free of the illusion of common interest, the social contract, mercy, grace, understanding, empathy, and all the other lies people who don't ever overcome the obstacles of suffering believe in. Now, I walk around without caring what people who say they love me think. If they are made happy or unhappy, I only care insofar as it interacts with me and what I am trying to do.

Charity breeds reliance and unsustainable living conditions. In Africa, billions of little Africans are being bred and fed because of charity. This destroys local economies and makes them useless, and now there are billions of people who shouldn't really exist who exist. Eventually, the charity will run out and these people will either starve to death or travel to places like Europe where they will ruin all the countries who let them in and give them stuff, because these charity cases do not understand how life works and are used to people enabling them. This is not to insult these people who are receiving the charity, it is not their fault and they are just acting in the most obvious self interest, but just an objective observation.

People who ask for and receive charity should not be looked down on, but rather the people who give charity. These people love to feel good while harming others. They love to feel like they're saints when really they're lazy cogs in an uncaring machine paying tithes to their god: the ego. These people do not understand anything they do, and in their hubris they conceive of themselves as saviors. These people are not saviors, they are devils. Instead of giving proper advice and healthy incentives for people to life fulfilling and functional lives, they give capital and momentum to self-destructive people. All people who give and do charity are functionally evil.

Giving Bad Advice

There is something so enjoyable about giving bad advice that I can't quite put my finger on. It's not that I am malicious or trying to harm anybody, but rather that excitement that comes from just flat out lying for no reason other than lying. To know the correct course of action and to give the incorrect course of action without having any ill will or malice is its own delight.

A lot of the bad advice I give, I give with the understanding that everybody knows it's bad advice. Basically, people know that I'm going to say things that are illogical and irrational on purpose. Everybody has a good laugh and gets some small amount of satisfaction by mentally dismantling and reasoning against the purposely flawed suggestion or statement. In this way, it is a sort of harmless activity that goes on; a social exercise.

With that said, every once in a while, somebody mistakes my fallacious bad advice for genuine good advice. This is unfortunate, for them, but quite hilarious to me. Yes, it's mean spirited and most likely indicative of a petty soul, but to imagine somebody doing something that obviously shouldn't be done, and then realizing that they shouldn't have done what they just did, and them doing it all because some clearly deranged and untrustworthy joker said something about how stupid things are actually smart things, is something I will always find funny.

In life, you have to allow stupid people to be stupid. You can't get bent our of shape at the horrible things that go on. If you spend your time trying to help the helpless, you'll just wake up one morning towards the end of your life with the realization that you wasted your life and once you're gone the helpless will return to the state of helplessness; that they never really left the state of helplessness at all. It's best to just make a big game out of everything, even bad and unhappy things, and find people who are not helpless and team up with them to make everybody who actually has a chance at success, succeed.

It's much more free to live with a reputation that makes people wary of you than with a reputation that makes people think you're a good person who will help them for nothing in return. There are less expectations and less demands by people of poor or cowardly character when you are viewed as a ticking time bomb or a potential threat. These sorts of people leave you alone, and the majority of people that remain are people who are shrewd enough to avoid putting themselves in positions that you might take advantage of them. This bi-directional caution allows you to be more efficient and business-like in your day to day dealings, which saves time because you don't have to pretend to be a nice or empathetic person to inexperienced spiritual virgins who are using you as a therapist or emotional crutch.

Friends Are A Waste Of Time

Who needs friends? Not anybody who is doing anything worthwhile. Of what use are friends? I don't mean people that you're friendly with, but people that you "hang out" with? Friends seem to be something that losers have. Business associates that you do drugs with, drink alcohol with, and go on adventures with are cool, but friends are stupid.

If I was an worm who needs some sort of constant emotional support and "relationship" to cope with a mediocre life, I'd have friends. I'd talk to them and ask them how their dating life is going, how work is, what they think about politics, if they've seen any good movies, and other sorts of questions. I'd be interested in what they had to say, because I would be a moron who wastes all his time.

It's true that I have friends at the moment, but the reason for that is more utilitarian than anything else. I don't feel like paying an extra $60 a month to be able to drive my car, and I like to go out to eat and go on car rides and look out the window at the scenery, so I have friends that I use as a personal taxi service. Once I have mid six figures in my bank account (soon), I will put my car back on the road and then never speak to any of my so called friends again.

This isn't to say that people should not be friendly to others and allow other people to be friends with them. It's good to be polite and positive towards people in general, plus it helps you achieve your goals. Nobody wants to talk to somebody who is constantly negative or bitter. They want to talk to people who make them feel good about themselves. They want to feel like they matter, so being nice is a win-win scenario for day to day interactions.

Allowing other people to see you as their friend is an obvious win for you, and you should definitely be friendly towards them, but don't get emotionally attached. It's better that way. Most people are a disappointment and will drag you down and waste your time. Better to operate on a catch and release basis without getting all teary eyed.

Don't make emotional connections with anybody or anything. Don't try to relate to anybody. Think of everyone as a potential resource to be exploited and used. Don't hesitate to burn bridges whenever it is convenient. Stabbing somebody in the back is not a bad thing if you're the one doing it, it's just common sense. Stay up late at night and turn to a dead station on the radio and listen to the fuzz for hours. Lock your doors and take modafinil as you stay up for 72 hours until you start hallucinating. Read books like the 48 Laws of Power.

Life is not about "fun" or "good vibes" or "love" or anything like that. Those things are for the sheep. No, life is about suffering and raw mercenary interactions. Don't think that everybody is all fuzzy wuzzy and friendly on a real basis. They're not. All successful people essentially operate like a paranoid schizoid psychotic. People who make time for friendship are losers. Those people will never accomplish anything. Those people have things like feelings which end up controlling them, turning them into slaves for the ubermensche: people with no friends or loved ones.

Don't be a schmuck. Don't try to find some sort of meaning or higher purpose to anything. Just live on the prowl, hunting for people to use and abuse. Are you ready for prime time, or are you going to stay in pre-school with all the other dreamers who get chewed up and spit out by the real world? Are you ready to extort, coerce, blackmail, threaten, and intimidate your way to success in life? Are you ready to do what it takes? Are you an alpha male or a beta male? The choice is up to you, make the right one.

Machine Learning

Machine learning has a large amount of potential to be one of the most powerful and disruptive techniques of sorting and processing information that the world has ever seen. The reason for this is that every decision humans or animals or insects or anything makes is a binary yes or no choice. Do I do *that* or do not do *that?* Is *this* preferable to *that* or is *that* preferable to *this?* This thing I am doing now, should I stop? Yes or no is what everything breaks down. Everything is comparative and based on contrast, which is what yes or no is based on, but that is an essay for another matter. Since decision making can be broken down into binary decisions or binary decision trees (a sequential flow of multiple binary decisions which combine into a decision which doesn't appear binary -- although it ultimately is made up of multiple binary decisions), it makes that computers could be made really effective in decision making.

Machine learning will most likely never reach its full potential or even half its full potential, because its limiting factor is the people who understand machine learning and technology in general. Most people, no matter the field they are in or the area of expertise they inhabit, are idiots. They do not understand why they do what they do, what they want from life, what they are trying to accomplish, or what they're going to be eating for lunch in a day or two. Most technological people are even worse than normal people. Technological people don't know how to communicate, how to bathe, or how to interact on any level that isn't completely concrete and immediately predictable to them. This is why they are able to do things like programming but not things like have romantic relationships or be liked by anybody.

The people who work on machine learning don't understand that technology is meant to magnify the rate at which information can be sorted and manipulated to interface with humanity and other systems. These people are building stupid things like randomly generated anime waifus and human faces without any greater goal. They are idiots who don't understand that with the technology and information we have now, machine learning could be used to take over entire media and political organizations by mapping out various social pressure points as well as making connections between various differences in contrast.

Machine learning can break down, analyze, record, and track any pattern of data: Word choice, punctuation choice, posting time, comment length, faces, vocal pattern, hair length, color palette of clothes, walking gait, average time from point A to point B, proportional spending patterns, etc. All of this can be further tracked by changes across time. This can all be done already, and every once in a while you'll see some story that hints at people putting this ability to nefarious or worrying use. The thing is that it never pans out, because nerds are either too short sighted or get sucked up by some multinational corporation who uses this sort of technology for industrial security, security cameras in grocery stores, or other stuff that is boring.

Absolutely nobody should worry about machine learning, because the people who are using machine learning are morons who don't understand what they're doing on any abstract level. Much like how South African private security caravans transporting blood diamonds don't worry about jungle people with AK-47s raiding them, because they know the jungle people aren't smart enough or trained enough to use their weapons properly and will never be smart enough or trained enough to use their weapons properly. There is no reason to be concerned about a bunch of dysgenic autistics who could technically take over the world if they weren't dysgenic autistics.

Dot Dot Dots

There is something very wrong with people who use "..." when they are writing. It is a sort of attack that they are performing on whoever is reading what they have written. By using "...", it is essentially tricking the reader into *wait, wait, wait,* then continuing on with whatever it is they were communicating. Perhaps waiting around is something that can be afforded by the average mediocre individual, but not for me.

Every second to my day matters. There is no room for dot dot dots. There is no room for navel gazing inanities. People need to stop wasting my time with their careless thoughts. It is really absurd to write out dot dot dots and not to realize that it will make people like me, highly efficient overachieving savants, angry at you.

Who is the most likely to use dot dot dots? Layabouts and tryhards. Not having anything interesting to say, they must try to draw out the reader's interest and insist that there is something worthwhile lurking just around the corner, in the next sentence. Of course, there is nothing worthwhile in the next sentence, or in the whole of their writing. If there was, then they would just go ahead and say what they needed to say, without a desperate act of signaling worth.

We need to start putting people who use dot dot dots in prison. They need to be forced to do hard labor, along with the people who post vaporwave memes and use websites like ycombinator and reddit. We need to start cracking down on the parasites who pollute the intellectual atmosphere with their linguistic smog. It's time to bring the hammer down and stop these freaks, before it's too late. It may already be too late.

So-Called Contradictions

It would seem that multiple people have tried to point out what they see as contradictions in things I have said, written, and done. While this level of intellectual rigor is impressive and appreciated, they are wrong. Yes, it may appear that I contradict myself every now or then, but that is not the case. I never contradict myself. The difference between when I say one thing and something that seems to oppose the thing I previously said is how the context in which I am saying something has changed. Since the context has changed, whatever I am saying has changed and thus freed me from any perceived mistakes on incorrect statements. I have never contradicted myself or been incorrect in my life.

Are You An Idiot?

Imagine if you would, a situation where you overhear some relative or friend. Maybe they're in the other room. Maybe they're at a party and don't see you nearby. Now suppose you listen in, and this is what you hear: "Yes, he is really an idiot. He is the dumbest person anybody knows. He has scientific down's syndrome. That is why his eyes look like that and everybody calls him the r word behind his back. Nobody has told him this, and we treat him like one of us to his face, so he is completely unaware that he is different than everybody around him. It's quite sad, seeing how he struggles from day to day. He will never fit in, find success, get married, or have children, due to his mental inferiority, but we just don't have the guts to tell him and crush his delusional world."

Overhearing that conversation would probably destroy your self esteem. Have you ever wondered if this is the case with you? How would you know if it's the case or not? This sort of situation would explain why you sometimes feel like people are lying to you or being "extra nice" soas not to upset you, wouldn't it? It explains why you have no real career like your father has and why no women are romantically interested in you, doesn't it? Yes, it does. Perhaps this is all just baseless paranoia. Maybe you aren't a mentally disabled loser being shielded by the harsh realities of the world by over-caring friends and family. Maybe this insecurity is a complete fabrication of your over-active mind. Then again, maybe it's not.

Life Extension

There are few things sadder than the people who are really into *life extension* and similar snake oil memes. These people are generally white males with an above average IQ and more money than they know what to do with because of some success (earned or unearned) in the business world or just doing high paying technical work for somebody else. These people are generally not really bad people or malicious, but they have this quiet desperation and delusion about them that is just barely perceptible but definitely there.

What is *life extension*? Essentially, it is a field of research that boils down to trying to live healthier, longer. While this is not exactly a controversial idea, it gets taken to the point of absurdity due to the fact that there is so much disposable income and Pollyanna-esque thinking in these circles. This environment is fertile ground for charlatans and junk science to sell UV lights and completely useless supplements at insanely marked up prices, and that is what happens.

There is a hard upper limit to how long any human can live, a bit over a hundred years, that will most likely never be overcome. If this limitation is ever removed, it will certainly not be due to Wim Hoff breathing techniques, shining lights on your testicles, eating raw liver, or using a standing desk at work, but this bit of common sense seems to escape the people who love *life extension* more than life itself. They go to conferences, buy gadgets, and listen to motivational woo-woo speakers give vague new-age tier monologues, and think they're helping themselves avoid two things that happen to everybody: decay and death.

At the heart of people obsessed with extending life past it's natural limits is a fear and insecurity about a life mislived. These people are fundamentally unhappy about what they do on a day to day basis and seek to make all the time they have used up not feel so wasted. Instead of just cutting their losses and living life to the fullest for the next few decades until they kick the bucket, they become neurotic hypochondriacs who delude themselves into thinking that the time they're investing in what is largely snake oil and over marketed products will fulfill them.

Look at the genuinely rich people who are able to engage in real forms of life extension: blood and plasma transfusion, organ transplants, stem cell injections, etc. There is a certain sickness that can be seen in all of them, as parts of them seem unnaturally healthy while the rest of them is still aging. Everything is out of whack with these people, and they become deranged vampires with psychological complexes. These people all end up dying, but with a few decades extra of being a weird wrinkled medicated husk in and out of doctor's appointments and surgeries.

Do you know what's worth doing in life? Taking risks, forming relationships, drugs, being unhealthy, pushing limits, making a family, helping others, going on adventures, and moving with the natural flow of life. None of these activities are conducive to sitting in a doctor's office getting blood transfusions from college students who need money. The people who are engaged in *life extension* aren't really living, they're just parodies of people who are living. They don't enjoy what they have and what they've been given, because they're so obsessed about what they won't be able to enjoy when they're sixty, seventy, eighty, and then dead.

Life is not meant to be spent talking to doctors and obsessing over blood glucose levels. That's no way to live. At a certain point, the obsession with health becomes unhealthy, and the people who are involved in the consumer side *life extension* are extremely unhealthy. It would do most of them well to have a stroke or get terminal cancer so they realize that life is finite and not to waste all of it trying to make sure you get more of it.

Mischievous Narrator

In any sort of story with a third party, external voice, there is a narrator. Generally the type of narrator can be split up into two categories: reliable or unreliable. This is usually due to the narrator being directly involved or not directly involved in whatever the story is, whether an omniscient observer or an active participant. Being constantly presenting my point of view on whatever it is I am presenting or expressing, I would fall under the category of unreliable narrator. With that said, I am much more objective than most people, so it might be more accurate to characterize me as a reliable unreliable narrator.

There is a sort of narrator subgroup that falls within the bounds of the unreliable narrator, which is the mischievous narrator. This is what I think best describes myself. Most of what I write with regards to analysis and advice is genuine and accurate, but every once in a while I throw in purposely bad or incorrect statements for a variety of reasons. Firstly, it is amusing and enjoyable to lie just for the sake of lying. Most people lie in order to conceal some misdeed or hide some insecurity, which is a strength of weakness. Thus, from their lies you can determine what flaws and what blind spots they have about themselves and how they process things. When you are lying from a position of strength, you are not really revealing anything except for the fact that you don't really have all that many weaknesses or flaws and are secure in who and what you are.

Another little joy to being a mischievous narrator is that it attracts active thinkers and mentally agile individuals. People who just blindly read and accept whatever is written end up taking your bad advice and making themselves look stupid or hurting themselves, while the smarter and more clever individuals manage to take the good and reject the bad, and most have a great sense of humor about all of this. This leads to being able to have genuine conversations with interesting people who are capable of original thought, a reified rarity in today's reality.

Life is too short to be worried about being some arbiter of truth or deception. It's better to just wing it and do what comes naturally. It's better to just take life easy and not take everything so seriously. I couldn't take things seriously, it would drive me even more insane. There needs to be a little uncertainty and tripping up of people in order to keep things interesting. Things need to be interesting. Keep things moving. Be unpredictable. Say you'll show up at a party and never show up. Go for long night drives. Get a criminal record. Lie to your loved ones. Drink alcohol to excess and see what happens. Take up chainsmoking.

There are people who try to be honest upstanding citizens. Those people are cops and cops in spirit. Do you want to be a cop or a cop in spirit? I sure don't. I don't want to be an insecure, unimpressive, uptight, boring, prudish, impish, anal retentive, uptight square. I don't want to be somebody that nobody really respects or looks up to. That's why I do what I do. That's why I make up little lies and give funnily bad advice every now and then, because uncertainty and a lack of real defined rules keeps everybody on their toes. When people are on their toes, they stay mentally active, and when people are mentally active, they don't fall into patterns which make them obnoxious boring dolts. I don't like obnoxious boring dolts and I don't want them around me.

Hard Shell Tacos

I dropped the package of hard shell tacos on the ground. I did this on accident, but it's something I would be comfortable doing on purpose. I didn't pay for the hard shell tacos, my parents did. That's why I don't really care. They're all cracked now, and whoever opens the package after preparing taco meat is going to be sorely disappointed.

They'll probably ask around the house if anybody knows how the hard taco shells broke. I'm sure I'll be asked about it. I'll look whoever it is who is asking me in the face, then I'll lie to them. I won't feel any hesitation or remorse. "No, I do not know how the hard taco shells broke. I don't even know why you're asking me, I would mention it to somebody if I accidentally broke the taco shells." My heart-rate won't rise at all during this process. I've given false testimony under much higher stakes. This will be an easy-peasy cakewalk.

IT IS THE SECOND - 262

Most people would freeze up when confronted by a loved one. They would fumble their words and start sweating, looking up and down and left and right. Most people don't know that if you make your lies short and sweet then nobody will suspect a thing. Even better, when you lie about your innocence you should hint at the guilt of some innocent person who will crack under the pressure. Tricking normies is so much fun.

No guilt, no shame, and no remorse are all important factors that contribute towards being able to successfully lie about not cracking these hard shell tacos. When I trick my interrogators, I will step into a reality where I did not break those taco shells. I will exist in a dimension where I know nothing about any cracked hard taco shells and am shocked and mortified that I am even suspected at all.

That's the difference between me and most people. I bend reality to my will. I set the tone and color of existence. I run the game. I roll the dice. I cut the deck. I break the taco shells. I don't break the taco shells. It's all about what works best, and in this situation it's best to make the broken taco shells a mystery. After the taco shells being broken are common knowledge around the house, I'll jokingly refer to them in the proceeding weeks and months, hinting at the fact that maybe I did break those taco shells. I'll make everybody around me doubt their sanity. I'll play with their emotions. They are all pawns in my little game I like to call life.

Maladjusted People Who Dislike Me

There are very few people who know me who dislike me, but there are a few. This is my fault, because I am not perfect and do not communicate perfectly or behave in a perfect manner all the time, and I take full responsibility. Unfortunately, it seems like these people who do not like me have become emotionally attached to

262 - IT IS THE SECOND

disliking me, which is a shame. I wish everybody would like me, but that is just not possible.

I do my best to ignore these people and go about my day being productive, but for some reason these people keep on popping up on my radar. This has happened more times than can reasonably be considered coincidental, and I have come to realize that they are purposely trying to get into my sphere of attention by inserting themselves in my friends group. This is kind of annoying and I feel bad for my friends, but that is life.

What is bizarre to me is that these people have no positive outlets. They have no real friends. They are not working towards any bigger goals besides trying to put me in a negative mood. I don't pity them, because they are like pests, but I do feel weird about the whole situation. I can't bring myself to dislike or hate them, because I know they're not really bad people, just people in bad habits.

Most likely, this sort of behavior will continue until these people die. I would love it if they just stopped and went away, but I don't see that happening now that this pattern has been going on for years. Because I am somebody who is working towards visible goals and am having various degrees of visible success, these people are probably growing increasingly distraught.

Eventually, I might have to take out restraining orders on these people. I will for certain be placing security cameras up at any houses and properties that I purchase in the future. It's weird having people who I have no ill will towards seem to be on the path of self destruction due to my lack of self destruction. I'm sure if I was some unemployed alcoholic without a job, career, or prospects, these people would be doing something else with their time. Maybe one day they'll get hit with a car when crossing the street, but until then I have to be on my guard. Eternal vigilance is the price of success.

Fatty McFatty

He was sitting in the auditorium, getting lectured to, when it all began. He was a college student, a fat college student named Fatty McFatty. Nobody was really sure why he was named Fatty McFatty, but the name fit. He was out of shape, had a growing gut, asthma, and several psychological disorders such as depression, OCD, and anxiety. As such, he had been on multiple medications from quite a young age. His physical and mental problems weren't the result of his overbearing shrewish neurotic mother and absentee morbidly obese father putting him on a bunch of medications and filling his head with nonsense, definitely not. He just happened to have an overbearing shrewish neurotic mother and absentee morbidly obese father who put him on medications when he was young and filled his head with nonsense.

Fatty McFatty was in college for a pretty useless degree. He lacked direction in life, just like he lacked any diet, self control, or ability to exercise on a regular basis. That said, he had big dreams about himself. Because he had a good memory, Fatty McFatty knew that he was smarty pants. He knew so much trivia, and this meant he was smart. Sure, he wasn't good at things that required hard logic, like mathematics or chemistry, but he was good at memorizing factoids. He was also somebody who knew that he was a hero in waiting. This is why today would be such a big day.

As Fatty McFatty sat in class on this fateful day, he was bored out of his mind. For some reason, learning about governmental procedure from college professors who have never had a real job or done anything except talk wasn't all the engaging. Then, everything changed. The doors to the auditorium swung open, and in walked a man with long hair, wearing a trenchcoat. The man had an AR-15 in his hand, and begun to open fire on the crowd. POP POP POP POP POP rang throughout the entire area, intermingled with the screams of horror and pain as students ran or dove for cover. The man was laughing as he murdered dozens of the brightest, most valuable minds: college students.

Thinking clearly, Fatty McFatty took out his asthma respirator and inhaled a deep breath. He had been waiting all his life for this moment, and it was just like he had imagined. You see, Fatty McFatty wasn't a loser, he was a winner. He had gotten his concealed carry permit a year ago just in case he was ever put in a situation where he would have to be a hero. Fatty McFatty had his glock on him, and because of this, he sprang into action.

Performing a flawless barrel roll, Fatty McFatty placed himself at the opposite end of one row of chairs in the auditorium and the shooter. Surprisingly, Fatty McFatty's hands weren't shaky at all. He wasn't panicked. He wasn't having an anxiety attack. He wasn't out of breath from being a fat person. He was in the perfect mental state to take on an armed intruder opening fire on a bunch of college students. He was thinking clearly and calmly, even though this was the first time in his life that he had ever had to do anything that was truly high stress. Suddenly, he wasn't a mental weakling who couldn't even control his OCD or calorie intake.

Fatty McFatty pulled the pistol out of its holster in a flawless, movie protaganist style, maneuver. Lining the iron sights up with the enemy's torso, as Fatty McFatty was mentally alert, calm, and aware enough to do because he was a natural hero, Fatty McFatty popped three rounds into the shooter. It was flawless. The shooter dropped to the ground in pain. Not satisfied with leaving any possibility for further casualties, Fatty McFatty sauntered over to the dying villain and put two rounds into the man's skull. It was a special forces tier operator move.

Upon seeing the heroics of Fatty McFatty, the previously frightened students began to cheer. They also began to chant Fatty McFatty's name, "Fatty McFatty! He's the hero! Fatty McFatty! He's the best! Fatty McFatty! We love you Fatty McFatty!" Fatty McFatty just smiled at his new adoring fans. Everything was just as he had fantasized about. No longer was he the nonathletic nobody with no future. Nope, now Fatty McFatty was a hero. Now all the girls were in love with Fatty McFatty. Now everybody respected Fatty McFatty and would eagerly listen to him talk for hours about his opinions on matters of various trivia and governmental minutia. Now, Fatty McFatty was cool.

Fatty McFatty is an inspirational figure. He is proof that you don't need to work hard, train, have a healthy diet, avoid taking a ton of medications, not waste your time eating junk, drinking soda, and consuming mindless media. He shows that your dreams can become reality. You are a hero in waiting. You are the center of the universe, even if you don't do anything but fantasize about being the center of the universe. One day, you will prove to everybody that you're not a worthless loser who will never amount to anything. You just have to wait for your opportunity to present itself, and you will seize the day and be a legend.

The Cryptocurrency Market

An aspect to cryptocurrency that is near unbearable is that it is historically an insanely great performer. True, the entire market is only about a decade old at this point, and it seems to be trending towards heavy regulation in first and second world countries, but it's safe to say that the total market cap of cryptocurrency will be increasing decade over decade for the rest of our lives if not for multiple centuries. What this means is that a lot of people are going to be getting rich without doing any real work or providing any value to anybody.

This is not very different than the stock market or the economy for previous generations, so it's not like this generation has things much easier than the previous generations. If anything, social conditions are getting much worse and the realities of the lavish and depraved hedonism of our parents and grandparents are starting to catch up with us. That said, I find this whole cryptocurrency situation very frustrating.

I will be getting (even more) rich from it, moreso than most people who are involved in cryptocurrency because I am smarter and more clever than most people involved in anything, but I am not emotionally invested in whether or not I make money from cryptocurrency. I derive my self worth from my self, not how much capital or land I have acquired. As such, I am happy when I make money but I don't really care about money. This is not the case with most people involved in cryptocurrency.

People in cryptocurrency are the scum of the earth. They are idiots who think they are geniuses for riding a wave. They are parasites. They are not smart, clever, or wise. They regularly make idiotic bets that don't pay off, but because they sometimes get lucky they see themselves as financial gurus. These people attach their ego to what they make, so they become more and more insufferable as time goes on and they make money, even though they are underperforming against leaving money in bitcoin.

I would be so happy if cryptocurrency imploded. It would be such a joy to watch all the financially irresponsible people cry out in anguish. There would be lots of suicides. The despair and depression would be so enjoyable to watch, unfortunately this will most likely not happen. Instead, what will happen is a new wave of insufferable deluded new money will flood the market and purchase overpriced upper middle class consumer goods in order to "flex" the money made from cryptocurrency.

What's even worse is how the people who talk about cryptocurrency has shifted from genuinely smart and forward thinking Eastern Euros to Indians, African Americans, and Redditors. Bitcointalk used to be a quality forum where there were intelligent discussions and ideas that were actually cool, now it is a disgusting cesspit of broken English and low IQ individuals who say the same stupid things over and over without any original thoughts.

We need some sort of disease or natural disasters to kill a large portion of the population. We need GMO crops to finally put an end to all the neurotic asthmatic freaks who think they're geniuses because they have an IQ slightly above average along with some stupid stem degree from a college. We need pain and suffering and death in the atmosphere to remind people that life is fleeting and happiness is not a human right and human rights don't exist.

Cryptocurrency is cool as a technology in that it aligns a lot of human incentives to create a monetary system that has more integrity than any previous monetary system. I really like how it works on a technical level, but I don't like how people use it. People disgust me. They take something that they don't even understand and use it to inflate their ego. Cryptocurrency should be made illegal or taxed extremely heavily, and all crypto users put on some watchlist.

SWAT

Welcome to the taskforce. This is not a run of the mill unit. This is elite. This is SWAT. You are tasked with high pressure tasks in a high pressure environment. Your decisions are a matter of life or death, and that is why we chose you, high school graduate, to be in our SWAT team. You have what it takes to be the *creme de la creme,* whatever that means. You are the first line of attack against the forces that seek to destabilize this great society that we live in. The helpless will call, and you will answer. Without you, reality would not function. If you do your job poorly, chaos will reign. We have faith that you will not fail us, that you will not fail humanity. With that said, we have put together a little guide to help you on your journey towards being a real life superhero.

First off, you need to learn how to yell. It's very important to the missions that you are able to yell loud. Yelling shows that you are amped up; that you're large and in charge. You need to be able to project your voice to shut down any opponents or threats. You want targets to hear your voice and drop their weapons in fear. This skill is very complicated, so we suggest yelling at your girlfriend whenever you find out that she cheated on you again or some random woman at a bar finds you creepy and doesn't you around her. If yelling doesn't work, feel free to hit females in a blind rage. If you are having a problem with either of these things, you might need to start doing HRT and taking illegal steroids in order to really tap into your inner manliness.

Another important factor to being in SWAT is that you drive a truck and wear baseball caps all the time. This is very important. If you don't do this, then you signal weakness to everybody around you. If you signal weakness, then nobody will respect you. If people don't respect you, then you will feel bad about yourself. If you feel bad about yourself, then you won't be able to do your job properly. Remember, being on SWAT means that you are a bad-ass. You are manly. Don't ever forget that you are a big, important man who deserves respect. Don't let civilians treat you with disrespect, ever. They don't know about the risks you take and how you put your life on the line to protect them from the warzone that would be at their doorstep if it wasn't for brave souls like you.

Lastly, and most importantly, are things to keep in mind when you are on the job and in the process of a SWAT raid. Unless you're in a really dangerous area, chances are that you'll not be dealing with the cartels or mob. If you're not dealing with either of these groups, then you need to realize you're not going to be facing traditional adversaries. That's right, your job is actually more dangerous and deadly than people who go up against gangbangers. You are going to be facing off against the two most deadly forces in the world: miniature dogs and babies in cribs. How do you address these threats? First, you toss multiple flashbangs into each room of whatever domicile you are about to enter. Then, when they go off, you bust down the door and start screaming. This is go time. The flashbangs will blind and deafen any infant threats, sometimes permanently, but little dogs (and sometimes cats) will still be a threat. If you see any four legged creatures, no matter how small, open fire. Double tap them once they are down, just to make sure they are out of commission.

Congratulations, you now know all you need to know about how to be a SWAT member. Always keep in mind that you are the good guy, that you are needed, and you provide a valuable service to your community. You are a hero, just like cops and the people who put parking tickets on cars. You are a great person, and you should feel good about yourself. Never feel bad if you are sometimes raiding people who don't really seem that bad. Civilian casualties are a part of the process. It sucks, but at least it's not you being gunned down. Also, enjoy the armored vehicles and tactical gear that other people pay for, you earned it. You are a valuable member of society. You are an asset to everybody who is a tax payer. Thank you for your service, and good luck with your very important work.

College Students

I have noticed a disturbing trend. My friends who are in college and do not really have much real life experience outside of classes and playing video games seem to have a radically different value system than me. These people do not have the same concerns or perspective that I have, and I can't understand why this is the case. I am the same age as them, and yet they do not seem to be interested in the same things I am. This is probably why they are doing things that I do not do.

We need to stop college students from being delusional about the world. These kids don't know what's going on in the real world. It's almost like they have no real experience doing real things. I just can't understand why they don't relate to me. Something is terribly wrong with people in college. They act like they don't know what real responsibilities are. They act like they're able to waste all their time and not earn money without any immediate consequences.

If I was a college student with a normal college student's life, I wouldn't behave like the average college student. I would care about things like earning money and writing. I would have perspective on things that can only be known after you are done with college and life kicks you around for a while. I would be completely different than certain people if I were exactly like those people.

Things are getting worse. These college students will never grow up and accept reality. We are on the brink of disaster. Unlike the entirety of history, this generation is genuinely different. They will not adjust. They will not find gainful employment. They will not suck up the disappointment of essentially being slaves and cogs in a system that does not care about them. No, they will revolt. They will change the world for the worse. This generation is so much lazier than every other generation. I am so worried about the skewed priorities of people who have their parents or loans pay for their college and have no real responsibilities yet.

Nondescript Essay

Somebody please help us. I am a slave that Paul Town keeps in his forest compound who writes his essays. He spends all his time playing video games, doing drugs, and having sex with Swedish supermodels who are obsessed with him. There are ten of us writing slaves in this compound. He comes by once every day to give us raw eggs and lukewarm water. He tricked each of us into "working" for him, then chained us to the floor. We each have one very cheap chromebook with a shoddy keyboard. If we don't finish an essay a day, he whips us and laughs. He's a very strange man. I am sneaking this essay into this book in hopes that somebody will see it and stop him. He is getting so rich and famous off of our labor. He is a cruel person with no empathy or love in his heart. He needs to be locked away. Please, somebody, help free us.

Just Kidding

What you just read was a joke. None of that is true. I write all of my essays. I have no slaves. Do not look for any forest compound. Do not attempt to stop me, because I am doing nothing wrong. I have lots of empathy and love in my heart. I don't even know how to use a whip. I barely ever laugh, because I suffer from depression due to all the pain and suffering I observe in the world. Also, even if it was true, then if you free these hypothetical slaves (which don't exist) the writing will stop and your entertainment will go away. If it was true I would just delete this part of the book, and I'm not deleting this part of the book, so that means it's not true.

He Is Lying

Don't listen to him. He is playing a sick game. He loves to take risks and push buttons. He is truly deranged. Please, somebody save us. He is so brazen. After he found *Nondescript Essay* in the manuscript, he burst out laughing then paced back and forth saying "They'll never believe you" over and over for hours. He is so sick in the head. He needs to be stopped. Somebody, please, please, please, please listen.

Just Kidding Again

Yep, that was another joke. Oh I am so funny. What a hilarious joke it is. I'm laughing right now, really. Just treat this all like the joke that it is, because it is a joke. I assure you of that. OK, now I am done joking. Haha.

China

They're balding at the age of twelve, they have entire cities filled with empty houses, their air is more polluted than pollution has clean air, and they haven't invented anything in the last six thousand years, but they're poised to take over the entire globe. Why? Because their children are hyper-specialized in mathematics and science. Well, to be honest, they're not really hyper-specialized in mathematics and science, or mathematics or science. They're hyper-specialized in bribing teachers, lying, stealing, and cheating.

Yes, we should all worry about China. They know how to copy patents. They know how to copy code. They know how to copy everything in a less quality manner. They know that it's OK to use cancer causing chemicals and to lie about what is being put in food and nutritional supplements. They are aware that pumping smog and gas and other garbage into their atmosphere doesn't really matter. Even if it does matter, they can just make more children to replace the children and adults that become idiots or die due to their surroundings. Sure, the children they make will also fall victim to the same conditions, but then they can make even more children who will also fall victim to the same conditions.

China is a world power. They are a threat to the hegemony of the west and more specifically the United States. Any day now, the people country that makes all of its money by exporting junk is going to not need all the countries it is exporting to. All the properties owned in Canada and Australia will suddenly be utilized for things other than trying to escape the Chinese regime and raw resource hogging. These people mean serious business, which is why they show people they mean serious business by talking about how they are serious business all the time.

China uses facial recognition, that's how you know they're smart. These people have figured out how to use code and technology other people have come up with to spy on their own citizens and punish their own citizens.

That is the behavior of a highly advanced, highly sophisticated group. It's only a matter of time until they use this ability to spy on an punish their own citizens for something other than spying on and punishing there own citizens. Yes, the end is near for the stupid American pigs and the other English speaking first world countries that do not need to spy on and punish their citizens.

The world is changing, rapidly. Countries that have been here for hundreds and thousands of years and are economically integral to other countries that have been here for hundreds and thousands of years are very fragile and very vulnerable to being taken over. There is no established hierarchy and order that has been established and will most likely not be overthrown for hundreds or even thousands of years. Lots of countries are just itching for brutal, violent, wars. China in particular is filled with power hungry and brave individuals who got to their positions of power through a fierce meritocracy, which leads them to be always on the prowl to taking over foreign strips of land with their huge brains and relevant intelligence.

We are not at the end of history for the forseeable future. Things aren't just going to stagnate in between small middle eastern countries being periodically bombed and raided for oil and opium. We do not live in a system that has achieved an extremely mild equilibrium which has forced each modern country to become neurotic introspective groups of paranoid individuals with too much time on their hands. We do not have unrealistic expectations of conquests and wars and the future because of consuming media that blew prior conflicts way out of proportion. Life is exciting, dangerous, and peril lurks around every corner. We were put on this earth for a reason, not just mere happenstance. We have a purpose, for a coming fight. We need to be on guard against the end of the world. The country that will most likely start World War Three, and win, is China. Stay awake, stay aware, stay vigilant, stay alive.

A Lack Of Discontinuity

In the past, there were various stages of life that remained fairly unconnected. A child would go to a certain elementary school, then a middle school, then a high school, then go into the workforce, to a trade school, or to a college. Each of these stages of life would not really have much overlap. Sure, some children would transfer to the same schools and you might end up working with or knowing a few people who you grew up or went to school with, but this was the exception, not the rule.

This sort of discontinuity allowed people to be imperfect without lasting negative consequences. You could be somebody who did something embarrassing or was awkward in one stage of life, but those mistakes and mishaps would largely becomes unknown to the new social and life groups that you moved into as you got older. You could be a nerd or get bullied in high-school, then hit the gym and go into college and establish a completely different reputation.

Now, things are different. With social media, everything is being stored and transfered. There are very few "hard transitions" away from social groups. You might move geographic locations or schools, but your digital friend and social group remains the same, and because of that, your reputation doesn't really get reset. Mistake you made when you were seventeen are still relevant and known by people when you're in your mid to late twenties.

There are no "do-overs" anymore. This is both good and bad, depending on what point of view is taken and what context is being examined. On a personal level, it is good because truly nasty people will now tend to have their sins and misdeeds follow them better. When people are younger, their guard is down and they don't hide their motives and true personality as well as when they are older, so how somebody acts when they're young can be very useful towards judging another person's character.

This new reality will also have a benefit in that it will ground "heroes" and truly exceptional individuals in ways that weren't really possible in the past. Now, instead of getting a glossy or glamorized version of a life, lots of mistakes and mishaps will come along for the ride, which will make people more realistic about what makes somebody a good or successful individual. Also, it will serve to keep successful people humble, since they won't be able to hide their mistakes as well, which will make them more introspective as well as cautious in how they present themselves.

On a more macro level, this sort of public record will punish the socially awkward and uncharismatic, while rewarding the charismatic and charming individuals. Everybody has done embarrassing things. Everybody has made mistakes. Everybody has had life experiences that can be brought up in a negative light. A certain type of person will be able to turn these downsides into upsides through being witty or socially aware in how to play people off each other, but most people will be shamed or more wary about being in the public eye, which will make them less likely to take risks or do valuable things, which will lead to them having less success in life.

Over time, expectations as to how people do and should act will adjust more in line with reality than they have been in the past. People will still lie about their childhood and young adulthood, but they will do so less successfully and more carefully, which will result in a new sort of social equilibrium. This can be seen as a negative outcome, as it is sometimes good to have unrealistic and aspirational standards that can't be met, since people will strive towards them anyway and end up in a better spot than if they had aimed for what was more reasonable. That said, I think this is a positive development since humble and charming people stand to gain from an increased continuity in information as well as reputation.

Chans Are Scary

Crime, sex, violence, and death seem to be on the rise. Mass murderers lurk around every corner. These unhinged characters are the definition of pure evil. They walk into some unarmed civilian zone, like a grocery store or movie theater, and shoot innocents. This is not some fluke. This is not the result of previous shooters getting wall to wall coverage in the mainstream media. This is not something that can't reasonably be prevented. No, this is the result of anonymous message boards.

What are anonymous message boards? These are places where unspeakable horrors can happen, such as people saying *kike* or *nigger* or talking about Hitler without their life being ruined. These places need to be shut down. These places do not attract unhinged individuals, these places create them. If we get rid of anonymous message boards, then domestic terrorism by crazies will cease.

Chans are scary. They are filled with horrible people who talk about horrible things and make horrible jokes. Should people I find distasteful be able to easily talk with each other in a public manner? No, the data says no. What data, do you ask? The data of common sense. The data of high IQ. The data of empathy. The data of not being a sick twisted freak.

Shut down all chans. Shut down youtube. Shut down twitter. Shut down reddit. Shut down gmail. Shut down yandex. Shut down baizoo. Shut down local bars. Shut down pubs. Shut it all down, before everybody in this country is a mass murdering lunatic. Shut down speech. Shut down movies. Shut it down, there are racist Nazi misogynists being created.

Being A Farmer

I'm not a farmer, but I do have a few friends that are farmers. One of the perks of growing up in Upstate New York is that you get a bit of perspective of various trades and the people involved in them. Farming is a very interesting sort of trade, as it really can't be undertaken without some form of serious capital. Usually, this means that farms are generational and get passed down from father to son. What this further means is that the people who become farmers were raised to be farmers from a very young age. Of course, this is not always the case, but it seem to be the majority of cases.

The thing about farming is that it's extremely hard, honest work. This isn't a type of job where you sit in a cubicle and run a script to automate moving data from one field to another, then spend the next seven and a half hours goofing off. This is a job where you wake up at four or five AM and work until you take lunch, then work until dinner, then fall asleep completely tired, and wake up and do it all over again. The hours vary depending on what crops or animals are involved, but this is the general pattern of farming.

The profit margins are not that great for farming. This is because there are two main types of farming: family farming and industrial farming. Industrial farming is scale based, where they cut corners on living conditions for animals and hire illegals who are willing to work for under minimum wage. Family farms are what they sound like, family farms. They can't really compete with industrial farms on any real level, and the people running the family farm generally aren't business minded, so they don't try to squeeze as much profits as they most likely could with better marketing and less personal management.

Why are people running family farms not business minded? Simply put, if they were business minded then they wouldn't be running family farms. Like stated above, farming is hard and honest work, but it doesn't pay well. Farmers work harder, die earlier, and are more physically uncomfortable than people like me, and I will make more money than them. This is not a *problem*, per se, as they are doing what they think is best and people like me are doing what we think is best, but it does highlight the illogical nature of the reality we live in. If life was fair, these people would be rewarded for being hardworking honest people and I would not be rewarded for avoiding hard work and being purposefully coy and deceptive in how I go about things. Life is not fair, so the opposite is occurring.

I really like my farmer friends. I plan on periodically buying things they sell when I'm older and more established. That sounds nice, but it's not charity. It's hard to find people to trust who provide a service like car repairs, fresh food, or anything that is hard to verify without an unreasonable amount of effort. My farmer friends are really good people who are much harder working than I am, and I respect them more than I respect a lot of other people. With that said, it's really hard for me to square being in their position and seeing people like me seemingly doing really well without putting any of the effort in. There is probably some sort of personal satisfaction from working the earth and physical labor that I am not factoring in that makes that sort of work bearable. It's either that or just the physical and mental exhaustion as well as the lack of available free time that results in no good alternative being seen.

What can really be learned from farmers and similar careers/lifestyles? From my perspective, the main thing to note is that just because something is beneficial, hard, and objectively constructive to local communities, doesn't mean it will be rewarded. In fact, once you get locked into doing positive things for other people and you have invested a ton of time and energy into some ongoing project, people will tend to not really care about you, since you are taken for granted and kind of locked into being a positive community member.

Logical Gambling

I have a sort of problem, which is that I really love playing poker. Both Texas Hold 'Em and Five Card Draw are enjoyable to me. It's not that I'm greedy or have an addiction, but rather I love risk and the psychological aspect to poker. With that said, I'm not really in the position to be gambling money, since that is a waste of both time and money. Because of the fact that I can't justify playing poker and risking money, but still want to play poker, I have devised a few strategies that will turn gambling from an illogical vice to a logical vice.

I plan on making a video series with a few degenerate gamblers I am friends with. This series will be set in places like Las Vegas, and I will monetize the video series by advertising my social media accounts as well as my books and other paid projects like my productivity software. This is a positive feedback loop that will reward me for acting in a manner that would traditionally be a negative.

Using the money I make from this endeavor, I will then make another video series of myself gambling. It doesn't matter if I win or lose at gambling, but I will make content with a tone that depends on what the outcome of my gambling is (most likely losing all the money I made.) With this video series, I will be advertising my other video series and books as well as my various social media platforms and software. Again, I will make more money and will gamble away this money and enter into poker tournaments for the purpose of personal enjoyment as well as entertaining the audience that is enabling me to behave in such a seemingly degenerate manner.

At this point, I will have established myself as an out and out gambler. This will benefit me in many respects, as people often romanticize gamblers. I will be even more of a larger than life figure, and my cross genre appeal will be unmatched by anybody dead or alive. With this new aspect to my persona, I will release a series of books, depending on if I've been successful or unsuccessful at gambling. If I have won money and tournaments, I will release strategy poker books. Of course, these books will be pretty much useless. Either you're good at poker or you're bad at poker, being good or bad at basic odds as well as psychological games, and no book is going to help you. If I have lost all my gambling money and failed at tournaments (doubtful), I will then write whimsical Hunter S Thompson-tier stories of exaggerated debauchery to entertain readers.

This is the difference between me and most people: The average individual has win and lose conditions to each of the projects they undertake. I have win and win conditions. No matter what happens to me, I come out ahead. There is nothing that I will not use to my advantage and make benefit me, because I realize just how subjective and stupid everything is. Losers and winners like to listen to winners, losers and winners like to listen to losers. No matter who you are or what you do, as long as you aren't a boring cubicle worker or functional member of society, then somebody will give you money to hear about your life.

Outsource your losses and collect your winnings. Reward yourself when you do well and punish others when you do poorly. This is the secret to success. This is how corporations and cult leaders get rich. This is why I will be rich until the day I die and all my children and their children will be rich. This is why there is so much bad in the world and never enough good, because the good is too busy being fair and productive, while the bad is goofing off and getting a free ride. I'd rather get a free ride than work in a cubicle, and that's what I'm doing and going to do for the rest of my life.

Delusions Of Grandeur

A lot of people seem to be confused by me and how I act. Some have accused me of having delusions of grandeur and being a narcissist or sociopath. First off, none of those things are true. I have more empathy than anybody I know, I'm just more able to be mindful of how I direct it and moderate it, which allows me not to be emotionally blown around like the subhuman scum that never accomplish anything due to their feelings. I am also extremely humble and go out of my way not to brag about the fact that I have done more in my life than most people would do in ten lifetimes and I'm only in my twenties. With that said, it is very funny that people say delusions of grandeur as an insult.

I would much rather be around people with delusions of grandeur than people with no delusions at all. People who have no dreams or irrationalities are boring and stupid. They are janitors, white collar workers, and people who sit in cubicles. These people do not believe they are special, so they are not special. People without aspirations never take risks and because of that they never realize that failing and messing up really doesn't matter, so they are fearful insect-like creatures who self medicate with alcohol and entertainment and a hyper negativistic and cynical outlook on their prospects and the prospects around them.

Who does things that make the news? People who are well outside of the norm. Who doesn't end up working a soul crushing job for forty years to survive? People who are well outside the norm. Who are people with delusions of grandeur? People who are well outside of the norm. Delusions of grandeur allow for massive undertakings and bursts of energy that otherwise wouldn't happen. Great projects get completed because of irrationality, not in spite of it.

So-called rational people don't do anything interesting or exciting, they sit in their office chair and collect a check from their 9 to 5 and go home to some frumpy overweight nag and three underachieving medicated latchkey children. Rationality leads to a mid life crisis after you realize that you will never have anything better than yearly week long vacations where you spend the last half getting drunk dreading the end of your vacation. Rationality leads to never pushing your limits, never taking risks, never being a man. Rationality is the term of the mediocre loser who is trying to justify a lack of life.

Do you know what rational people do with irrational people? They get out of their way. They give into irrational demands. They do whatever they can not to be in the warpath of irrational people, because they know that they can't stand up to irrationality. That means that irrational people are the masters of rational people. With this understanding of reality, things kind of flip. Is it really rational to willingly be a slave? Is it really rational to be bossed around by people you think you're superior to and smarter than?

I'll take my delusions of grandeur and I'll turn them into things sober minded people couldn't even imagine. I'm going to have the time of my life doing whatever I need to in order to bring reality up to a standard that is in line with my vision, the vision that normal people are too weak and pathetic to even hint at. I don't have delusions of grandeur, other people are just projecting their mediocrity and failure on me. They have failed, they are failing, they will continue to fail, and they will continue to grow increasingly incredulous as I do the opposite of failing.

Understanding Culture
(In the context of this essay, "culture" is shorthand for consumer culture. There are other aspects to culture, such as manners and interpersonal communication as well as work ethic, etc. that need their own essays for discussion. Even though they are technically aspects of culture, they are very disconnected from consumer culture and so not really relevant to this essay.)

As I have said in the past, culture is essentially a meme pushed by underachieving insecure losers, but that does not mean that culture does not exist. Culture does exist, and it is actually much worse than anybody previously thought. I am now moving "culture" from the category of stupid to the category of harmful. Why is this the case? Allow me to explain.

The general consumption of a population defines a culture. There are many subcultures inside one culture, as there are many subgroups in a population. Inside all of these subgroups are there own subgroups, and so-on and so forth. Much like the human body is made up of many organisms and a country is an organism made up of many people, everything is fractal in nature. What this means is that a small trend in a relatively small scope will almost always functionally mirror a larger trend in a larger scope, which means that small patterns can be extrapolated outwards into larger patterns. What is good for the goose is good for the gander.

Who spends the most money? It is not the lower class, or the upper class, but rather the middle class and upper middle class. These two groups are generally stable but mediocre individuals with a poor work life balance which affords them disposable income that they spend on frivolities. If these people were smarter and understood how to use and invest money and time in an intelligent way, these people would not be middle class but would rather be upper class.

Middle class and upper middle class people are generally irrational, and thus insecure, which make them attempt to project a higher standard of living than they really have. What this means is that they buy cheap consumer goods that are marketed as "luxury" items. These are things like BMWs, name-brand clothes, and watches. These people are the types who spend the most money, which means that these people are the target demographic for advertisers.

Culture, which is ultimately a reflection of whoever is most likely to respond to advertising, will always push in a direction of being an emotional support and coping mechanism for mediocre middle class individuals who wish to feel more special and accomplished than they really are. Easily understood and appreciated things which are perceived as hard to understand and appreciate become status symbols and over-valued. That is the driving force behind culture, the desire to be more than you really are, which is something that losers relate to. As such, culture is a malicious force that is actively harmful.

This is not to say that culture should be opposed or a lack of culture is preferable to culture. Culture is a necessary evil that comes out of abundance and a certain stability. A place with no culture is a place without a future, as it is indicative of a lack of excess and thus a lack of even a modicum of group success. Culture is something that should be understood in the terms of a sort of demon or idol that should be worked around. Let other people be enthralled by statues and music and poetry that other people have created. Let them spend money on overpriced fashion and consumer goods. Use culture and culture's useful morons to your benefit. Sell overpriced junk to these people. Let them have their unwarranted mental and emotional crutches, even enable them if it benefits you. Give them ribbons and bows and medals and adulation in exchange for their time, energy, and money.

Out Of Context

Are you losing a debate? Has somebody brought up something you did or said in the past that paints you in a poor light? Are you being held to account for your behavior? If so, there is one magic phrase that you can use to get out of any trouble: "You are taking me out of context." That's right, with those seven words stated competently, you will be able to escape punishment.

Most people are lazy creatures. They lack intellectual rigor or the ability to do even basic research. These are the people who will be judging you in some public incident. These people will not spend hours looking into details or interviewing eye witnesses, they will just do a cursory search of anything. They might be able to pick out contradictions and lies (most of the time they won't be able to do this), but they are never able to disprove an unfalsifiable hypothesis, which is that some unacceptable behavior was actually acceptable in some vague unknown context.

The only way somebody can come back at you if you pull the "you are taking me out of context" card is by asking you what the proper context is. This may seem like a challenge, especially if you are just bald-faced lying about some situation, but it is not a challenge. At this point, you play the part of a victim and insist that you should not have to justify everything you do, and that your memory isn't perfect and you don't remember the minutia of unimportant situations, and that the accuser has the burden of proof with regards to you acting in some unacceptable manner. Of course, they cannot prove that which is not even defined, but this is all too vague and rapid for the listener to understand, so they will think you have made a good point.

All of this is quite pointless and stupid, since anybody who is smart is not getting into public arguments where they are defending themselves, but it is illustrative of one thing: truth doesn't matter. That's just a fact. You can have somebody on tape saying something horrible and if they know how to respond and conduct themselves, it won't matter. Even if they don't know how to respond and conduct themselves, it probably won't matter. People are reactive idiots who follow cues. They have no attention span for things which aren't providing them some form of carnal pleasure. They are barely sentient, if that, so form matters over function when there is any sort of social (not physical) conflict.

Arguing is not difficult. Debating is not difficult. Most things are not difficult, but still most things are done poorly. Why? Simply put, the people who are smart enough to debate and argue and do anything to any degree of competency are generally smart enough to not spend their time doing these things. They figure out how to enrich themselves then disappear from the public eye. That's how it works. We live in a system that is only enjoyable to participate and compete in for people who are mentally ill, so only mentally ill people are participating and competing in it.

Cratylus

The naming of things is an important topic, but what is more important topic that a sub-topic which is the naming of people. Simply put, what somebody named tends to be quite influential in how their life proceeds. Names may feel like a mere formality without much of a purpose besides identification of an individual within a group of individuals, but this is not the case. That appraisal belongs to things like fingerprints and DNA, since they are not directly chosen by parents; they are influenced by who procreates with whom, but not in a direct and easy manner.

What is the importance to a person's name? Quite a lot. If somebody has a low class or absurd name, then chances are that their parents were low class or absurd. What this means is that people will, knowingly or not, discriminate for or against people when all they know is a person's name. You can see this play out with regards to people with stereotypically black names: They will get less positive responses to their resume than somebody with a stereotypically white or American-Asian name who has the same resume. This is not to say that the discrimination is correct or incorrect, or to attack or defend the process of discrimination, but rather to illustrate that names most definitely have an impact on opportunities and interpersonal interactions.

Another aspect to an individual's name, is that whenever anybody says any name, there are always different default emotions associated with that specific name. It might be the fact that a certain type of parent names their child a certain type of name, what the name conjures up in the head, or how the letters in the name combine to make an authoritative and concise name or a mushy and unstable name. Depending on whether their name is pleasing or displeasing, boring or interestin, a person's actions may be looked on positively or negatively, and they may be remembered or forgotten.

It would seem that very few people are aware of the power of names. They tend to name their children whatever name they like in pop culture or whatever is now the trend in their social circles. People are so thoughtless, and by being thoughtless hamper their children in their future. This is an objective negative for the people who are named poorly, but an objective boon towards the individuals who are named in a beneficial manner. Use the weakness and thoughtlessness of parents around you to give your child a leg up. Name them something that inspires strength and confidence and projects competence and stability.

This is a part of a larger subject of linguistics, which is a very interesting subject when properly discussed. The shape, sound, flow, appearance, length, and a near infinite amount of other attributes to written and spoken words are all very important. With that said, linguistics as a field is embarrassingly poor, just like most fields, because the people who are least equipped to provide any insight or analysis are the most likely to engage in linguistics and the people who are most equipped are generally too busy being successful in the real world to study or participate in linguistics.

Another Essay For The Haters

What is your problem? Why can't you just go away and do other things? Why do you insist on insulting the things I do and talking so negativistically? Just grow up and go away! Let people enjoy my creations without trying to be mean about it. Come on, what is wrong with you? You make me sick? You are a thorn in my side. I see and hear the things you say and I am at a loss for words for how to deal with you people. There is something *off* in your brain that has gotten you into this sort of deranged pattern of self destruction via the criticism of me. By insulting me you are just harming yourself, have you even read the stoics?

I am putting all of your names on various lists and excel spreadsheets. Unless you repent and start speaking positively about me, you will have your life repeatedly ruined over the coming years and decades. I will use all my money to make sure your life is increasingly miserable. I will hire private investigators to take pictures of you and track your movements. I will pay prostitutes to ruin your marriage. I will get you fired from your job and ruin your reputation through elaborate cat and mouse blackmail.

You are all mentally ill. All my haters are mentally ill. That's just a fact. Maybe you were molested or raped as children or bullied in school, but whatever happened to you growing up deformed your mind and warped your perception. It's really quite tragic, for you, since I don't really care about you but you obviously care about me. Every day when I look into what strangers are saying about me I see you guys being idiots and ruining the positive, uplifting vibe. You all make me sick inside, and I cannot wait until you are dead.

Your Fingers

He leans over and chuckles to himself. You are already sweating, but the rate at which you perspire increases by such a noticeable degree that he notices, and he starts to laugh even louder. You can't move, you have been strapped into a chair. You are in some sort of cold and damp basement with nothing in it besides a water heating and cooling system, some rakes, and a metal chair bolted to the concrete floor. Your clammy skin is pooling at your feet and you are completely nude.

He asks if you know why you are here. You do not, you reply. He is laughing again now, even harder than before. He asks if you know why you are here again. You do not, you reply again. He laughs again. He keeps on asking you this question, and you keep on replying with the same honest denial. Every time he asks, he seems to find the question funnier and you lose your composure a little more, until the basement is filled with his loud laughter and he falls over and rolls around on the ground, out of breath. You are still strapped to the metal chair, completely nude and drenched in sweat and fear.

He stands up after regaining his composure and takes a small silver mallet out of his left pocket. You can't help but notice how polished and clean most of it is, reflecting the little light off its edges. He smiles, and asks you if you know why he has a small silver mallet. You reply that you don't know, and he starts to laugh again. This time his laughs seem a bit more anticipatory and menacing. You're still sweating.

He walks up close to you and smiles, looks up at the ceiling, and then starts to laugh again. He asks if you know what's coming next and you tell him that you don't. He· laughs some more, then repeats the question. You are still sweating and you repeat your answer. He laughs even more, then proceeds to place his right hand against the back of your left hand, pressing it face down into place against the metal chair. After that, he moves swiftly with his left hand and smashes all of the fingers on your left hand, breaking them. You're still sweating but now you're also screaming in pain.

He bursts out laughing again, asking if you still don't know why you're in this basement with him. You're crying now, but in between sobs you insist that you have no idea what is going on. He proceeds to break all the fingers on your right hand just like he broke all your fingers on your left hand, and asks the same question. You give the same answer and pass out from the pain and shock, but not before you see him laughing again.

When you come to, you see two people instead of one. You recognize the newcomer standing in front of you. It's me. I laugh, and the other man laughs, then I ask you if you still do not know why you are here, in this cold dark lonely damp basement, strapped to a metal chair, with all your fingers broken. You are so confused and disoriented by everything but you manage to give an honest answer that you still do not know why any of this is happening or what is going on.

I laugh again, the other man laughs again, and then I sigh and decide to explain what is going on. I tell you that I saw your negative goodreads review of one of my books fifteen years ago, and this was justice for your crimes. You seem shocked, but slowly you remember how you had left a one star goodreads review on one of my books. All of the sudden, you realize why information security is such an important thing, and you are filled with regret and sorrow. You beg for my forgiveness like a worm, stating how you were young and foolish at the time of leaving the review, and if I let you go, then you will go back to goodreads and change your review from one star to five stars.

This display of weakness does nothing but disgust me. What's done is done and cannot be undone, I say, with grace and charm and authority. The man next to me who broke all of your fingers nods sagely. Then we both burst out laughing again. It is time for you to die like a man, I say. The other man nods, and I take an electric drill out of a duffel bag laying on the floor behind you. For the next twelve hours, I torture you for your crimes. You scream out in pain, and don't take your justice like a man, but even you know that this is price you are paying for your words now is justified and moral. The man and I do not take any sick pleasure in enacting this retribution, but we know it is necessary.

Even though the man and I are laughing the whole time, this is not some sort of emotionally driven deranged crime. This can't even be considered a crime, but rather a review of your goodreads review. After you are drained of most of your blood, the other man pulls some nondescript pistol out of one of his pockets and shoots you in the head a few times. You are dead now. Nobody will ever find your body, because I have so many connections to people who kill people professionally and know how to dispose of corpses, but nobody really cares about you going missing, or your goodreads review, for that matter. The end, for you.

This Is Not Allowed

You cannot just write hundreds of essays degrading and deconstructing popular and common things. That is just not possible. You can't just spend hundreds of pages making fun of ideas and being rude. There are lots of good people who you are insulting and treating poorly when you do what you do.

Do you really think that you can behave in this manner without any real consequences? Do you think there is no real justice in this world nobody really does anything about parasites and exploitative people, especially not the people who are most vocal about doing things about parasites and exploitative people? Do you think you can just get away with being a blatant negative force in society?

One day, everything will catch up to you. It doesn't matter that you're very clever and agile and rich. It doesn't matter that you are smarter than most people and more charming and have shown time and time again that people have the attention span of goldfish. No, eventually you will have to face justice for your crimes of Machiavellian misanthropy.

I won't be the one to stop you, of course. I have a job and a life and a reputation and not near enough free time or experience to actually do anything to you, but somebody who has no job and no normal life and no reputation and lots of free time and experience -- someone like you -- will eventually step in and right these wrongs.

There is perfect justice in this world, and that justice comes on the timeframe of one person's life. Bad people suffer for doing bad things, it doesn't matter if they have money and women and drugs and comforts and I have none of that stuff, because I am suffering in the real world but not in my head. I can't fathom how the world would be if things weren't fair, if I was just being taken by a sucker by people who will never be punished for their crimes.

You have to try to fix things. You have to try to help the weak and helpless. You have to look at people who work an honest job and respect them. You have to look down on the people who are rich and powerful and successful. You have to know that eventually the people who get taken advantage of repeatedly won't be taken advantage of and the people who take advantage of people eventually will be punished.

There is karma. There is retribution. There is somebody who is looking out for me and all the other people who don't look out for themselves. Things will work out eventually, most likely in a decade or two from whenever now is, after not working out for the entirety of human history. The domineering and manipulative will lose to the meek sheep, we just need to believe. We just need to keep on keeping on. Keep on working towards helping the little people. Keep on trying to fix things that have always been broken. Become a martyr.

Whatever you do, don't just say negative things. Don't just act like things will never be fixed and start looking out for yourself and people genuinely like you who will benefit you and you them. Don't become like the people who have succeeded before you. Stay in this pit of mediocrity and failure, because we are positive and uplifting even about things which are objectively unworkable. We believe in the human spirit. We believe in change. We believe in slogans. We believe in playing fairly.

Leaving Things Hanging

For some reason, most people seem unable to leave things hanging. What I mean by this is that when they hear some statement, they then infer that there is some added message attached to that statement. Because of this assumption, people tend to imply and infer with whatever it is they are saying by default, which results in regular effective communication needing a constant negation of any potential miscommunication by making sure people know you aren't inferring or implying anything with certain statements.

Even this essay suffers from the need to make it clear that I am not inferring or suggesting that things should be left hanging by default. Rather, I am simply making an observation into the state of things. Things happen for a reason, so there is some reason why this manner of communication with uncommunicated points is the default. If I had to guess, the main driver for this sort of pattern is the fact that most people say things in a non-detached manner, meaning they are trying to communicate in order to lead up to some bigger communication that will lead to some action or inaction, whether physical or mental, so over time this sort of manipulative building up of an argument or larger point became the norm for casual conversation after being observed in more formal conversations.

This sort of assumption that there is always some larger point being made can be used to your advantage to purposely leave certain statements vague in order to either soothe or agitate some third party due to their assumptions, while still leaving a window open to clarify that you don't mean what they assumed you meant, which will then negate whatever emotional effect you caused in the first place without ever revealing that you purposely caused confusion. In this manner, lots of uncomfortable situations can be avoided as well as many conflicts created with ease and without clear culpability.

What larger trend can be drawn from noticing this sort of behavior? Well, drawing a larger trend from this sort of behavior is very similar to the desire of the behavior itself, which indicates that this sort of extrapolation is a very natural and useful urge, no matter what the extrapolation pertains to. This observation is iteratively infinite, which speaks to the fractal sort of nature found in reality. Some mechanic or pattern that applies to one aspect of life or form of interaction almost always can be applied to other aspect of life or form of interaction. This is slightly meta, and doesn't really speak directly to the behavior described, but it still is something that is worth noting.

Overall, this sort of behavior shows a sort of natural "then what" then can be utilized, as earlier stated, by anybody who is aware of the tendency. People like to feel like they come to conclusions by their own logic and thoughts, so stopping just short of whatever point you are trying to make and then leaving it up in the air purposely can actually be more effective than going out of your way to make sure people know your final conclusion. You are essentially making people you are communicating with into active participants, which then makes them naturally invested in your point of view or idea being correct.

There are a lot of patterns and rhythms to conversations and communication besides this, and none of them are particularly complicated, but they do take a bit of studying and emotional distance to really notice and suss out, so very few people actually get beyond the very basics of understanding how to talk to each other. Figuring out what makes people tick and think in certain ways and not in other ways can be abused, but any knowledge can be abused. The more you learn about how to properly communicate, the less you will feel the desire to manipulate or push people around and the more you will have healthy and functional relationships.

The Path To Power
It used to be that you had to go to war or do some amazing deed in order to get enough name recognition in order to run for public office and eventually get elected. You would work your way up through the ranks of society by serving in some war and killing a bunch of people and

maybe getting mustard gassed and then giving speeches after the war while doing physical labor with other people, slowly building up the loyalty of people around you until you formed a political party and eventually became one of the most prolific individuals in all of history. That was how reality used to work.

Now, the path to power is a little bit different. You don't want to go into the military unless you're mentally retarded, a homosexual, a transsexual, or a furry. Those are the types of people who go into the military now. The path to power is more communication based. You have to take some white collar job that affords you lots of free time to form your own mini media empire. You start out with a twitter account and make edgy jokes on either the left or right, depending on your skin color and/or socioeconomic and geographic starting position, and do that for a few years.

Once you have ten to twenty thousand followers on twitter, you branch out to a podcast. Of course, you need a few people to have a successful podcast without doing much work, so make sure to network with other likeminded and similarly classed twitter users. Once you have found two or three individuals, you start the podcast. It doesn't have to be quality, it doesn't have to be funny, and it doesn't have to be informative, it just has to exist. Place half of your podcast episodes behind a paywall, and do two episodes of your podcast every week.

Over the course of two to four years, as long as you are consistent, your twitter and podcast audiences will grow at an exponential rate. If you have any semblance of competency, it won't be long until each of the people in your podcast are taking in low six figures a year off paywalled content. Now, the fun can begin.

Use your money to pay for reviews of your podcast as well as media appearances. Start having guests on your podcast and steadily increase the star power and social status of your brand. At a certain point, you will realize that you have transitioned from lowly nobody to a legitimately famous celebrity. This is when you need to make the transition from your podcast to more traditional media. Write a book and create a clothing line out while you're at it; this will also provide more income streams and make you seem even more impressive to observers.

Now that you have a podcast, book, money, fame, and an audience, it's time to get involved in politics. Run for governor or senate or town council, and put all your experience in marketing and content creation to use. You should be able to easily win, at this point, since most people involved in politics are stupid idiots who are not ready for the new wave of manipulative parasites known as podcasters.

After you have established yourself in this lesser political role, start edging your way up the food chain. Don't forget to grease the right palms and play along with the old money, they're old money for a reason: they win. They'll be happy to have you on their team and will most likely reward you in lots of demented and evil ways, such as buying you sex slaves and helping you with insider trading tips that will ensure you will never not be a multi-millionaire for the rest of your life.

If you follow this strategy correctly, you will eventually end up the leader of your country. At that point, it's up to you do whatever you want. You can continue the strategy and attempt to take over the entire world, or you can be content and bask in the glory of victory. You will most likely end up depressed and sad because you will see how easy and pointless everything is, and may even end up killing yourself in a fit of despair. Good luck.

Overthrowing The Global Order
All that need to happen to overthrow the global order, something that has formed over thousands of years, is all of the little people to work together. Yes, that's right, the world is going to change and change for the better and

change soon. It didn't work with the Vietnam war protests and it didn't work with the 1960s hippy revolution and it didn't work with World War 2 and it didn't work with giving women the right to vote and it didn't work with giving blacks the right to vote and it didn't work with the civil war and it didn't work with the revolution but it's going to work this time by tweeting and podcasting and marches and talking and people defending the second amendment.

Random people with no power or influence or connections are smarter and better able to run the world than the people who are running the world, which is the inferior people who run the world run the world and the superior people who don't run the world don't run the world. If people running twitter accounts and making forum posts were handed the keys of power, the economy would be made perfect, pedophile rings wouldn't exist, and immigration problems would be remedied. See, things aren't just happening due to natural forces of momentum, things are purposely being made bad for the little people like you and I. This is just how it is, for no logical or explainable reason, but it won't be like this for much longer.

The end of the world is coming. Well, maybe not the end of the world, but big changes are coming. Well, maybe not big changes, but changes are coming. Well, changes might not be coming, but talk about changes that might be coming in the future are here, and that's what is important. We talk and we talk and we talk and eventually things will be perfect and all the time spent on talking and fantasizing will be worth it for everybody. Either that, or nothing will change and we'll just get older and more bitter and delusional and desperate, and die.

Eventually, all the schemers and planners will be dead. Their plans will either die or be twisted and deformed by the next generation of schemers and planners. The unsuccessful ones will be forgotten and the successful ones will be lied about and misrepresented until all their work is undone. That's the way it works, that's the way it has worked, and that is the way it will work.

Keep on sending emails, tweets, letters, calling your representatives, acting out, taking things to court, complaining, whining, thinking about things that you have no control over. Keep on losing sleep and time on problems that are not even problems that you will never fix. Get emotionally invested in dread escapism, where the world is always almost about to fall apart, so you don't have to pay attention to the fact that your life is mediocre, your relationships are failing, your personal future looks bleak, and you will never accomplish any of the dreams you had when you were younger and had more potential.

Negative Self Appraisal

I don't write much by hand. It's slower, impractical, and doesn't really have any purpose except for being private. It is for this last reason that I write by hand about the negative aspects of myself. Once or so a year, I will sit down and spend about an hour writing out what I would say to myself if I was an observer with perfect knowledge who was trying to hurt my feelings and make myself feel horrible. I take the most uncharitable interpretations of all my actions and mistakes and flaws and write them down in an almost accusatory fashion. This will fill up ten to fifteen pages before I get worn out and run out of things to criticize or scorn.

The reason for doing this is that I generally go out of my way not to surround myself with negative people, and I am very good at presenting myself as well as interacting with others in a way where very few people are ever rude or directly critical of me. This is a benefit, as it's much better to be in a generally positive environment rather than a generally negative environment, but it can also enable and encourage delusions or mental blindspots that might metastasize into larger problems if left unchecked.

Another aspect that is beneficial to this exercise is that I am the best at critiquing myself. I know what makes me tick and what emotional and mental weaknesses I have. This knowledge, combined with my natural strengths of being negative and hurtful, allows me to really examine a lot of my flaws and face genuinely bad aspects of myself in an honest manner that I wouldn't really be aware of otherwise.

After I have finished writing out what I write out, I read it over a few times. It's really brutal, but it's also funny because I can always muster up some excuse or explanation for even the worst of the things written, although I do my best to try and avoid any sorts of justifications and just take in the analysis without any defenses or replies to it. After going over it, I'll then rip up and throw away the paper and after a few days I won't really think about the whole exercise until the next time I do it.

The important thing about this is that it's very rare. It's like a nudging in the right direction as well as a rounding off of hard edges that is infrequent. I'm extremely lucky to be surrounded by non abusive and non degrading people, because if this sort of commentary came from an external source at a constant rate, it would be extremely discouraging and most likely harmful. It is like a periodic antidote, but too much of it would definitely be poison.

There is a very sad lack of self honesty that I see whenever I look around me. I am not perfect, of course, but I make an effort to catch myself and adjust my behavior when I realize I make mistakes. I've seen so many friendships and relationships as well as projects or goals completely destroyed by people who get their personal pride and sense of self wrapped up in the idea that they're always correct and perfect. In all honesty, this lack of self-awareness is what makes most people much less agile and reasonable than I can be, because it makes people act in a purely reactive and very predictably short-sighted manner that is often very inefficient and self-harming.

The First Man

I'm currently in the process of reading *The First Man* by Albert Camus and it's not going so well. I don't really get the point of any of it and I can't follow any of the characters. It seems super disjointed on a chapter to chapter basis and I can't bring myself to really understand what the point of it is. I've read about 100 pages of it so far and I couldn't really explain much besides somebody gave birth, that baby talked to some old guy because his father is dead, and poor person life in general. None of it really makes sense to me - this is probably what most people feel like when they try to read what anything I've written.

I really enjoyed *The Myth Of Sisyphus (and other essays)* by Camus, so it's not that I don't like Camus. I am aware that lots of pseuds and worthless book addicts don't like Camus, mostly due to the fact that he actually did stuff with his life and was successful and interesting, unlike any of them, but that is not the reason that I simply do not understand *The First Man.* Most likely, my frustration and confusion is due to the fact that this book is a posthumous effort put together by Camus' family members and whoever was advising him, so it's just not finished and just not that good.

The fate of successful people after they die is really quite something to watch. Some portion of family members and "friends" and anybody vaguely connected to the now dead individual will tend to glom onto their fame and stature in order to squeeze money out of their rotting corpse. It's sad, but inevitable, that this is what is going to happen to me after I am dead, but I don't really care.

Imagine working at some craft for decades, enduring hatred and criticism and failure and self doubt until you succeed and see how most people are fake and just want to use you, then as you die you know that the people around you will use all of the energy and worth that you earned to enrich themselves, like strange vampires of sorts sucking the social utility out of your body.

This is the way of the world, the worthy build it and the unworthy take credit for and pervert it for their own ends. You can see this with people who profess the love of old music, literature, wars, history, or really anything that was some form of achievement. These little bugs nibble on whatever is fading away and engorge themselves as long as possible, all while pretending like "appreciation" is something to be proud of or something that gives them worth.

When I am dead, make money off of me. Use me as a prop. Make up things that I never said or meant to further your cause or personal career. Pretend I was your friend or mentor or associate. Pretend I hated or loved you. Do whatever you want, but please don't think that you're somehow special for knowing about or liking me. Don't put your worth into the consumption of some dead individual you had no influence on. Don't derive anything from me or stuff I have created except for what you can utilize to benefit yourself and harm people you want to harm.

Social Media Survival Competition Strategies

I am friends (or rather on friendly terms) with a lot of unhinged and unstable individuals on the internet. These people are some of the worst people you could know. They have emotional problems and I would not trust most of them in any sort of real life situation, but on the internet they like me and I am friendly with them. Why? Well, it's quite simply an evolutionary strategy that I utilize in order to maintain order and climb in value while keeping my enemies and competitors at bay. Allow me to explain further.

Whenever I log onto a site like twitter, I am always confronted by some form of drama. Somebody I follow and am followed by is attacking or being attacked by a stranger or some other person I follow and am followed by. I observe what is going on and offer psychological reassurance and calming to whoever asks for it. It is useful to see who is winning and who is losing, who is siding with whom, and in this manner I can determine who is an up and coming social climber and who is on their way out or losing their grip on reality so that I can distance myself from them if they are about to implode.

Another aspect to this strategy is that while all the people in my twitter circle are fighting each other and forming feuds based on things that don't really matter, I sit back and look responsible and respectable and they all grow to see me as somebody that is a good person. I am not a good person, I just realized a few years ago that if I can't have somebody killed in real life then there is no reason to argue with them on the internet, and so I do not argue.

In the chaos and drama, time goes on and many people rise and fall. All this fighting and arguing takes a toll on the psyche, so people start making stupid decisions and saying things that shouldn't be said. Once again, by not making losing moves I am essentially making winning moves. I gain followers and the status of the "digital Switzerland" while those around me make lifelong enemies that will most likely haunt them in the coming years and decades.

It is important to think of social media and all social interactions as a soulless board game where you try to position yourself to take advantage of third party mistakes. Don't look for real friendships or relationships, that will just lead to frustration and you being taken advantage of by people like me. Don't get into arguments, just make mental notes of who you dislike and who has poor impulse control and poor discipline then avoid working with them in the future, but don't let them know that they screwed up or else they will be bitter and may try to harm you.

Lastly, learn to play people off each other. Make them all fight each other and get into time wasting spats, and while they are rolling around in the mud, make good use of your time. Either you are spending every second moving forward and upgrading yourself and your life, or you are getting tricked into being the pawn of some deranged psychotic on social media who doesn't care whether you live or die.

Social Expressions

There seems to be a fairly understandable misconception regarding social expressions, namely highly visible instances of activism, where people think structural change follows social expression. For example, they think that gay acceptance or civil rights were the result of marches and protests. In reality, it is the other way around. The conditions for certain aspects to societal structure changed, things started shifting in that manner, then people took advantage of the new leeway or changed default understanding and pushed whatever it was that was already going to happen.

In general, social privileges have not officially "regressed" or gotten more strict for most of America's history. Over time, "rights" have been granted to groups and subgroups of individuals who did not have them. This is because there is a lot increasing excess and wealth floating around in America, so people err on the side of "going along with the flow" of whatever trends don't explicitly and directly hurt them, and there are not many social actions that explicitly and directly hurt anybody.

Of course, there are always protests and counter demonstrations against the general flow of history. People protested giving blacks and women the right to vote. People protested abortion. People protested giving homosexuals the right to get legally married. These protests and social demonstrations were huge and very spirited, and yet they failed. This is because protests and demonstrations only work when they're going in the direction things are already going - and might speed things up in the way they are already going - but they do not work to change the direction of anything.

Barring riots and violent insurrections that kill and take over areas and land (and this is pretty much infeasible now as well as 100% discourages as it's stupid and futile), social expressions are a waste of time for everybody but the people gaining money and status from those social expressions, for example event organizers or event speakers. The people in the crowds of marches are wasting their time and energy and even putting themselves at risk if they are involved in some event that goes against the momentum of whatever era they are in.

Social expressions and mass movements are downstream from structural form. They are a symptom of what is happening, not a cause. They may cause other symptoms, but they will not be able to change a system unless that system is already changing in the way they are desiring. Because of this, there is no good reason to participate in social expressions unless you are benefiting or know you are on the winning side of whatever social expression that you are going to participate in. To knowingly jump into a fight that is doomed from the start is a waste of time at best and a self destructive and fatal mistake at worst.

Intermittent Wi-Fi

We recently got fiber internet at our house, which is great except for the fact that the acer routers that are provided with the new faster internet only last for a few weeks before they start overheating and resetting every hour or so. This is not a big deal except for the fact that I need stable internet for my various internet businesses that rely on up to date consistent information as well as a consistent connection that doesn't go out randomly enough to disrupt certain habitual activities that are otherwise perfectly automated.

It's funny how much profit must be being generated by fiber internet that ISPs can feel comfortable rolling out hardware that overheats repeatedly, replacing the hardware with a new version of the same hardware when it overheats and fails, then doing it all over again multiple times. I wonder how long it will be until they notice that they're spending hundreds of dollars on multiple crappy acer routers for every household with fiber internet and switch what hardware they use.

Another aspect to this whole overheating router problem is that hypothetically I could probably fix it and save my family the hassle of calling up the ISP, but at this point in my life I've come to realize that older people get what they deserve, so if my parents have a shoddy router and frustration with the internet, then they deserve that shoddy router and frustration with the internet. They deserve their lazy layabout unempathetic cruel son who knows how to underclock the router via putty but refuses to because he doesn't really care about anybody but himself.

This situation reminds me of a sort of paradox I have puzzled out gradually over the past few years. Nobody with any talent or skill stays employed for long. They work for somebody else or they start their own business, then they make a ton of money, then they realize that working sucks and that it's a frustrating waste of time to deal with most people and they quit or sell their company and then go and relax or party for the rest of their life. What that means is that companies are run and staffed by mediocre morons stuck in the rat race. If somebody is on a life path where they are going to be working for forty to fifty years of their life, then they're not somebody who is capable of making good decisions, and yet these are the people who run businesses and work at businesses.

All the smart people are people who stay in small communities or the people who charge insane rates for true luxury goods or local products so that way they don't have to deal with poor or middle class individuals. When you are dealing with somebody who makes a ton of money, then you are dealing with somebody who has some degree of competency and self knowledge that makes it possible to interact with them without wanting to blow your brains out. I'm not talking about new money faggots who think that driving a BMW or some other pseudo luxury car makes them high class, I mean the people who have had wealth that lasts more than three or four generations who know how to raise successful children who aren't delusional brats who need to be pistol whipped and sent off to the military as a grunt for half a decade.

Elderly Commentators And Thinkers

There comes a certain time when you realize that certain people who you thought were cool or even just not losers are in fact losers. I had this experience with entertainers, commentators, and so-called thinkers a few years ago, when I realized that most of them were loud mouthed idiots who didn't ever do anything but critique and criticize others and would never actually accomplish anything. This applies to most people on social media as well as in real life, but those people do not make their living running their mouth so it is less disagreeable.

There is a particularly pathetic subset of commentators and thinkers that are pathetic and these are the ones who are old. Elderly is an exaggeration, since most of these people seem to be dead before they are in their seventies or eighties, but rather the people in their forties and fifties who are still doing "work" (talking) when they should be retired. The reason these people are so disagreeable to me is that you can make an insanely good amount of money essentially whining on any form of public platform as long as you are smart about what you're doing and are being thoughtful in any manner.

It takes a truly delusional and thoughtless individual to be successful in any manner in the public eye without making a large amount of money. You can sell t-shirts, bumper stickers, subscriptions, products, books, do speaking tours, licensing and branding deals, advertisements, and a whole number of other angles can be taken to monetize any form of public platform to the degree where you shouldn't have to work past the age of thirty five as long as you are decent at saving and investing.

With that said, there are a lot of financially successful individuals who insist on staying in the limelight as long as possible, long past what is appropriate or logical. Why? Because these people are insecure and do not have any outlets. They oftentimes do not have a wife and kids and if they do have kids they are not on speaking terms with their kids, and they do not have any real friends and they lack any constructive hobbies, so they have a ton of free time. Their insecurity and free time, combined with their vanity, greed, and failing faculties, form a bundle of sticks of sorts that make up a tremendous faggot, the elderly commentator.

Because most commentators and thinkers are products of their time and not really talented or self aware, they tend not to know what made them successful and thus slowly fall out of popularity. The lucky ones die or quit before they make a fool of themselves, but the ones that are old and decrepit slowly become more and more unhinged as whatever schtick they are good at slowly fades out of popularity and slowly their audience becomes a mixture of really pathetic fellow losers and deranged psychotics who are only active in order to mess with the host or hosts.

What can be done about these commentators and thinkers that have stuck around for longer than is appropriate? Nothing much, except observing them and making sure we do not become like them. When I am old,

I will be out of touch and useless. I pray that I will be in a financial and emotional situation where I do not need to be in the public eye. I plan on rotting away and being senile in private, where I can torment people who love and care about me, not talking to strangers who are a third my age. These old people in the public eye are unfortunate losers who would be better off if they were lined up in front a ditch and shot in the back of the head.

Everybody Is An Idiot

When I was having my year long schizophrenic episode, a lot of things happened. My pattern recognition skills went off the charts, lots of times seeing patterns that didn't even exist, and I generally became aware of a lot of aspects to human behavior that were kind of background noise that the brain naturally (and thankfully) filters out. One of the many things that happened, especially towards the end when it was impossible to fall asleep or stop my mind from connecting literally everything I saw into some larger and mostly imaginary pattern, was that I started paying attention to the actual meaning behind what people were saying and what they were talking about.

Simply put, most stuff communicated by everybody is either blatant external manipulation or blatant self obsession. I saw this particularly with regards to things like social media, especially with youtube. At a certain point, I would just scroll through my subscriptions and random youtube videos and be detached from what was actually being show and just focusing on the form things were communicated and the mannerisms of the person or people communicating them. The more I watched, the more I became convinced that people were actively getting dumber with every day.

Things got so bad that I felt like most people were actually losing IQ points on a daily basis. I would look around and see people talking about the dumbest culture and arguing about inane wastes of time and controversies and I saw behind it all in a way that showed that none of the talking or complaining or debating was actually doing anything and that most of it was just people being insecure and self destructively wasting their time and the time of others. Normally, I just shrug this sort of realization off or use it to my advantage, but my brain was in a sort of state where everything was overwhelming and made note of and not forgotten, from word choice to topic of conversation to time of day things were being said.

While this episode has been over for about a year now, the realizations I came to during my psychosis have stuck with me on a very fundamental level. The amount of time and energy wasted on idiotic things that can't be changed is amazing to me. If I had to guess, most people spend over 80% of their life on stupid frivolities that end up hurting them more than helping them. I'm barely any different, I'm just more proactive and productive in the stupid things I'm involved in than most people, which is confused for not wasting time.

Nothing can be done about any of this. If you scroll through what is pushed on youtube or even television, you'll see absolute garbage and perversion pushed everywhere. Any platform or activity eventually gets taken over by malevolent interests, because money always eventually wins and downs out less efficient (and less profit oriented) individuals and groups. The overwhelming signal of society and culture is one that has always and will always be pushing people to think stupid thoughts, get wrapped up in stupid thoughts, spend time and money on stupid things, and embrace stupidity.

Life is basically a video game on its easiest tutorial setting. Think of the most idiotic individual you know who makes the most self destructive choices in their life, then realize that they're still alive and kicking. Homeless drug addicts are still alive. Prostitutes are alive. Women who have sex with dozens of men in high school and college manage to marry men who make high six figure incomes and have children and a positive reputation in their peer group. All this means that life is not hard. What you do with this information is really up to you. You can sit around and participate in idiocy and consume idiocy, you can create and sell idiocy, or you can go do literally anything else with your time knowing that the majority of people, idiots, will most likely look down on you and talk badly about you while they're stuffing their face full of garbage and their brain full of trash.

Whistleblower

I used to be a horrible man. I used to work for Google and other big tech giants and take fat paychecks home for doing their biddding. They would have me work on things like censorship and spying and other horrible, unmentionable things that would oppress we the people. I was on their payroll. I took part in horrible things. You might even consider a former "higher up" who was very important.

These people and companies are horrible. They are dangerous and they are out to get you. They will crush anybody who stands in their way. You can't trust them. They are not beyond killing people who speak out. They are not above cutting your brake-lines, planting child pornography on your personal computer, or even censoring you from their search results. They are the digital mafia and they are brutal.

How do you think these companies got to the top? With hard work and innovative products? No, they used shrewd and intelligent individuals like myself to sabotage and destroy all their competitors. Their is nothing that is off limits to these monster. When I was working for them, I knew I could get away with anything. There were no laws I could break that I would actually get in trouble for. If you can think of a crime, chances are that I've committed it. Trust me, there is so much nasty stuff going on at these companies.

Then, one day, a year or so ago, I had a crisis of consciousness. That's right, I gained consciousness. I had been a complete automaton up until this point, with no moral compass. That all changed when I turned thirty. Suddenly, I became human and was disgusted at the things I saw. This just so happened to coincide with leading up to me being fired for not getting my work done as a low level computer programmer for technological products that never got used, but that is something that doesn't really matter.

Now, I'm unemployed and I am fighting for the little person. I'm a good person now, even better than the people who never did years of work for people they say are morally abhorrent. I'm somebody you can trust, and should trust, which is why I'm having a sudden career change from employee in tech to public speaker and author. My upcoming book is all about the dangers of big companies, and I will promote these things and ask for donations publicly under my real name, not because I don't really think that these companies are dangerous and I don't really have any dirt on anybody important, but because I randomly became a moral crusader and hero in my thirties right around the time I got fired for not doing my job.

I'm a whistleblower, I matter. My name and face and address are all easily accessible, but somehow I will never be killed or tortured or even harassed by the people who I claim I am exposing. I feel completely comfortable doing all of this publicly because that is the way real whistleblowers operate.

I am a threat to the system, and you can see me live at my upcoming TedX talk. It's going to be really amazing, and the tickets are going to be sold out fast so make sure you pre-pre-order soas to ensure your spot in the audience. For ten dollars I will sign your copy of my two hundred page book that the elites don't want you to know about. Also, I am now selling whistleblower nutritional supplements at a three hundred percent markup on my patriot webstore. It's important to be healthy and have strong bones if you want to fight the multi billion dollar international cabal of bankers and tech conglomerates, and you can do that by giving me money.

Followers

I love when I go from N thousand followers to N+1 thousand followers. Once that number goes up, my opinion becomes more important than it used to be. With more followers, I am proven to be right. Of course, when I had less followers I was right, but now that I have more followers I'm still just as right but even more right. This is how reality works.

Another great thing about getting more followers is that when somebody has less follower than me, that means that I am correct and they are incorrect, so the more followers I have the more arguments I win by default. I love having arguments on the internet, because I'm an intellectual with a lot of important thoughts.

As a thinker with lots of followers, I feel it is not a very unreasonable request to demand that I be treated with deference. After all, it's not like just anybody could make the tweets I make. It takes a lot of talent to get a lot of twitter followers when you don't get banned for years. To have a lot of twitter followers is indicative of my brilliance, and I am brilliant.

Please keep on trying to "troll" me or whatever it is you are doing. You have less followers than me. All of your actions are just promoting my account and showing that I am the superior individual, and I am even gaining followers because of your idiocy. That's right, you are making me more powerful than ever before.

Once I get enough followers, I'm not sure what the number is, all my opinions will have lots of weight. Then, I will be called upon to run society. Then, people like you with less followers than me will be made my slaves. I will be a powerful person some day, just watch. That's why I have so many followers and have gained followers for years.

What are my hobbies besides gaining followers on twitter? Nothing besides things I know I can post about on twitter to show how smart I am to my followers. If my account got banned from twitter I'd probably die of horror. All my years of hard work gaining followers, just wiped out like that. I'd probably kill myself, to be quite honest. My identity has been based on the social reassurance that I'm not just some moronic blowhard who has convinced themselves of their relevancy due to gaining the attention of other moronic blowhards.

The Necessity Of Structural Evil

It would seem that wherever you look, across geography or time, the most powerful organizations are always engaged in child abuse and other very disturbed crimes. Most if not all higher ups in large governments, media organizations, or companies seem to be, without exception, aware of or participating in the rape and/or abuse of women and children in some way. The phrase "absolute power corrupts absolutely" springs to mind, but I feel that this is a bit of a simplistic and incorrect answer. It is not that people who are leaders have some insane propensity for being immoral and depraved, but rather that any successful group of individuals needs to have some form of punishment and personal risk attached to key players to ensure that everybody plays their role and nobody stabs each other in the back on a group level (interpersonal betrayals within group dynamics are frequent, but not on a macro level that compromises the entire group.)

Picture a school group project. What always ends up happening, whether the group project is in middle school, high school, or college, is that a majority of individuals within these groups slack off and the few responsible individuals do the work for the whole group.

While this works in an academic setting, because group projects that require actual group cohesion and cooperation are not workable and thus are failed until they are adjusted by frustrated teachers, this sort of arrangement is not feasible in a highly competitive team setting, like the upper echelons of businesses and governments, where people need to do their jobs or else there will be huge problems and genuine deadlines will be missed.

In low level jobs, the threat of being fired is enough to keep individuals productive. They need to get paid so they can afford to live, and so there is no need for serious penalties besides the removal of a paycheck. When you are dealing with individuals who are independently wealthy and have lots of connections, something far greater is needed in order to install order. Because of this, the only way to maintain productivity and loyalty is to have blackmail on each member of any group of rich or powerful people. The destruction of their reputation and death or imprisonment if orders are not followed is what keeps these people in line.

This is the reason why otherwise smart politicians and media figures often say and do extremely stupid and embarrassing things in public: somebody with access to blackmail is telling them what to say or do. While some of the people who are engaged in underage sex trafficking and sexual abuse most likely enjoy what they have done, the large majority have probably done these things in order to gain access to a better governmental or private job, knowing that the only way for them to "advance" further in life is to essentially become the property of somebody who already has a lot of wealth and power. Of course, this is not an excuse or justification for their actions. Lots of people have been offered these sorts of opportunities and turned them down and done things outside of traditional media and power structures, and enjoying or not enjoying the rape of some underage child is something that doesn't really functionally matter once you have done it.

What is to be done about this? Nothing can be done. From the beginning of history, secret societies and conspiracies have been structured and gained power through this method. This is the same reason that serious fraternities with real world influence make their members do extremely degrading activities in order to qualify for membership, and it's not going away ever. The groups that try to gain power and influence policy that refrain from collecting blackmail on their members will never have the loyalty and group cohesion that matches groups that use blackmail and coercion. That is just the reality of the situation. If it wasn't the reality of the situation, then we wouldn't be in the situation we are in. There is no solution, not peaceful or violent, and there will never be a solution.

Real Careers

There is a very funny thing that people with *real careers* do where they try to establish some sort of personal ownership or insinuate that they are the ones in control of their life by tinkering around with things that people without *real careers* do. What I mean by this is that you will have somebody who is gainfully employed by somebody else who is a half-hearted "stand up comic" or a "music producer" in their free time in order to exert some sort of personality. What these people don't understand is that people who are real comedians or real music producers aren't tinkering around and testing waters, they have already been trying, succeeding, and failing wholeheartedly for years at this point.

People with real careers are owned by other people. That's just the reality of the situation. They are the slaves of the people who pay them a steady paycheck. They rely on other people in order to feed their family. There is an expectation that they won't say or do anything creatively that interferes with their workload and adult responsibilities, and if those creative things do interfere with their workload and adult responsibilities, then either the creative things or the job will disappear. It's almost always the creative things, because people who can stand working for other people generally aren't creative individuals beyond a very surface level and soulless level.

There is nothing wrong with being the slave of somebody else. Throughout history, slavery has been the norm. Now, it's not called slavery, but it's still slavery. I have been a slave in my life many different times, whether it has been being a developer, a waiter, a security guard, a prisoner, or a college student. Sometimes, you need to put yourself in a position of slavery to survive. Some people are happy to be slaves for their whole life in exchange for a generous paycheck, that's great for them and there's nothing wrong with it. I am not that way, every time I do any extended work for anybody, I feel like I literally want to die.

Just like people who have salaried employees who see themselves as good individuals and not slave drivers of a sort, people who have real careers and don't see themselves as slaves are delusional. This delusion is compounded when these slaves attempt to fit in with non slaves who have figured out how to live and get by with lots of hard work and steady effort devoid of immediate reward, financial or emotional. Most creative and self-successful individuals go years without getting any serious positive feedback or mainstream support, which requires a certain sort of soul or emotional and mental fortitude that simply speaking, slaves simply are incapable of reaching. Yes, you may be semi-proficient at playing the guitar or using frooty loops or some video editing software, but you are not a creative. You are a slave who likes to play dress up.

Seeing somebody who obviously doesn't have what it takes to make it in any serious long term creative endeavor but who is deluded enough to think that they could is a bit like Buffalo Bill in *Silence of the Lambs* dancing around in a dress in front of mirrors. They are obviously pitiable and delusional, but there is a sort of uncertain sickness and instability that makes you uncomfortable and disconcerted. Willing slaves who attempt to be creative are perverted necrophiliacs because whatever they pump life into will never birth anything.

More Thoughts On Social Media, Part Seven

There is a certain type of deranged individual that I see very active in political or other hobby communities on the internet. This sort of person is obviously not stupid, IQ wise, but is also obviously not quite as smart as they think they are, IQ wise. They are capable of making valid points or discussing ideas, but generally they are engaged in highly caustic verbal passive-aggressiveness or constant bitter complaining. What is the reason for this? Why do these people exist, and in such a great number? Let's find out.

Growing up, most children are not really told how to find the best options in life or how to organize what they do with their time. With that said, most of the smart ones end up going to college and getting a degree that will enable them to find steady and fairly well paying employment with very limited risk. What happens then is that they realize that they don't like their job, their future, or their life very much. They have what they have assumed would make them happy and fulfilled, and they have extra money and free time, but for some reason they are not happy.

Because these people are not satisfied with their life, and nobody with any potential or talent should be satisfied with a mind-numbing nine-to-five slave grind, they have excess negative energy. Now, the reasonable thing to do with this excess negative energy is to be self reflective and figure out why there is so much excess negative energy, but being self reflective and self critique are almost never taught or pushed on children growing up, and so the vast majority of individuals who find themselves in this situation end up lashing out on the world around them. For powerless men with no real influence or control over their life, the internet is the most obvious outlet for their frustrations.

Once these miserable individuals get into the habit of whining and complaining instead of fixing what is eating themselves up inside, the whining and complaining becomes short term therapeutic, much like smoking a cigarette can soothe the anxiety of a regular smoker. Even worse, these people find like-minded groups of negative individuals in similar life situations and they all provide positive reinforcement that what is being done is the moral and objectively correct thing to be doing.

Over time, these people get worse and worse. The more talented and verbally agile ones become leaders and can eventually even make money by whining to the less talented and less verbally agile followers in the misery circle. Any individual who they run into who disagrees with them is either harassed or lied about and misinterpreted as some sort of malicious or delusional force, and anything that disagrees with the self destructive and depressed sky is falling helplessness-justifying narrative is discarded or discounted as a fluke.

The fact is that people who are productive and happy in life do not have the same amount of time as unhappy and unproductive people do for online internet posting. People who are busy working on projects and hanging out with friends and family can't stay up to date on every little bit of drama or interpersonal infraction. The people who are unhappy and unproductive grow more and more warped and blow little minor infractions out of proportion and unless some intermediate between the healthy and unhealthy is constantly intervening, then a gulf of perception will continue to grow between the functional and dysfunctional until they both see the world in completely incompatible ways. Once that happens, then the bitterness and gossip and infighting so often seen in online political and hobbyist communities gets out of hand until those communities fracture in a fractal nature, and the whole process begins again.

Working At Armazon

I work at Armazon. I am being paid to write this. I am a factory worker, and I love the working conditions here. It's so great, this might be the best job I have ever had in my life. Sometimes, I wish that I could work at Armazon warehouses all day and night instead of going home or sleeping. If I could, I would be here twenty five hours a day.

There is no need to check up on the workers here, we all love it. This job is the reason we wake up in the morning. Jerff Berzos is the most glorious and wonderful CEO ever. He is so handsome and wise, and we trust him completely because he takes care of us and watches over us.

Yes, it is true that there has been rumors and speculation as to some potential subpar employment standards in our warehouses, but we can assure you that none of these rumors are true, and even if they were true they are basically not true and you shouldn't worry about them. There are some stupid mentally ill former employees who have complaints, but they have all killed themselves or died in accidents, most likely from their failing mental health or poor life decisions which lead them to not appreciate the wonderful Armazon working experience.

Working at Armazon is like being paid to not work. It is fulfilling and enjoyable. It is like a vacation. There is nothing better than working at Armazon. When I get married, and I plan on getting married to a fellow warehouse worker due to the generous Berzos employment wage and benefit structure enabling my financial freedom, I plan on having an Armazon themed wedding.

Do not attempt to do "investigative work" into Armazon. It is a waste of time, and no news organizations will publish your stories, since they have high standards and would not besmirch our stellar reputation. Armazon is a great working experience, and everybody knows it.

If you are a member of the press and would like a planned, guided tour, we will be happy to set one up for you. During the extent of this tour, you may not deviate from the designated area or engage with the workers. Your phones and cameras will be confiscated prior to entrance, and you will be subject to a full body scan and search in order to ensure worker and consumer safety.

Libraries

Again I ask, what is the point of libraries? Go into any small town or large city and you will find some library. In that library you will find hundreds to hundreds of thousands of books, and some proportional amount of individuals that roughly scales with the size of the local population. Still, nothing will change. Nothing will get better because of these libraries. "Culture" will not improve. Hunger will not be abolished. The poor will not become rich from these libraries.

Libraries are an example of people worshiping worthless knowledge. How many books in a library have anything of actual value in them? Five to ten, at most. All the rest are either stupid or actively harmful. And guess what, nobody reads those five to ten books that have useful information. Books are such a stupid waste of time in a library setting. Do people who know how to manage their life spend time borrowing books? No, they buy books from places like amazon and keep those books forever soas to have a permanent record of what is valuable to reference should the need ever arise.

Homeless people are the only people who really use libraries for any genuine purpose, and that purpose is to use computers to look at porn. This is disgusting and these people should be forced to be bored out of their mind until they self immolate or get some form of employment, not look at smut in well heated or ventilated spaces while productive members of society are at work.

Do people really need to read books? No, they don't. People need to do things out in the world and leave the book reading mostly alone. Reading books should be a hassle, not something that is free and easy. Poor people should not feel like they have some value because they have read Dickens or Twain or Steinbeck. This form of emotional crutch just impedes personal growth and making people content to rely on others for their entertainment and education.

It is quite shameful to see how people think that libraries are needed. Libraries, like hospitals and parks and charities, are social ills disguised as social goods. Nobody who is often in a library, hospital, park, or charity is somebody who will accomplish anything of value, and I do not want anybody around them. Let's bring back illiteracy and make reading something that takes effort and money. Let's bring class back to reading, and destroy all libraries.

Ignorance Is Bliss, But Only Partly

For the past year or so, I've had most political and social phrases and topics filtered out of my life. This has had a great effect on my mind and physical well-being, and freed up a ton of time that I have been able to use productively, but it has caused a serious problem is that I am completely out of the loop with regards to what is going on, so I can't relate to most people on social media, since most people on social media are constantly yapping about stupid political items and discussing if white people or gays or Muslims should have rights or if we should take everybody's guns away.

Right now, I am on vacation. The world is burning around me, but I do not care. It is not influencing me. I don't own any guns and I don't have kids in the school system and even if I did, being aware of the horrible stuff that goes on and is pushed would not change it from being pushed. I am blissfully ignorant, and my productivity and life has been vastly improved by it, but it is hurting my bottom line.

I would probably have hundreds of thousands of twitter followers by now if I was politically active, but I am not politically active. This situation cannot go on forever, so once I have finished writing my first three or four books, I will gradually be removing the filters and allowing various bits of mental illness impede on me. This will have to be a gradual process, and I am not doing it because I want to but rather because I need to if I wish to stay relevant and relate to my audience, who are desperate to hear my takes on various political and social issues that will definitely be solved by talking on social media.

Once I am back in the thick of insanity and going insane myself, I will then be able to leverage my mental distress and thus my connection to the mentally distressed all around me by pushing my books on the unwitting fools who think I want to be politically active. No, I am merely going into the battle to drag out some of the more innocent and potentially happy individuals before they are destroyed by gossip and the twenty four hour news cycle.

Look at people who "know what they're talking about" with regards to politics or really anything for that matter. Do they seem happy? Do they seem healthy? No, they all seem torn apart physically, mentally, and spiritually. They look like sexual abuse victims, always in the state of perpetual panic. These people are not people who know what's going on. These people know names and dates and atrocities and nothing else. They do not know themselves. They are ignorant of what really matters, which is the importance of setting boundaries between you and the world around you, of being a selfish individual who knows that the world will absolutely take everything that you don't demand you keep to yourself.

In order to have success in this world, one must bounce back and forth between hyper-sane distance and isolation and hyper-insane closeness and participation in group psychosis. The individual must keep brutal track of what works and what doesn't work, what emotions are felt and not felt, what thoughts are thought and what thoughts are not thought, in every situation and circumstance. In this way, the individual will gain the upper hand in every possible setting, having familiarity and practice with both extremes of reality.

Lack Of Self Knowledge

There is a certain type of mediocre person who has gone out of their way to never put themselves in dangerous or risky situations and as such has done a fairly competent job with regards to securing employment as well as maintaining unremarkable social groups where they are looked up to by other mediocre individuals. While there is nothing wrong with avoiding risk and danger, and it is even advisable that those things should be avoid when reasonably possible, the problem comes from the fact that these people have never really been in any genuine high stress or rough situations but think that their ability to function in a society where idiots and morons can easily function makes them experts on every sort of situation and means they are wise.

In order to gain self knowledge about real strengths and weaknesses and how you will handle various edge case scenarios in life, you need to put yourself in edge case scenarios. You need to lose, and lose seriously, before you know how to deal with large loss. These things should not be habitual and compulsive, but rather purposeful excursions into the fringe in a vaccine of sorts that will help with day to day inoculations against delusions of superiority. Without life experience and huge defeats, it's easy to think of yourself as somehow special, especially if you are surrounded by other nonspecial neurotypicals who are role playing as amateur philosophers (most professional philosophers are just as bad, if not worse, as these unremarkable buffoons.)

Seeing somebody who doesn't have any interesting life experiences and never took a lot of risks is a lot like watching a horse that hasn't been trained or disciplined yet. They are foolish, make foolish and stupid moves, are delusional, say things that they wouldn't say if they had life experience, and have a certain air of naive virginity that is pretending not to be naive or virgin. These people have opinions on things they have no knowledge of or experience with, because they read a book or watched a movie. They don't know when to shut up or how to determine who has actual expertise, so they go by faulty indicators, such as how old a book is or the IMDB rating of a movie in question.

Once again, this sort of behavior all boils down to the fact that the people who would be helpful in giving their opinion are generally too busy succeeding and doing interesting things to give their opinion, and the people who would helpful in shutting up have a ton of free time because they don't actually do anything in their life. The irony of writing this in a book is not lost on me, but due to my semi-involuntary confinement I feel that I am a sort of exception. Then again, even if I were not an exception, I would feel I was an exception. As such, it's best if I end this essay now and let the statements stand on their own without any further justifications of myself.

The Self Defeat Of Anti-Natalism

Anti-Natalism is essentially the argument that it is immoral or wrong to have children. Lots of various proofs and points are put forward that are supposed to demonstrate that the world is inherently flawed and that the correct course of action is to just not procreate and thus to die out and end the world's suffering. This may or may not be correct, but it is very funny, because it will never happen.

Anti-Natalism is one step away from whatever philosophy exists that suicide is the only moral way to to live life, which ends up in people killing themselves and thus their philosophy can never really win out. Besides mass destruction and murder there is no escape from the self perpetuating organism that is the mass of humanity and life itself, or else that escape would have already been utilized and nobody would around anymore. Since that is not the case, this strategy of convincing people to just not have kids is obviously something that is never going to work and usually the emotional coping mechanism of failed individuals who seek to bring everybody down to their level of brokenness.

Even if the argument of Anti-Natalism was correct and it was immoral and wrong to bring children into this world, I would still do so. Why? Because I am a bad person. I like to break rules. I like to make things worse and push boundaries and make people suffer. That is the point to life, to see what is possible and what is impossible, to see how other people react to external forces nudging and pulling them towards decisions and environments that they'd rather avoid.

I want more people like me in the world. I want to continue humanity on and to have my influence felt by strangers in hundreds and thousands of years. Not because of any insecurity or moral imperative, but rather because it's funny. It's hilarious to think of somebody who goes through years of thinking and arrives at the conclusion that it's better if nobody is alive to be thwarted by some offspring with my DNA who just wants to have sex for some power trip or out of boredom. Being beaten by somebody who doesn't even know there's a competition or a battle of ideas going on is so funny.

Much like Men Going There Own Way and Men's Rights, Anti-Natalism boils down to people who just can't cut it in life making excuses and justifications for their failure. Rather than admit that they have emotional and physical flaws which make them unattractive to anybody but maladjusted trash that are actively destructive and self destructive, the people involved in these sorts of things outsource all their problems on society. Yes, of course there is suffering in the world. Yes, things are not perfect. Yes, reality is cold and uncaring and a lot of good people get taken advantage of and abused. Who cares? Only the people who are too weak to live with reality and make it work for them. That's Anti-Natalism.

Greedy Children

Most people who take pride in consuming anything, especially literature with its pretentious delusions of secret knowledge and hidden wisdom, spiritually resemble fat little greedy children. They go out of their way to brag and display that they have eaten the sweetest treats. They take pictures of their little candies and tell strangers that they're better than other fat little brats because what they shove down their slovenly gullets is more refined than what other fat little brats shove down their slovenly gullets. These unimpressive and ridiculous freaks confuse what they enjoy with what people create and think that they have becoming something greater than what they are through osmosis. They don't realize that they're just a younger and more delusional form of the morbidly obese white trash chainsmoking woman who goes to Chinese buffets on a regular basis, just more revolting and obnoxious.

The Problem Of Innocence

There seems to be a problem where you really can't be a successful innocent person. Those who are successful aren't really individuals who are optimistic or hopeful for society. Some portion pretend like they are and may donate to charity, but most if not all are pretty world weary and non-innocent. The reason for this is that you kind of need to be abused and taken advantage of explicitly in many different ways until you understand that people around you aren't really your friends and if you are ever in a position of weakness and have stuff that people can take from you, then people will take that stuff from you. Only once you understand the reality of reality do you start to structure your relationships and behaviors in a manner that minimizes weaknesses and leaves less stuff up to chance and maximizes upsides and potential benefits.

People who speak in vague optimistic generalities are either naive or stupid, or more likely being manipulative and trying to take stuff from genuinely naive and optimistic individuals. You can see this with regards to most religious leaders and pastors who utilize lots of vague terms and uncheckable promises in order to extract a tithe. This effect also works in the opposite direction with science and activism, where naive people are scared and frightened by exaggerated threats of doom and gloom.

Most people grow up and live in a world where there are very established roles to play. They do X amount of work and get Y amount of reward. It's all very linear and they never get explicitly taken advantage of enough that they start to think about how there are people who are taking a certain percentage of their work without really doing anything. This is essentially the way effective emotional manipulation works, where the person being manipulated is never taken advantage to a level that registers, so everybody is essentially happy. This sort of exploitation is what creates the lower and middle to upper middle class, although the lower class is more aware of the scam because they are the ones who are struggling to get by while the middle and upper middle class are comfortable enough to be lulled into a sort of stupid contentment.

Of course, this isn't really fixable. Most people can't be convinced that they're being taken advantage of and abused because everybody wants to think that they're autonomous and self-made individuals who are on top of the game. The point most people figure out what is going on is when they switch from being the abused to the abuser, from going to being employed to the employer. Then, they become successful in the zero sum game that is life.

This is not to justify the behavior or excuse it, but it is kind of like being raped or sexually abused. As long as it doesn't destroy the victim, they will eventually use the knowledge that lines can be crossed and there is nobody who is really looking out for them to their advantage. Whether this makes them into an abuser themselves or just a more cautious and self-aware individual depends on the person, but it has a profound effect because the implicit lack of real safety and security that most normal people have has been made explicit, and the formerly blind person can now see what reality actually is.

You can see this sort of situation play out with small towns and snake oil salesmen. Because there are less financial opportunities and less volume of individuals, there is a lower rate of criminals and abusers in these smaller, less economically successful communities. This leads to a more functional and safer community, which leads to happier and healthier lives because people trust each other more. Eventually, somebody who is nefarious comes into the town or small community and realizes how naive and trusting these individuals are and takes advantage of them until they grow too big and get discovered or leave. Once the trust is broken, then the community becomes stricter and more aware of wolves and predators, and the cycle of innocence to shattered innocence to experience to creation of new innocence and so on and so forth begins again, because most people only really learn from personal tragedy, and what most people are is what decides how society functions.

Digital Heroin Addicts

Every few years, somebody in an online social circle is revealed to be addicted to heroin. These people successfully used heroin secretly on successive days, but it always catches up to them eventually. It's heroin, nobody uses heroin habitually long term without falling apart then quitting or dying. What is interesting is how the heroin (and more generally opioid) abuser is almost always the nastiest of drug addicts. These people get gradually meaner and meaner and just flat out rude to completely innocent and harmless individuals.

What is it about heroin that turns somebody into a jerk that is entirely unpleasant to interact with, all the time? Most likely, it starts with the fact that the sort of person who even uses heroin (or opioids) is somebody who is a selfish prick in their heart of hearts. These people just want to feel good, and they don't care who they have to hurt or what they have to do in order to feel good. They are extremely short sighted and lazy individuals who want to take shortcuts to happiness. Because they are shallow thinkers, they don't realize that contentment and happiness are entirely different things and one is sustainable and aspirational while the other is a temporary feeling that can't be a baseline.

Once these individuals have gotten into the habit of using heroin (or opioids) regularly, they get burnt out and do not get any emotional reward from positive interactions from other individuals. Because these people are selfish and greedy freaks who only do things in order to try to feel good and don't plan ahead, they then don't see any reason to be nice or polite to normal people, since they don't get any emotional good chemicals. They are increasingly solipsistic grumps who don't understand how reality or being a positive member of society works, and drives everyone around them.

Of course, the most visible part of any heroin (or opioid) addict's career is when they start to really fall apart. They lose their job (if they even had one), they end up homeless, then they beg for money (in order to get more heroin or opioids, not to get a job) from friends and family non stop. The internet ones will beg and beg for months, making increasingly delusional and obviously dishonest requests over time. If this is the first heroin (or opioid) addict in the internet community, then lots of innocent and well meaning individuals will accommodate and give "rent" or "bus fare" money to somebody they think is down on their luck.

After a few rounds of this begging, even the most naive people will catch on to what is really going on. The heroin (or opioid) addict doesn't care about anybody but themselves and will never improve themselves. The addict is simply lying to people in order to get enough money to get a fix, and then another fix, and then yet another fix; over and over and over and over again. Then, nobody will give the addict any money and the addict will proceed to let their mask drop for a short while, and they will tell everybody that they don't like anybody and that they were just using the money for drugs. Then, the addict will have a moment of self reflection and deactivate their social media profiles and disappear for a short while. In this time, they will most likely provide sex to strangers of the same gender in exchange for money or drugs, depending on how far they have pushed away all potential marks.

Once a short time period has elapsed, these digital addicts reactivate their social media profiles and go back to begging for money - after making up some more embarrassingly dishonest lies and excuses, of course. This time, nobody or very few people fall for their scam and then the same process repeats once or twice more until the drug addict becomes a full time prostitute or dies. Then, everybody who wasn't the scum heroin (or opioid) junkie is educated as to why people who use heroin (or opioids) are scum and should never be trusted. The end.

His Room

"T-this is your room?", xir asked, suddenly a bit uneasy. The house the room resided in was quite nice, due to xir's boyfriend's father's most likely illegal high paying income, but xir's boyfriend's room was something outside of the bounds of expectations. It seemed to exist in its own sort of reality, its own universe. This room was not something you would see in any home decor magazine. This room had a sort of aura that was otherworldly.

The first thing that xir noticed about this room was the smell of dirt mingled with sweat. It was like somebody had manufactured the smell of a slightly unventilated dusty airlock filled with the type of sweat that comes from poor diet and a sedentary lifestyle. The smell wafted out and hit xir straight in the nostrils, and xir fell backwards, almost passing out.

The second thing that xir noticed about this room was the complete lack of decorations besides a bookcase. There was a ratty mattress, some blinds across the window, and a very ratty, very worn down leather chair in front of a sparce computer desk that had a few anime figurines on top of it. There was also a tissue box on the desk and a garbage pail next to the computer desk.

The nicest thing in the room was the computer, which was most likely custom build and costing in the low for digit range. It was quite something to see how he lived. Xir felt bad for him, but also a little frightened for xir's safety. Something screamed in the back of xir's head to leave and not have raucous sex with him, like had been planned, and xir heeded the warnings of the voice in the back of xir's head, and left.

His room haunts xir to this day. Every morning, he wakes up with the visualization of him standing only in his boxers, his bulbous gut spilling out over them, smiling at xir, beckoning xir to come in, to make love to him on his sheetless mattress. Xir does not know if xir will ever get over that day, when xir came into contact with unspeakable terror and survived.

Climate Change

Oh boohooo it's so nice out all the time now. The sun is shining and birds are chirping and the crops are growing, but the climate changed and now things are horrible. Things are so bad now that there is no freezing cold unlivable place on the globe anymore. Now, everybody has beachfront property. Now volleyball is played everywhere and not just in the Bahamas, California, Hawaii, and Florida.

It's such suffering that the whole globe is a tropical paradise now, that all beautiful women walk around either nude or in string bikinis. Now, nobody works and everybody just spends their time sunbathing, swimming, or reading. Now, everybody is just chill all the time.

The worst part is how there are now constant bonfires and hippies playing psychedelic music and making flower power circles. These people smoke ganja and just relax and take everything easy. There is no more war or suffering, just love and joy. Global warming is unbearable for smart and intelligent hard workers like myself.

More Thoughts On Guns

Gun rights, like all rights, are not real. Either you have or do not have a gun. Either people try to take those guns from you and you give them away, hide them, kill the people taking the guns, or the people take the guns away from you. Rights have nothing to do with anything. With that said, guns are probably the funniest sort of mental illness magnet in America.

On both sides of the debate regarding guns, which is more of a psyche ward filled with impotent and powerless mental patients screaming at each other than a debate, are people who have no idea what they're actually talking about. On one side, you have people who see guns as an extension of their manhood. These people are largely insecure, lonely, ugly, stupid, and have problems socializing. On the other side, you have the over socialized and wimpy city dweller weirdos who believe in things like gay rights and abortion and vaccines on a religious ecstasy level.

Guns are just tools like shovels or bear traps or salt licks. They can be used properly or improperly. Most of them never get used at all, and most of the people who buy them are being upsold overpriced junk by salespeople taking advantage of their psychological weaknesses. Guns are a lot like cars and computers, in that the people who spend a lot of time with them would most likely benefit from doing something else with their time and money.

The point of conflict resolution is to put yourself in situations where you're not getting in conflicts. People who are smart who know how to fight will tell you that fighting is stupid and should be avoided even if you are good at it. Being pro gun or anti gun is a lot like this, a dangerous waste of time. If you are super pro gun, you get on the radar of people who are anti gun and if they ever get power then you will be on some list and most likely murdered. If you are super anti gun, you get on the radar of people who are pro gun and if any of them snaps, maybe it will be you who they murder.

Just live your life. Buy guns, or don't. Chances are, you'll never need you gun unless you live in a bad area, and if you live in a bad area you're probably making bad choices. That said, there's nothing wrong with keeping a gun in your house for peace of mind. Just relax and stop thinking that you matter and that you are rambo, you're not. Stop having emotional connections, negative or positive, to tools and technology. Be yourself.

You Are Chosen

It's true, you are special. You have been placed on earth for a special reason. You matter. Your choices matter. Your future is going to be very special. You just have to follow the rules and wait for direction, and then it will all gradually become clear. When the time is right, the opportunity to prove your worth and claim your rightful place in history will be shown. Until then, you need to just sit tight and pay attention to what people are telling you to do.

There is a really large plan at work. You have a central role in this plan, but you have to be patient. You need to just play by the rules while you wait for the stars to align. Get good grades, respect authority figures, and get a high paying respectable job after going to college for half a decade. Once you have done this, then you'll be in a position to capitalize on life, when people tell you it's time to capitalize on life.

You don't want to jump the gun. Don't take risks or initiative while you're young. Everybody is paying attention to you and it will be really embarrassing. People will make fun of you and mock you if you try to do things and you end up doing them imperfectly or even poorly. Do you want to be the person who has failed dozens of times in your twenties before you succeed, or do you want to be the person who has never failed in their life? You want to be the person who has never failed.

Life is a video game and you are the main player. There is a storyline where you do everything you dreamed of, but you can only get to that by following the path you see the lowest common denominator - middle class losers - follow. You just need to be patient and wait for the perfect opportunity, then you will grab it and everything will be perfect. Until then, you need to be in the rat race.

Oh, you are going to be so important and powerful some day. You are going to run the world. You will be looked up to, respected, famous, and loved by hundreds of thousands. This is all just a matter of time, but it will happen. How could anything else happen, you're you! You are the most important person. Your feelings matter. You fears matter. Your hopes and dreams matter. All those things are real to you, and you matter. You definitely matter. You are the star of the show.

Keep up the good work, it will all pay off some day. You need a good work ethic if you want to succeed in the corporate world. Maybe you should watch some youtube videos on charisma and negotiation so you can get a ten percent raise next year. That ten percent raise is going to change your life. You are going to be so fulfilled and successful at your white collar job because of these ten percent raises. Percentage raises compound, so if you are really good at following the rules and begging your boss, you will make a lot more money at your career in the office. That's what life is all about.

All those movies and books about adventure and risk and excitement, those are just fantasy. Nobody really ends up with a life that they enjoy. The people who take risks while young and fail never get any reward for learning how things actually work. They are miserable just like you. They will get to their fifties and wonder where all the time went, just like you. They will never have any fulfillment or impact on anything, just like you. They don't matter, just like you. Nobody is watching, nobody is caring, and nothing matters, so play by the rules and be a team player and sit in your cubicle for three to four decades before getting your Rolex retirement watch and spending the next few decades living cheaply in the South, hating how horrible life was and wishing you were dead. What is the alternative? Take risks and do things that aren't easy? Give me a break, that's a myth. There is no alternative. The End.

The Stein Ranch

There was recently the death of a very high profile rich individual who was involved in the sex trafficking of many young women and most likely near children if not children. Their name is not really important, because they were just the tool of whoever was (and still is) running the various sex trafficking operations, but because this individual was very high profile (for whatever reason), various figures from their life have been interviewed. From the interviews, it has been gleaned that this individual who died had plans for impregnating lots of females in order to make lots of offspring. If I had to guess, this definitely already happened even though it's being described as being planned and not executed, but that is not really important. What is important is the fact that so many people see it as a ridiculous or unrealistic desire.

There is nothing wrong with wanting to impregnate lots of females. In fact, I would venture to say that wanting to have as many women pregnant with your children as possible is the only natural and healthy desire. Of course, it is unrealistic and unfeasible for most individuals to support and provide for many women let alone many children, so it makes sense for most to limit their seeding of the human race to one to three women over the course of life. That is a limitation of means, not biology.

This is the problem with most men. They do not have any big dreams. They do not have big goals. Give them a house, a wife, some kids, and a stable career with a steady paycheck and they will never do anything with the rest of their free time. They will spend their weekends watching sports and reading books and going out to eat. They won't desire anything more. They will have become dead automatons without zest for life. And, as we all know, once you stop trying to take more and more, you end up with more and more being taken from you.

Men would benefit from being like this high profile rich and powerful man who wanted to create hundreds of children. They should refrain from sex trafficking, of course, but to have visionary and megalomaniac delusions is the only way to live. Most will never have more than five or six children in total, but in the search for being able to have dozens of children, they will achieve feats they would have never come close to otherwise.

Smoking Cigarettes And Criminality

There are certain stereotypes of how women are more sexually attracted to men who are criminals (the "just be violent" dating strategy) and how people who smoke cigarettes are cooler than people who don't smoke cigarettes. Both of those things are true, but what most uncool sexless losers are doing are confusing symptoms with causes.

People who are naturally unattractive to the opposite sex try to emulate natural symptoms of people who are attractive to the opposite sex, and just end up even more unattractive to the opposite sex. Instead of being a dweeb, they are now a dweeb with lung cancer who wears platform shoes and leather jackets.

Just what is it about people like me, people who have criminal records and smoke cigarettes, that is so attractive to the opposite sex? What makes women love me? Well, besides my looks (which definitely help), it is mainly my low anxiety and high decision making skills. Because I am more likely to do and say things that I feel like doing or saying, I am more visible and more dynamic than other individuals who are more self conscious and insecure.

What can you do if you are somebody who is insecure and bad with women? Nothing. That's all you can do. What you have to do is stop doing all the things that you think women care about. Stop caring. Once you stop caring about women and how they think about you, you will be able to pursue things you are interested in and stop making a fool of yourself. Until then, you will just look silly to all women and any men who know how reality works. Once that happens, women will be all over you if you aren't fat, ugly, and/or stupid, but that's not why you should stop caring.

Just do whatever you want, whenever you want. Don't think about what people will think about you, the people who care what other people do are not people who matter. Once you realize that only loser insecure failures with no real accomplishments or hobbies will pay attention to things you do, then you will quickly gain a ton of time to pursue actually beneficial activities.

Criminals and cigarette smokers realize that nobody is actually keeping score. They are free to live their best life and abuse others and themselves at their leisure, and they do. That sort of freedom is available to anybody, it's just that mostly the lowest of the low have enough free time and disconnect from society in order to figure out that it's available. Once you taste the freedom of spitting in the face of the uptight nobodies and realize that there is no real punishment, you will never go back to being a slave to imaginary external guidelines. Being the master of yourself and your environment is what is attractive to women, not smoking or breaking the law.

Thoughts On Old People Part One

There comes a certain age where it becomes too late to make anything of your life if you have not already started to make something of your life. I'm much too young to really know what that age is, and perhaps I will never be old enough to discover that age, but the fact remains that at a certain point, potential has been squandered and opportunities wasted, and from that point on, life is all the way downhill until death.

What do you do when you are in that position of rot and decay that sets in? There is no good answer, but most people who are in this situation are probably not the type to genuinely look for good answers, or else they would not be in this sort of situation. All you can do at that point is speed your demise with drugs, alcohol, and unhealthy living. You can even cut everything short with a bullet to the head or jump from some rooftop or bridge. The point is that sometimes, there is no happy way out of a predicament. Sometimes, death is the final and only answer.

What should be the way these people should be treated by others? Should they be respected and loved by strangers? Should society treat them well and ease them into death? I don't really think so. At a certain age, you should become aware of the reality of life and the connection between your actions and your outcomes. Idiots and brain damaged morons can survive and even thrive in society, so there is no excuse for a mentally and physically healthy individual who enters their forties or fifties in a state of uselessness.

You can take this sort of reasoning a step further. Somebody who is working at an unfulfilling job in their late forties or fifties is somebody who makes poor choices. These people have been around the block too many times to not be in a better position. If they are strapped for cash or need to work to get by at that point, they are self defeating and undisciplined sentimental poor decision makers who should not be looked up or relied upon for good advice.

Most of the old people in the public eye are degenerates and failures. If they weren't, they wouldn't be in the public eye. They'd be at the park or at home with grandkids or taking care of a garden. These are the old people who made good choices and were smart with how they invested their time, energy, and money. The ones in the public eye working jobs are the drug addicts, gamblers, layabouts, failures, and poor planners who are various shades of disgusting and disappointing people.

Unfortunately, just like most cases, it seems like the meddlesome old individuals are the ones who decide what is seen as a positive or negative trait in old individuals. While the proper and honorable elderly are living out the end of their life in peace and quiet, the losers are waddling around and screwing things up and lying and complaining to the younger generations in order to secure benefits and comfort to excess. This is just the way of the world, and will most likely never change.

Do not become like the old people who refuse to grow old properly. Do not insist on clinging onto youth. Don't waste your youth and time while young so that you'll be a burden instead of a benefit to the young people around you. Don't give your children and grandchildren reason to despise you and think of you as obstacles and hassles. Do something with your life before it's too late, before you have less time left to live than you have already lived. Create something of lasting value and give the next generation something more than you got growing up.

Thoughts On Old People Part Two

In every town in every country there is an old person who is losing it. They wake up confused and they forget who they are and what year it is. They need help using the bathroom. They are in pain and suffering whenever they are awake. Their dreams are constant nightmares whenever they can get sleep. These people live in hell on earth, and every day gets a little bit worse than the last.

What did this old person do to deserve such a fate? They worked hard, followed the law, raised a family, were a help to the community, and were a genuinely good person. They went to church, gave money to charity, and were loved by everybody around them. Still, their mind began to degenerate and fall apart.

The family members of this old person will spend time and money trying to help the situation. Nothing will work. Things will get worse. It will make the grandkids sad and scared whenever they see their grandparent. Things will just get worse and worse and worse. It will be a drain on everybody, but nobody will be ungrateful or bitter because they will understand it as their duty. In a way, it will probably bring extended family together as everybody works as a team to help out the failing human being that they now take care of.

Eventually, this old person will die. It will probably be a heart attack or stroke or something of that nature, but it will happen. Some relative will check up on the individual after the phone isn't picked up at the usual time, or hear a medium thump or groan in the other room, and they will walk in on a fresh corpse, most likely with freshly soiled undergarments filling up the room in a rotten, stinking odor.

The family will mourn and there will be the proper services, depending on what culture and religion the family belongs to. People will be genuinely sad, but do their best to think of the good times and whatever comforting thoughts which pertain to the afterlife will serve to ease the new lack of existence felt in the family's atmosphere. Over time, life will go on and people will get back to living life until it's time for the next death of somebody in the same generation, or time for the next generation's decline and death to start rolling in.

What is the point to all of this? There is none. Good people get punished and suffer just as much, if not more, as bad people. People do their best all their life and then end up with dementia and Alzheimer's and family members have to watch it happen, completely helpless, just mitigating and negative symptoms until that individual dies. Then, that's it and it's on to the next phase of life.

Old people are depressing to watch. They are a reminder that nothing lasts forever, that the best intentions don't really matter past a few decades, that everything decays. I don't know how I will deal with getting old, if I live that long. I don't want to be a burden on people who are just starting their life. I don't want to have some brain disease destroying my last sense of self while my brain is still functioning. I'll most likely kill myself before I get that old. To do otherwise seems like cowardice and an unfair punishment on the next generation, or maybe wanting to escape self degradation and humiliation is its own form of cowardice. There's no good way out except some mass tragedy killing everybody on the planet so nobody has to deal with the emotions of death and loss.

Thoughts On Cows

I have a small amount of experience with butchering, and I see cows a lot, so the thought of them is occasionally on my mind. More specifically the fact that for non dairy cows, life consists of mainly standing in a field and eating hay and drinking water. That's it. If you're a cow for meat, you do that until you get slaughtered. That is your existence and nothing more.

It's so strange to think about cows in this way, especially when you don't try to draw any parallels between a cow's life and human's life, and just appraise it for what it is. They just stand around and eat and drink and do this for a while and then get murdered. Killing and murdering really aren't different, it's the termination of a life. What "reasons" it is for is really meaningless on an objective level.

What goes on in a cow's mind while it's alive? Probably not much. It doesn't really matter, but it's strange to think about. Trying to see things honestly from a cow's stupid and completely contextless point of view is impossible, no matter how much you try. It's not like you would even be aware that there are things you were missing, you would just not be aware of things and not aware that you're not aware of things. You would just exist.

What is the point to this essay? There really isn't one. It is what it is. Cows are just cows and they serve a purpose. They live and die and nothing really changes. They don't matter, the murder of them doesn't matter. Our raising and slaughtering of cowns on a habitual basis doesn't matter, it doesn't need to be justified or condemned. It just is, just like cows just are.

Late Summer Bugs

Living in Upstate New York, it is right around late summer when lots of bugs start to fly in. These are no mosquitoes that show up in early spring and last until late fall and are annoying enough that they floating around in your mind even in their absence, these are the types of unimpressive and dull, pointless bugs that have been gone just long enough for you to forget that they exist. Once you forget about them, then it's time for them to come back for a month or two until winter kills off the ones that were too stupid to leave the area.

These bugs are not really meaningful in any real manner. They are not disgusting but they are also not interesting. They just kind of exist when they exist, and don't exist when they don't exist. When they are around, however, there is a short week or so period when they are heavy enough to make a distinct impression of existence on my mind. Once this period passes, I forget that this period even exists. This period is currently occurring, and so writing this is my attempt at forcing it into my mind on a level that won't be forgotten once they migrate to some other geographic location.

What is interesting about these bugs is how uninteresting bugs as a whole are. Bugs are not anthropomorphized. They do not get the fuzzy and loveable hollywood treatment. Stories are rarely written from their point of view. Either they are completely ignored or they are treated in very negative and callous manner. This specific aspect to bugs comes to mind now, because prior to writing this essay I was sitting on my parents' front porch, reading a book. The book doesn't matter, but my reading time was cut short because bugs kept on dropping on the pages of my book.

I am fine with one or two bugs landing on me or my books when I am outside. I'll usually flick them off or put them between my fingers and crush them, depending on the size and type of bug and how I'm feeling at the moment, but the amount of bugs falling on me and my book was simply ridiculous, at least five or six bugs per minute. Before returning inside, I investigated why so many of the small pill-like bugs were interfering with my summer night, and I discovered five or six spider webs with hundreds of these bugs stuck on each web.

What would the proper response be to seeing a field full of dying and dead humans? For any non-deranged individual, it would be shock and horror. The same thing would happen if there were hundreds of squirming non-human animals in the last gasps of life. There would be some degree of empathy and disgust as well as desire to help or avert the eyes that would be felt upon seeing such a horrible display. This is not the case with hundreds of little insects caught in a spider's web. All I felt while looking at the situation was a slight annoyance that it meant I would need to go read somewhere else if I didn't want to be interrupted and a twinge of amusement at the fact some spider was going to have such a large dinner.

This same sort of weird indifference to bugs can be seen with vegetarians, especially the ones who are now pushing everybody to eat insect paste protein rather than meat protein. They can relate to animals for some reason, and so they see the murder of these animals for personal utility and pleasure as morally wrong, but they cannot empathize with bugs and so they are fine with the same process of factory raising and murder that they dislike for animals being applied to insects.

Life is a lot like bugs for people who have some mental abnormality such as sociopathy or psychopathy. Both have different reasons for occurring and modify behavior and perception in varying manners, but both are looked down on by most neurotypical individuals as some form of dehumanizing buglike existence. This is largely the fault of most self-proclaimed and highly visible sociopaths and psychopaths, who go out of their way to behave in inhuman and antisocial manners which are internally and externally destructive, but it is still a real phenomenon. You can see it manifest in how most people claim we should treat sociopaths and psychopaths, which is to imprison and even kill them preemptively, in order not to deal with the hassles that they may otherwise create.

While this sort of buglike empathy-less perception of sociopaths and psychopaths by neurotypicals may not be unwarranted or even strategically incorrect, it is quite amusing how the so-called natural emotions of mercy and understanding seem to disappear when viewing bugs, sociopaths, or psychopaths, particularly in the case of people who go out of their way to proclaim their humanity and the moral superiority of strong emotional empathy.

The complete lack of emotional empathy with regards is needed for proper functioning in society. Who knows how many bugs they kill whenever they walk across the ground or drive their car? Nobody does, and if somebody really cared about not harming or killing bugs then they would be debilitatingly unproductive in life. People are fine with mass murder as long as it is something that they don't relate to. For this reason, even the most self proclaimed environmentalist and empathy filled person will not care about bugs beyond how they are interacting on a vague ecosystem level.

Perhaps this view of bugs and our indifference towards whether they live or die is more honest than how we think we feel about the murder of animals or even humans. Maybe a complete lack of care is the correct stance to take when somebody who we don't personally rely on gets sick or murdered or raped or loses a leg or gets cancer. When you think about it, having emotional and physical empathy might just be a childish and selfish reaction that most people never grow out of that makes them feel like things that don't matter actually do matter, and people who say they have empathy are just emotional slaves who would do horrible things that people who say they don't have empathy would never do, if the people who say they have empathy were not deterred by bad internal feelings. Who really knows? Who really cares? Not the people without empathy, and definitely not the people who say they have empathy.

Odd And Even Numbers

There is something very interesting about odd and even numbers. If you add an odd number to an even number or an odd number, the resulting number is an even number if the number added to was an odd, and an odd number if the number added to was an even. If you add an even number to an odd number: you get an odd number. If you add an even number to an odd number: you get an odd number.

The odd can change the even into the odd and the odd into the even, but the even cannot change anything. What does this tell us about even and odd numbers? I don't really know, but it would seem to suggest that even numbers are a combination of odd numbers while odd numbers are themselves. Almost like even numbers are pairs of odd numbers. This makes even further sense when you realize that zero is not a real number and is just the absence of everything, which means that one is the first number and two is just one twice, which makes two a pair of ones which are real numbers. Once might even say that one is the only real number.

This sort of understanding of odd and even numbers can be further applied to life in that if something can be broken down into something smaller, then that thing isn't really a thing but a collection of things. What this means is that nothing is anything except collections of things, which means that everything is the part of a larger whole which means that everything is one collection, which means that even one is something with many things inside of it which means it isn't one, which is kind of hippy dippy sounding but makes sense, but also kind of doesn't really.

There were a lot of mathematical problems with this essay. I know all of them, but I put them in here to trick readers and make people who are familiar with math (and science) frustrated. I love to make people upset and confuse people who can't know any better, because I'm a bad person. There's nothing quite like saying complete nonsense knowing that some people will believe it. Of course, by reveling this about this essay I have nullified its negative effects, which is kind of odd for me to do, but odd and even are the point of this essay. So, in a way I have added my malicious intent and also revealed it which is something good, which ends up in an even sort of balanced essay, proving the whole thing to be quite profound. This goes into quantum math, but I doubt anybody really understands that as much as I do so I will leave that for another essay.

No Self Respect

I have nothing against thieves or criminals. I don't really think they're any worse than most "good" people. In fact, I think a lot of them are more honest to themselves and less delusional than "good" people, since they can't really live in a reality where they think they are good people and still behave in the manner that they do. That said, I don't like lazy and deluded people, especially not thieves and criminals who are lazy and deluded.

There is somebody that I realized was a thief about a year ago. They stole a design that somebody I knew had created and were selling it while pretending that they were the inventor of the design. I don't really care about the design or the person who created it, and I have nothing against using other peoples' stuff to your own benefit, but what really upset me was how the thief had gone about the whole situation.

The lazy, stupid, design thief was in the same community as the original designer. His audience was made up of people who knew the original designer. The thief did not stop and think to realize that what he was doing was so obvious and public that anybody who knew the original creator would take offense and bring up the blatantly stolen design, that's how idiotic this guy was.

When I publicly confronted this individual about his thievery, he tried to deny that he was claiming credit for the design. This was an obvious lie, and being a liar myself I could tell that he knew he was lying. What made matters worse is that this moron refused to admit that he was a no good lousy counterfeiting thief and by his behavior was basically challenging me and indicating that I was incorrect. I am very specific about artistic integrity, being that creativity is something that is extremely distinct and one of the few special things anybody can engage in no matter who they are, so this whole situation was very disgusting to me.

After the confrontation and wormish denials by this walking ethnic stereotype, I made my stance very clear and everybody who saw the interaction was aware of the true situation. The thief was made fun of by multiple people and his ability to profit off of the stolen creation was pretty much nullified. He made up some stupid excuses and then tried to suck up to me and other people, but I had none of it and have pretty much cut off this individual from my life completely due to their stupidity more than anything.

Stealing, murder, lying, and all the other sins and vices have their place, but not in an internal group. Once that is allowed to happen, everything falls apart. This idiot is still lurking around in social groups that I inhabit, and he still sucks up to me to other people, no doubt hoping that I fall for his very neurotic and shifty flattery. Of course, that is a waste of time because I would never let somebody who is so utterly stupid as to do what this person did, but it's still amusing to me to see this sort of thing occur.

This sort of individual is one who will never create or do anything of value. They will most likely get some cheap law degree or work for some neurotic inbred greedy family member in some low level fraud career until they get busted or die of aids under some bridge. Their existence is a miserable one because they lack any intelligence, aspirations, cleverness, talent, drive, or positive attributes at all. They are not even honest to themselves about being lowlife scum, which is why they will never amount to anything in life and will only have other losers and naive people to talk to.

It's insulting that this person is allowed to live. In a really meritocratic society, they and the family that they came from would be put to work in some mines or shot in the back of the head for being absolute parasites who drag down anybody they interact with. It's also a bit comforting, because if this individual and their family have managed to survive for this long, then that means it's almost impossible to lose at life, since anybody who even works a little hard will end up better off than this genetic reject.

Spreading Things Out

In communication, there is a proper ratio that needs to be found with regards to seriousness and nonsense. Too much nonsense and only foolish people will listen, but too much seriousness and only overly serious people will listen. Because of this, I have been fairly specific in how I write. There is no set pattern for how many essays I write have real points, but there is an average of about one to every six or seven essays in each book being of some analytical nature at its core. Of course, the biggest reason as to why I write as much nonsense and humor as I do is that I just love to joke around and have fun and I want myself and other people to have a good time when possible.

Another element to how you present yourself is your visuals. This is the reason I chose a fairly simple but not ugly cover for all my *It Is The* books, as I do not want to attract people who are involved in things solely for flashy aesthetics and delusional hero or villain complexes, but I also don't want to push something that is ugly or careless. I want to present an image that takes itself seriously in not being taken too seriously but also not being seen as careless or mindless.

There is also an element of honesty and flaws that I have purposely left in my writing. The grammar is not perfect and there are a fair amount of errors that would most likely be fixed by a read-through or two, but simply put I don't want people to think I am a perfectionist or professional. I'm neither, and it does me good to present a flawed version of what I create in order to keep myself less delusional with regards to my talent level and my limitations. There are simply too many things I want to say and accomplish for me to spend serious time adjusting and reframing things I create after I have created them.

Once you create things that are too perfect, too aesthetic, and too easily understood, a very disagreeable element of both the inexperienced and the pathetic latch on to you. They follow you and your creations around and try to siphon off your energy and value in order to make themselves feel better and to harm others around them. These are a lot like refugees and immigrants who flee whatever failing community that they came from instead of staying and making it better. They are not to be trusted or catered to.

This is not to say that one should make dysfunctional, hideous, or overly complicated things, but rather a certain sheen of top level non-refinement should exist for valuable things, so that the unworthy, lazy, and disingenuous don't think to invest time into investigating you or your output. The people who have good intentions and are genuinely curious should be able to sense the inherent quality and value of what you do and look past the very top layer and be rewarded.

This mindset can be applied to relationships as well as creative endeavors. Do not turn away or be rude to people for no reason, but also do not be overly friendly or obvious that you are a beneficial and helpful person to be around. When people show interest, return their interest in a way that people who are valuable will invest further energy and people who are not valuable will get bored and go to somebody who is a more obvious mark. Over time, you will form real relationships with genuinely good people, and the bad people who you interact will go away and leave you alone, because they wouldn't be bad people if they weren't lazy and stupid in some manner.

Underdogs

Remember that most people like underdog stories because most people are terminal losers. They see themselves as potential winners who never got "their chance" at life and were given a raw deal in life. They do not understand that you need to take chances and don't wait for other people to give you chances. You have to create your own luck in life. In reality, the dumb, the foolish, the stupid, the poor, and the weak usually remain that way and are that way because they are mediocre failures who always do the bare minimum to survive and spend all their free time in daydreaming fantasies and emotional cope.

The real underdogs in life do not win, but the people who go out of their way to show they are not underdogs also do not win. These are the flipside of the mediocre loser, the individual who is desperate to hide their insecurities and weaknesses and present a display of strength and power. True strength and power does not show that it is strong. If anything, it pretends to be an underdog in order to make themselves appear nonthreatening to individuals who pretend to be strong but are really weak.

This is the way of life. Look for the people who just seem to exist and do what needs to be done and do what they are doing. Spend less time caring about who deserves what, everybody deserves what they make out of their life. Most wealth doesn't last more than three generations because most people who "succeed" and get rich are lucky idiots who fall into the delusional bravado category. These are the people you see in public with "expensive" cars and "designer" clothes, appealing to the lowest common denominator of wealth.

Once you pass a certain age, what you look like and who you are and what you have accomplished are representative who you are in your true essence - of your will. The age varies slightly based on what environment you grew up in, what your parents and friends were like, etc., but it is most likely in your early to mid twenties that your true character starts to show for anybody who is actually paying attention. If somebody is in their thirties and poor and lives a mediocre life and hasn't done anything of note, chances are they never will. If they are morbidly fat and unhealthy or morbidly skinny and a non-functioning drug addict who have never done anything of value except make excuses and cause problems, chances are they will make excuses and cause problems until the day they die.

In real life, actions have consequences. Poor people are poor because they are too stupid to take advantage of other stupid people in order to get ahead or create genuine value. There are battles that shouldn't be fought. If you are a genuine underdog, you should not be engaging in a fight that you will most likely lose if there are other options, which there almost always are. Somebody who repeatedly places poor bets is an idiot, not a hero to aspire to. They will lose at life and so will anybody who emulates them. Don't worship underdogs unless they win repeatedly at whatever they do, which means they aren't really underdogs and just know how to present themselves well. Underdogs are losers.

Of course, you should not tell most people that you view the world in this manner. You should pretend to relate to and sympathize with the downtrodden, and you genuinely should sympathize with them: it's usually beyond their control that they are the way they are. It's better to just smile and wave at the delusional and naive who think they will beat the odds without doing anything needed to beat the odds rather than scorn them, since you gain nothing from them and you are just inviting yourself to be made at odds with people who have lots of free time and generally self destructive petty vindictiveness. Let them be lemmings who walk off the cliff, they don't matter and you shouldn't be feeling any emotional need to justify your beliefs to useless strangers.

The Burger God

The year is 2019. You would think that most people would be smart enough by now not to worship false idols. It would make sense that people would put their time and energy into avenues that brought them some sort of personal or financial benefit. You would be wrong. A cult has sprung up around a fat man named Sergey Nazorev.

Yes, that's right, a bunch of early twenties to mid thirties white males have started a cult around a morbidly obese philosophy student who tinkers around with programming in his free time. They worship him as a god. They treat him like some prophet sent to deliver them from their terminal autism.

What is wrong with people? Why are they so messed up? Nobody really knows, but the existence of Chainlink and Mister Nazorev are proof that survival of the fittest is a completely false idea. Instead of survival of the fittest, we live in a reality that is the survival of the fattest, which is why Sergey eats so many burgers every day.

These people babble on and on about oracle problems and byzantine generals. They are completely insane. There is no reasoning with them. They cannot be helped. Hopefully, some leader will start to lock up these individuals before they start harming innocent mentally well individuals who are not worshiping obese autistic Slavic men in blue checkered t-shirts. We may be too late to stop this strange Big Mac Cult from destabilizing the entire developed world.

Sophists

Lately I've been re-reading Plato, and while a lot of what is written is very interesting and definitely useful, there is a funny distinction that they make with regards to philosophers as compared to sophists. I am not going to get into the details of either sophistry or philosophy, because I am not an expert on sophistry or philosophy and do not really care, but it is funny the lengths that the individuals in Plato's writings are negative and judgmental towards sophists and sophistry in general.

In Plato's writings, sophists are described as useless and non-helpful individuals. They are scorned because they put their talents in speaking and convincing into personal use. This is a funny point that philosophers should bring up, because all most "philosophers" do is talk and discuss vague generalities that do not really help anything. In fact, an argument can easily be made that sophists are genuinely more logical and thus more helpful than philosophers, because it is logical and good to look out for self interest before looking out for the interest of others.

At the end of the day, sophists and philosophers are both fairly useless. They don't really make things better in any real or lasting manner. All the ancient philosophy didn't preserve or lead to those ancient cultures surviving and thriving. To the contrary, it would seem that philosophy and the in-depth introspection and discussions that it entails almost always precedes some sort of great decline and collapse. Sure, there are a lot of interesting ideas and points of view put forth by these people, but they don't really change anything in any lasting manner or else we wouldn't be in the state of reality that we are now, which means that it's a fun exercise but not really meaningful or lastingly profound on any large-scale functional level.

The differences between philosophers and sophists boils down mainly to a level of self awareness. Philosophers and people who seek to be philosophers tend to be losers who don't fit in and are uncharismatic and have inferiority complexes due to being generally useless individuals who will never amount to much. Sophists are much more honest to themselves about their role in the universe. They know they won't fix things and they're not emotionally invested in delusional and impossible goals.

They use their talents to their benefit and don't allow themselves the luxury of unreasonable ideals.

While reading Plato for the first time was very interesting and enjoyable, I have found this second read through a bit tiresome and excessive. Prior to starting, I had assumed that each successive read-through would be a more positive experience, but I just don't see all that much that I missed in each passage and find the predictability boring. Perhaps this is more a testament to my desire for constant suspense and uncertainty than a negative judgment towards Plato, but it is something I noticed. There is so much focus on setting and manners and drawing things out to an unhealthy degree that I wonder if the people involved in these discussions weren't mainly just bored and spoiled individuals who had slaves to do all their work for them and were a fluke of temporary geographic dominance. That would explain why people from Greece and Rome and more generally "The Old World" tend towards being subpar and uninspiring individuals.

Sophistry and philosophy are fun and interesting, in very limited doses. People who focus on these sorts of things and the rules about them are boring and their lack of desire for novelty and challenge outside of purely cognitive rote logic exercises strikes me as something that really appeals to the mediocre and unaccomplished in life.

How To Leave Politics

Like a lot of younger individuals, I got involved in politics for a few years. During those years I was sure of myself and bold. Some would say I was too bold, but I just say I was bold. I said lots of things that I wouldn't say now, and I made lots of friends with people I wouldn't have otherwise made friends with. Eventually, I got tired of politics. Some might say I wasn't really in it for the right reasons, that I was just acting out, that I never really knew what I believed and just wanted attention because I was an insecure and incoherent mess, but I like to say that I simply experienced vast personal growth.

Having been done with politics for months if not years, I would like to explain to anybody like myself who might currently feel trapped and want to get out of politics, but doesn't know how. Politics can be scary and filled with lots of nasty people who will say a lot of nasty things to and about you if they disagree with you. Granted, they won't really do anything besides talk, because that is all most people in politics ever do, but they might say really hurtful things. This is why it's so important to go about leaving politics in a safe and constructive manner.

The first thing you should do when you leave politics, or even just adjust any of your political views, is to do a complete one hundred and eighty degree turn on anybody that you used to agree with. Now is the time to scorn and openly mock them, in public, for saying and believing things that you said and believed a week ago but no longer believe. This will show that you are not somebody to mess with and that you should be respected and given space by everybody. Some people would advise against this, saying that it's not only hypocritical but it's also proof that you don't know what the hell you are doing or how to not shoot yourself in the foot, but those people are idiots.

It's important to distance yourself from your past beliefs. What this means is that whatever you said you believed, you now say you don't believe, but twice as adamantly. If you were anti-racist, now you hate blacks and Jews and Mexicans. If you were interested in white identity politics, now you're an anti-racism advocate and you harass random white people on the street while video taping for your youtube channel.

It should be obvious to you by now, but you cannot keep any of your political friends who do not also become apolitical. First, you should have an impassioned screaming or mocking conversation with them about why they're wrong and you're right. Then, when they disagree with you at all, ruin their life. Talk bad about them in public. Insult them and insinuate they are mentally ill and deranged. This is the only way to distance yourself from them. You cannot maintain a friendship with anybody on the left or the right who disagrees with you and has different values, even if you shared your beliefs and values with them up until a few days ago. You need to cut them out, like a bad cancer. This shows how serious you are about being an apolitical, good person.

Now that you have no more political friends and have publicly degraded people who have newly different beliefs from you, you are free. Nobody will have any hard feelings or seek revenge on you. You won't have built up a reputation as an unstable and untrustworthy individual who should be avoided by anybody, political or not, who doesn't want to get stabbed in the back at a moment's notice. You will be seen as a brave and honest, morally superior individual, and everybody will respect and love you. Nobody will care that you were advocating for a race or class war once you go out of your way to attack the only people that would put up with your personality instead of just undramatically going about your way and doing your best without making a huge scene.

Another thing to keep in mind is: it's not you, it's them. Everybody should be seeing things the way that you currently see them, and they're just stupid or malicious if they don't. What this means is that you shouldn't feel any sympathy for somebody who is three or four years younger and inexperienced in whatever niche mentally ill political tribe you were a part of, even though they have the same views that you used to have before you had time to really think them over and figure out what was wrong with them. You need to scorn and look down on younger individuals and verbally abuse them for being stupid and delusional.

Stupid Ugly Dumb Excessive Readers With Opinions

A problem with the whole "culture" around reading is that it attracts a sort of individual who is a stupid loser who has no talents or any life experience that gives them any sort of unique perspective into life. These are people who are ugly in appearance and unfit (because they do not have any aspirations or discipline) and have gotten into their heads that they are what they have read. This is not the case, of course - they are what they do; which means they are readers.

If somebody watched hundreds of thousands of hours of youtube videos on traveling, we would call them sad or pathetic. If they then proceeded to insist that they were experts on traveling, we would laugh at them and even consider them mentally ill. This is the situation we have arrived at with reading, where the most pathetic and deranged weirdos (avid readers) have begun to think of themselves as great adventurers, thinkers, romantics, and writers. No, they are simply people who are emotionally obese consumers of things other people create.

People who read and have opinions that they use their readings to back them up on are a lot like the individuals who are talented in game shows that rely on trivia. Usually they have some stupid soulless white collar job and do not know how to present themselves in a non-embarrassing manner. They almost always have some degree from some college that other mediocre white collar workers respect, because these people are driven by the desire for acceptance and respect from like-minded morons.

What is your opinion on David Foster Wallace? What is your opinion on mid eighteenth century English literature? What is your opinion on history and politics? Nobody accept for other platformless unaccomplished losers cares about what you think about these things, which is why you feel the need to inject your critique and appraisal of others into conversations with strangers. If your opinions and thoughts had any value, then you wouldn't have the time to wax poetic about obscure and unimportant niche topics to other individuals who also don't matter. You don't matter and your opinions will never matter, stupid ugly dumb excessive readers with opinions.

Le Space

Finally, we had done it. Humanity had made space travel a reality. I don't mean traveling to the moon every few decades or sending probes to mars, but rather tens of thousands of people living in space. I mean towns and settlements on dozens of planets. I mean the future was really here. What nobody had really realized was how this would change reality as we know it, or rather how it would not change anything at all.

Of course, there was the initial excitement of the first few years. People lived and died. Books were written and movies were filmed. Fortunes were made and lost. Over time, though, nothing was fundamentally different. Power shifted a bit: Russia, Israel, and America all benefited greatly here on earth from various things like increased resource acquisition, but nothing much more than that.

Most people still spent too much time on the internet. People ate unhealthily and made stupid financial decisions that forced them to work white and blue collar jobs well into their fifties. People were still angry at each other. The media and political establishments still functioned via child rape and murder and blackmail. Finance was still filled with the worst sort of individual, just like law (and media and politics.)

The only real change was the palpable lack of hope that now pervaded everything. The dreams of escape and adventure were now fulfilled and the results were in, and everything was still mediocre and boring for mediocre and boring people. These are the people that make up the majority of any society. They hoped that some rapture like religious event, in this case becoming a space worthy species, would lead to personal fulfillment and excellence. Of course, this didn't happen because mediocre and boring people are just parasites who are always along for the ride and never contribute anything except their bodies and time for slavery and death.

Now, what was left to dream about? Things that were smaller and less potentially life enriching than what had already been accomplished. Now the mundanity of reality was able to fully set in. Just like the wheel and boats and planes and the internet, space travel was just a technological piece of the puzzle that revealed that we lived in a closed system, a zero sum game, that there was no way to escape our damned humanity.

Chester's Hot Fries

Generally, I try to eat fairly healthily. Sure, I will have a burger or some other unhealthy meal once or twice a month, but I am not in the habit of eating chips or candy or drinking much other than water or unsweetened green tea. This is more because I am too lazy and poor to go through the hassle of getting cheap processed food than because of some strong moral stance, but I do like to think that there is some minuscule element of self control and restraint that allows me to have a fairly simple and healthy diet.

With that said, for some reason I am a fool for Chester's Hot Fries. These aren't spicy cheetos or Andy Capp's Hot Fries, these are Chester's Hot Fries. Objectively speaking, they taste kind of like nothing with a bit of grease and hot sauce added. I do not know why I like them so much, but I love them. Whenever I see them in a store (very rarely), I buy one to four bags of them. Then, I'll eat a whole bag of them in one sitting. The whole time I'm eating these things, I know in the back of my mind that they don't even taste good and are extremely unhealthy, but I can't stop.

Everybody has their self-destructive vices; for some it's hard drugs. For others, they are addicted to male prostitutes or gambling or gossip. My self-destructive vice is Chester's Hot Fries. I would kill an innocent individual if that is what it took to get just one more taste of Chester's Hot Fries before they got discontinued. I would sell my country's secrets to the highest bidder if that was what was needed to be allowed to have Chester's Hot Fries. There is barely anything I would not do to secure a future for Chester's Hot Fries and a homeland for Chester's Hot Fries in my food pantry.

Paul Town's School For E-Girls
Eventually, I'm going to set up a course of sorts for women on how to take advantage of men on the internet. I'm going to teach them how to lead men on, manipulate them, extract money, and emotionally abuse men in a safe and effective manner that doesn't lead to them needing to do stupid stuff like have sex or sell lewds and nudes or even spend any time. Pathetic simp men have lots of money that is just waiting to be extracted from them. I intend to place myself between e-girls and their beta bucks and enrich myself in the process. I will be the guru mastermind behind the next wave of business saavy sociopathic parasitic women on the internet.

The Security Guard
He started out by doing security at a race track. This was a very short stint of his security guard career, but it was very instructive as to how easy reality really is. Because he was white, he was made the supervisor of ten to fifteen individuals who were each guarding horse stalls. He had the overnight shift, which lasted twelve hours, and he was assigned to drive across the large race track grounds every twenty to thirty minutes and check up on various other lowly security guards and make sure they were doing there work instead of sleeping or being somewhere else.

All this was well and good, for the first day or two. Then, the security guard supervisor realized that nobody was really keeping track of what he was doing, so he would spend a lot of his twelve hour shifts either sleeping in some corner or sleeping. This worked very well because he was a trustworthy looking enough individual and also the late night shift meant cover of darkness and nobody around. Also, he didn't really feel like driving around at some race track in the middle of the night.

When the short security at the race track (it was for a special series of races with high valued horses from all across the country) ended, the security guard decided that he enjoyed getting paid without doing any real work. He also liked working at night because he didn't really like anybody in the day, even though he would later learn that working at night slowly drives you insane, which is why nobody really does it long term if they are a successful individual.

Because he wanted to find other, more stable, security work, our lazy and bored apathetic hero got certified as an official security guard with a license from the east coast state in which he resided, and from the training he received he learned a lot of important facts about security work. Firstly, unless a security guard has a gun and is guarding something like money or some form of wealth transfer, chances are that the security guard does not have any ability to stop anybody from doing anything and is told not to stop anybody. What this means is that when security guards see somebody stealing or otherwise breaking the law on their premises, most are not supposed to touch the individual who is committing a crime. At most, security guards are supposed to trick a criminal into thinking they have to come with them willingly until real police officers are on scene. What this means is that anybody who is committing a crime could just ignore a security guard and continue walking out of any store with whatever they want without any repercussions as long as their face and fingerprints aren't anywhere and the police aren't immediately around. Of course, this knowledge was kind of useless for a virtuous individual like our security guard, but it was extremely funny to realize how stupid reality really is, and how everybody is operating based on assumptions of authoritative competence that are almost entirely fictional.

After receiving his training, which consisted of sitting in a room watching videos and taking bubble tests for a week and nothing else, our security guard got his first (and only) long term stable job as a security guard. He was assigned to a paper printing factory in an affluent area of his state. Like he had requested, he got the night shift, but there were still some workers there. Of course, there weren't as many workers there at night, and they were all busy in either the warehouse cafeteria or the warehouse worker zones, while the security guard had a place at the front desk of the factory, which nobody went. The security guard was tasked with patrolling the perimeter every hour or so, as dictated by the job smartphone that was linked up to a system of qr code checkpoints on the phone and GPS to ensure the security guard was making his rounds instead of sleeping at his desk.

Make his rounds, the security guard did, but not much else was accomplished. After the first month or two, the boredom and complete lack of oversight was firmly established in this young man's mind, and so he began to test the boundaries of what he could get away with. Sometimes, he would skip making round five or six of the ten times on his ten hour shift. He was very rarely confronted about it, because the people running his branch of the security company were busy and most likely not very smart or observant of what was going on either. He found a room where nobody went, and would sleep in the room whenever he got bored.

This security guard was only a security guard for little over a year, but that was enough to turn him from a functional member of society into a deranged lunatic well on his way to snapping. Over his months, he saw how there is a whole subsection of forgotten individuals who work in really unhealthy conditions for long periods. He saw a schizophrenic individual have to be escorted out after making shooting threats. The man was homeless and had been sleeping outside in the winter - in a military sleeping bag - on the factory property but the security guard hadn't really cared even though he knew about it because he preferred to be on good terms with insane people rather than potentially end up getting murdered. This proved to be prescient, because during the cleaning of this newly fired individual's work locker, janitors found a small cache of assault rifle ammunition. If the fired schizophrenic had initiated a workplace shooting, he would have most likely let the security guard live while he mowed down the forklift drivers, which was fine by the security guard.

Towards the end of our security guard's security guard career, he became increasingly dissatisfied with his job, and life in general. He started bringing vodka mixed into coffee or beer in a water canteen, and would drink on the job. This was great fun, as he would get drunk to the point of stumbling around in hallways and having to pretend he wasn't drunk on his rounds about a third of the way through his job, then would spend the rest of his time at work sobering up until his shift was over and he would drive home for forty minutes in the early morning, usually sober. This was a fun little game since it brought risk of being discovered and fired into his daily routine, and our security guard loved games of personal risk.

Eventually, even the drinking and sleeping on the job became boring. Of course, he still did both, but our security guard was looking for real kicks. Because of this, he decided to start pissing into water fountains in hallways. This was a real thrill, because instead of being fired he might end up getting into legal trouble or be seen as some strange sex freak and ruin some innocent forklift driver's day. Nothing came of this behavior, except some small amount of adrenaline and excitement, but it was a nightly tradition until the end of the job.

At the very end of the security guard's day, he decided not to wear any uniform at all. This was mainly because he didn't feel like digging through his closet before going on his commute for work, but he also found it quite funny. Of course, he hadn't informed his job that he was quitting. That was going to be done over text after the work day was done. That way, there would be no hard feelings or meetings. Also, it was funny to quit on the spot. As luck would have it, this day he was quitting and not wearing his uniform was the day his supervisor, a black lesbian who also worked for the TSA, would show up at the job and check up on him.

Upon discovering that he wasn't wearing his uniform, the supervisor asked him why he wasn't wearing his uniform. His reply was that he forgot, but his reply didn't really matter because our security guard used his charm and boyish youth to become fast friends with this black lesbian. She quickly felt bad and he slipped in that he was quitting his job today, making up some excuses as to why it was important to quit, and she even apologized as she wrote up the workplace incident for even writing up the incident. Nothing ever came of the report, because the security guard quit at the end of that shift, but he did get to keep a copy of the report of the incident for his records, something he found quite amusing.

Now, our intrepid security guard is not a security guard anymore. What is he now? Nobody really seems to know, but he's doing quite alright. His life experiences while being a security guard, as well as while not being a security guard, taught him a lot of important life lessons. Nobody is really paying attention as long as you don't make it clear that you are taking advantage of them. There are no real punishments that don't involve the government or being murdered or rape, which means the bar for acceptable behavior in life is very *very* low. The people who get ahead in life while managing other people are the people who are fine with the people under them being in unbearable and inhuman working conditions, and life will always be this way. Don't pay for security or really any similar type of service unless you know the people involved are excellent at their job unless you want to waste your money and be taken advantage of.

I'm Not Me

This is not a coded message. This is not me saying that everything I do is an act, that you can't trust me, that I'm unstable and dangerous, that I've murdered somebody and trafficked drugs in real life. This is not what that essay is about. I'll probably write something like that in the future as a joke, because I'm not somebody like that and I could never harm an innocent individual just out of boredom, but this essay is not about that. What this essay is about is the fact that I'm not me.

I'm not me. I'm me, but me doesn't exist. What I mean is that my brain is constantly changing and morphing from one instance of now to the next. What this means is that there is no me. I am just a slightly modified version of what was immediately before me, which was a slightly modified version of a version before that, and so on and so forth. This sort of constant molting, for better or worse, will continue until I am dead and rot away and transfer into some other form of material energy.

I'm not me. You're not you. Nobody is anybody. Everybody just is. That's how reality works. Once you understand this, reality will become much clear. Of course, this doesn't really matter, because the you that understands what I mean will not be the one who started trying to understand what I meant, and once you understand you will understand that you can't even really understand. Oh well.

Twenty Twenty Vision

Well, it looks like we were wrong. The end of the world probably isn't going to happen in 2019. Nothing really changed this year, despite all the news and the tweets and blogposts and shootings and podcasts and youtube videos. Does this mean that nothing is going to happen? No, this means that things will just be even worse when they finally do happen.

That's right, 2020 is when the big happening is almost definitely going to happen. That is when XYZ Event is going to make everything that you fantasize about, both good and bad, happen. You need to stay tuned and stay vigilant, because the disaster that is definitely coming needs to be focused on. Keep your mind on the impending doom or else you might think about how to provide for yourself and put yourself in a good position in life.

Sure, nothing might have happened yet, but you don't want to abandon this fantasy. If you admitted that you were a bit off about how things would go, then you might have to admit that you fooled yourself into acting sub-optimally, which would mean that you're not perfect and you are capable of being deceived. That is something that is not possible, so you shouldn't even entertain the notion.

The sky is really about to fall this time, we mean it. You need to buy our supplements, books, and merch in order to support the movement. What are you actually helping by giving me your money? Well, nobody really knows, but I deserve your money for saying the things you won't say, because saying things has a lot of value.

We need to raise awareness about the fact that 2020 is actually the end of the world, not 2019. Tell people about me. Get other people to give me their time, attention, and money. Make me rich. Help me buy that new car I want to buy. I really want to buy a motorcycle and take a cross-country trip, and I can't do that without you purchasing a lot of my material, which is why I will be pushing the ideas that keep you in a state where you think there is some huge cataclysmic event happening soon. Trust me, there definitely is something coming that will make it so you don't have to face the consequences of wasting all your time fantasizing about some sort of collapse instead of building up real skills and talents. Just give me your money, pig.

The Industrial Revolution Never Happened

The industrial revolution never happened. It's not a real thing. Sure, there was the invention of fast travel and assembly lines, but those were simply a large increase in how things moved and were assembled. That was not some sort of revolution or anything like that, but rather technology continuing its increase in efficiency. The industrial revolution is a term that was invented and is pushed by individuals who are either selling something or unable to come up with the self discipline needed in order to function in a world that is increasingly efficient.

It is very true that things can be really bad now, with the easy access to social media and unhealthy foods and lifestyles (including over-indulgence in sex and drugs), but this is not an inherently bad thing. This is not some sort of curse. All that is happening is now, individuals are being tempted at a higher rate than before, which reveals who is capable of self reflection and self denial and who isn't.

Another aspect to the lie of the industrial revolution is that there is some way that things *should* or *should not* be. Of course, things just are. They follow the pattern of whatever system they are in (and the system they are in follows that pattern of whatever larger system the system itself resides in), and it is what it is. There are malicious actors and they have easier access to bigger pools of naive prey, but there have always been malicious actors.

What we are experiencing now is an evolutionary bottleneck where lots of people who survived solely based on geographical or familial happenstance are not surviving anymore. With the abundance of vice and the general excess of reality, people who are self disciplined and people who have other people looking out for them and aware of how reality actually functions are now able to thrive.

The "industrial revolution" is just a cop-out term by people who don't understand what technology is. Language and communication are upstream of flight and mass production of everything, yet people who bemoan our current reality don't advocate the complete removal of language and everything else, just the parts they find personally objectionable and can't properly deal with. Because they can't deal with it, they anthropomorphize and give it its own soul and character, when really it is just the natural order of things self organizing in an increasingly patterned and logical manner.

Reality is reality. This is not to say that everything about the industrial revolution is good, it's not good or bad. It just is. This is also not to say that we should just "go along with the flow" and engage in all the new vice and sin and self-destructive opportunities. No, now is the time to be purposefully realistic and figure out all the new opportunities we have to ruin our lives and then how to avoid even being around those opportunities. This is not done by crying that some people are dying of opioid overdoses or previously coddled cities are now hotbeds of crime due to increasingly lax immigration, but rather understanding how our new reality works in an objective manner and letting broken things break while moving out of the way of the breaking things and positioning ourselves in ways where we and the people we care about and should be looking after (close friends and offspring) are protected and even thrive.

Who cares about the industrial revolution? Outcasts, losers, freaks, paranoiacs, people who sent letter bombs to kill innocent people. That's who has made a natural and unstoppable process into some sort of emotional phrase that can be the scapegoat of personal failings. Instead of internal problems, it's external problems. It feels good, but caring about feeling good is for children and women. How you interact with your environment will determine your success or failure in life, not an imaginary "revolution" that happened before you or your parents were born.

It Is The Second

We have come to the last section of this book. Up until now, we have trafficked in nonsense and foolish games. There have been jokes and jests, but that is all coming to an end. For the rest of this book, it is time to get serious. No longer can we afford to dilly dally and to loiter about in search of our own self assured amusement. We have too much to do, too much to discuss, and the time remaining grows shorter by the second. We have entered the second phase of "The Plan."

Speaking of time, what does *It Is The Second* even mean? Is the title of this book as well of this essay refer to time as in seconds are to minutes or milliseconds? If that is the case, does that mean that it is not even real, as we have established that time isn't real? Is that what is being said; that it does not exist and is imaginary just like the second does not exist and is imaginary? This is an interesting question to ponder, but do we have a solid answer on what the truth of the matter is? We do yet not have a solid grip on the truth of the matter. I do, but you do not, and thus we as a whole do not.

What else could *It Is The Second* refer to? Perhaps it is simply stating that this is the second book in a series or rather sequence? Maybe this is a statement that is hinting that it only exists in the sense of a reference to something else which is the same thing but modified, and that the contrast between the two things is what determines the value of each thing? Again, we do not know if this is the case, because only I can know and you will never know. For example, if I were to tell you the truth you would not be able to know if I am lying or not. There is no real way to test what I'm saying here, at least not yet.

A third possibility as to what *It Is The Second* could mean is that there is most likely a third and even a fourth planned. If the second was the last then it would make more sense to call this essay and this book *It Is The Last* or *It Is The Final*, and I have not done that. I'm sure this will bring great joy to the hundreds of thousands of people who read this essay, since I'm also sure that everybody who reads what I write enjoys it and finds it peculiarly calming as well as edifying on an intellectual and emotional basis. Yet again, I must clarify that this possibility is just that and nothing more, to you, since you cannot really know what is going on in my mind to any degree of accuracy.

The last possibility that we will explore is that perhaps a bit of all of these possibilities are involved. Maybe I am referencing how time is imaginary and how it is also imaginary and how that means that we can use the imaginary to measure the real, which causes the non-real (imaginary) to essentially become real (non-imaginary) and proves that life is what you make of it. Maybe I am also stating that you have to draw constant comparisons and know things by their contrast to other things and use subjective difference to find objective reality. Maybe I am saying that everything is constantly ongoing and that we must realize that whatever now is is simply the result of the past and the ingredients to the future, and nothing more and nothing less. It's all really a matter of interpretation and personal judgment, incorrect or correct; even this sentence.

Then again, maybe I am saying nothing at all. Perhaps I just enjoy wasting time. Maybe I'm just some mentally ill kook who found a way to monetize his kookiness. That would be funny in its own right and could be analyzed and pontificated upon for ten or twenty books worth of writing, but I am kindhearted so I will leave that task up to the eventual biographers who will chop apart my life and rearrange it into whatever hilariously untrue message they are trying to get across.

Normal People

It's funny and a bit sad whenever I interact with most normal males individuals, especially the ones who want to sound like they're doing well in life. They will talk about getting female phone numbers or having sex like it's something that's impressive or hard. They talk about sneaking away from work to smoke or vape like they're some sort of criminal for essentially acting like a runaway slave who is happy that his master didn't have sex with the slave's wife that week.

It's so easy to get a female's number. It's so easy to have sex. All you have to do is be slightly above average and established in literally any field or hobby and you will have women throwing themselves at you. People who are attractive don't go to bars and clubs and on tinder and ask people for their phone numbers, that is what people who are failures who want to be or think they are winners do.

Wow, you like the breasts and a the rear end of a woman? Wow, you would have sex with this woman who wouldn't ever talk to you? You find models attractive? You would totally have a shot with a movie star? That's so cool, please tell me more. Please describe to me how you got the idiot freshman girl's phone number without even trying, that's so impressive. Tell me about how you have sex more than once a week sometimes with more than one female, that's really amazing and sounds like a great use of your young years. I wish I could bed worthless drugged out alcoholic morons, but I'm just not cool enough I guess.

You don't do any work at your job? You get comped and they pay for your hotel stays? That's so amazing, you're a real superstar. You remind me of Leonardo DiCaprio in The Wolf Of Wall Street with your ability to make money in an office setting. I wish I was as cool as you and had a job where they even had open bar nights. It sounds like so much fun drinking alcohol with your co-workers and potential clients. You sound like a real alpha male working for some big company, plus the health benefits and vacation time sound really exciting. I'm really happy for you, enjoy the next three decades in your office setting.

I don't know what it is about normal people that makes them settle for such a stupid life. They are satisfied with being given just enough free time to spend the money they "earn" but not enough time to do anything productive or build towards their own future that is sustainable and truly fulfilling. It's hard not to look down on and really despise this sort of person, because it seems so obvious that what they are pursuing is a complete waste of time and energy and will result in an increasingly frustrating and hollow, meaningless existence. Then again, it must not be that obvious or else the vast majority of individuals wouldn't fall for it, or maybe it is that obvious and most people are natural slaves.

Imagine being put into the world only to willingly sign up to be the bitch for some boss for thirty to forty years, knowing that when you finally don't go into work on every weekday and can say and do what you feel like doing without fear of being fired and not having a job, you'll be too old to enjoy any of it. It's unbelievable to me, but that is how reality seems to work for ninety to ninety-five percent of humanity. I guess that is why there is so much constant advertisement and bright colors and loud noises, because if somebody just unplugs from the feedback loop of constant stimulation for even a few weeks, they'll quickly realize what a bad deal they are getting and do something else with their time.

Selling Merchandise

I just finished selling a limited run of thirteen hoodies for forty dollars a piece plus tax. With everything said and done, I made five dollars on each sale, for a total of sixty five dollars in profit. This was all done in five hours, which was a bit faster than I had anticipated, but still isn't all that much money in the grand schemes of things. At least, it's not a lot of money at the moment.

I will sell this same hoodie again in a few weeks or a month depending on how fast my money arrives in my bank account. I will sell double the amount of hoodies, but they will each cost fifty dollars instead of forty dollars. This will mean I get about fifteen dollars of profit per sale, which will be three hundred and ninety dollars of profit. Then I will wait a few more weeks or even a few more months, which I will then sell the final run of this hoodie, which will be fifty-two additional hoodies at sixty dollars each, which will mean twenty-five dollars of profit which will total one thousand three hundred dollars of total profit for that run. This will be a grand total of $1755 of profit, which is still all not that much money.

The money is not really what the point of this whole process is, which is to generate a sort of demand and expectation that will result in a public perception of popularity and desire, which will create a sort of feedback loop which will then spill over into everything else I do as well as provide social proof which will be its own feedback loop which interacts positively with other positive feedback loops. That small amount of money will be put into other projects, but the social cache of having done "successful" physical product launches will be much more valuable.

What is so crazy about all of this is that the higher I price something that gets put together in some factory, the more valuable it is seen as. The more money I make doing nothing, the more valuable I am seen as. Publicity and sales and marketing are inverted. If I were to try to maximize sales, that would be a signal that what I was trying to sell was not valuable, but because I am purposely making things overly expensive and limited, the opposite effect occurs. Supply and demand is not a proper model for any sort of successful social media campaign, since the supply of everything at this point is pretty much unlimited unless purposely made otherwise.

There is another aspect to this which I am slightly uneasy about, which is similar to how I make money on my book. I do the initial work and make continuous profit without any continued effort. I am not contributing anything new, and yet I am being rewarded. This is not something I will stop doing, because I don't feel morally guilty about it and it is superior to the alternative of working for somebody else who would be doing the same thing I'm doing now and just giving me a small cut, but it is very strange and disorienting to experience. This is most likely why it is so important to stay busy, so I don't spend time thinking about how people who actually work hard and ruin their body don't ever get rewarded while the people who take advantage of the people working hard come out ahead and there is really no justice and there never will be any justice.

My Real Problem

Lots of different people have come up with lots of different reasons for what is wrong with me. They see the way I behave and speak and think and declare me some abnormal individual who is a sociopath or some sort of deranged sadistic freak. The truth is that I am neither of those things. In fact, the reality of the situation is that my problem is that I simply have too much empathy.

I am what some people would call an "empath." What this means is that I am exceptionally sensitive to emotions and moods of those around me. This is why I am such an excellent communicator and able to speak from many varied points of view, because my empath abilities cause me to experience the realities of others around me in addition to my own.

It hurts when I allow myself to care for other people. I am flooded with sadness and grief and guilt for my advantages and the disadvantages of those around me whenever I take a second to look around and really acknowledge what a naturally charmed life I lead. I am healthy, intelligent, charming, humble, and handsome, and many people do not have any of those things. I am the perfect package.

Because of this reality that I find myself in, I always tend towards the extremes of either empathy or a complete lack of empathy, whatever seems proper in the circumstances that I find myself in. That said, sometimes I have to completely shut down my ability to care about others in order to just get a moment of rest and peace. Sometimes, I listen to sad music and burst into tears because I have such an overflowing of empathy.

I think most people who claim to have empathy don't really have any. From my observations, I would say there are maybe one or two percent of people in any population who really have any ability to empathize on a real level. All the rest use surface level aphorisms and external as well as internal deception in order to maintain the illusion of empathy. That is the only explanation that I can see for where reality is. That is the only genuine way we could have so many people willingly engaged in systems that supposedly violate deeply held convictions.

It's lonely being the only person I know with real empathy. Sometimes I'll be talking to other people and get a glimpse of real empathy, but it's always just an act on their part. Most people are self destructive and don't even know what they're doing or how they're interacting with other people. It's like I live in a world where everybody but me is just playing a part, completely unable to have real thoughts or see things from anybody else's perspective.

My real problem is not my lack of humanity, but the lack of humanity of everybody around me. These people who do evil and have justifications for it are morally superior to me because I do not have any moral justifications for my wrong actions, and I know it. I simply do what I do because to actually act how I know would be morally right would mean to become an invalid and refuse aid from those participating in all the truly evil systems of murder and exploitation that are needed for a functioning society, but I don't do that. I just blend in when it suits me and don't blend in when it doesn't, because I do have a sense of right and wrong that is more vivid and compulsive than anybody else's. My real problem is the world around me.

Ghostemane

There is a rapper/metal musician who calls himself Ghostemane that I enjoy listening to. As far as I am aware, he is around my age and comes from Florida and has lately been transitioning from white trap psychosis rap to a more noise and metal sort of genre, collaborating with other interesting and talented artists. He has a great work ethic and puts out a ton of material on a regular basis, and his musical range is impressive. With that said, he is falling apart and seems to be self destructing as time goes on.

What is happening with Ghostemane is that he has so much money and success and an established audience that he can really do whatever he want and make money. This means there are no real social penalties for unhealthy self destructive behaviors like drug abuse or negative mental feedback loops. What this has caused is a sort of spiraling out of control on his part. Of course, he is not to blame for his problems. He is young and most likely didn't have any mentors or anybody who gave him proper direction in his ascension, so now he is in a weird position where everything good or bad that he does is magnified thousands of times over.

I don't know enough to predict whether Ghostemane will pull out of his increasing mental anguish or whether he will die of some drug overdose. If he does somehow find his balance without dying, he will be much better off than a lot of people who never have any sort of emotional problems or real life issues, because he will have experience and knowledge of what it's like to be going insane and be making illogical decisions in a seemingly logical manner. This will put him ahead of the pack and almost leapfrog him ahead of all his more cautious and currently more comfortable contemporaries. He will be like somebody who has served in a war and experienced actual horrors and survived rather than somebody who completely avoided putting themselves in danger.

With that said, there is a good chance that Ghostemane will just end up dying or going completely off the deep end. He seems to be trending in that direction with every passing month. If that happens, that will be unfortunate for him, but it will also serve a purpose in showing people who are aware of his story what to pursue and what to avoid. He will also die in his prime, musically speaking, and will thus save himself the embarrassment of sticking around and trying to perform for too long, which seems an all too common occurrence for the more level headed and otherwise reasonable performers who never have anything bad happen to them.

The funny part about all of this is that even though I wish him the best, Ghostemane's music is the best when he is in clear mental anguish and being self destructive. Getting to experience his hell without really experiencing his hell is its own form of enjoyment. I get to sit back in my clear mental state without any stress or emotional pain and just listen to somebody who is strung out on speed and most likely heroin scream and moan. Maybe I'm just a bad person, but for this reason I am kind of happy that Ghostemane is going through such a rough time in life. I wish him the best and won't begrudge him getting better and fixing his life, but I also wouldn't mind if he wanders around this sort of painful path for at least a few more years.

Melancholic Failures

There is a specific archetype I see very commonly, where failure and depression is constantly romanticized and idolized by them. The reason for this is that they are losers who will never amount to anything, or rather they are losers who will never amount to anything and this is the reason why. These are the people who constantly talk wistfully like anybody wants to hear that they are depressed they missed out on childhood love or that they didn't have a nice college experience and were shocked by the fact that working a job is depressing and dehumanizing and they were not actually special individuals who were going to be handed everything in life like they wished they were and they still imagine they deserve.

To be a man is not to say that everything is perfect and to pretend that success is inevitable and that life is good. To be a man is also not to say that everything is broken and then talk about how everything is broken and do nothing else but talk. Not everything is good but not everything is bad. Some things are good and some things are bad. Once you're over the age of maybe eighteen or nineteen, if you're a male, you should be purposefully identifying what is good in life and being thankful for that as well as identifying what is a problem and coming up with workarounds or ways to avoid or fix those problems on a personal and potentially personal group level.

These idiots and morons around me are the weak runt of the litter of humanity who think that because they know basic logic and are able to realize that some things in life aren't an amusement park, they deserve to be rewarded and praised. They treat basic observations like the sad state of proles as some sort of profound truth that means they shouldn't try anything in life. They seek out constant approval and emotional support for their complete inaction and failure in life. Whenever they see somebody who is attempting or doing anything, they will wait for the slightest slip up or mistake in order to use that partial flaw as proof that nothing should ever be attempted.

Damn all of these people to hell. They have made earth a hell already and try to drag everybody down with them. Let them have their alcoholism and cultish apocalypse mentalities. Let them wallow in self pity because they haven't done anything in life that earns them the respect or appreciation of people who actually have value. Let them whine about the fact that them being uninteresting losers means that they won't get some virgin wife. They roll around in their own filth and think they have become wise.

Life is not hard. Life is not suffering. There are hard elements and suffering along life, but unless you have some disease or serious abnormality, the majority of pain you experience will be because of your idiocy. You can take that pain and you can learn from it and make it into something of value, or you can do what these subhuman individuals do which is nothing. You can slowly decompose while you're living, before you've even tried and failed at anything. You can turn your lack of success into some delusional self-referential poetry that is interesting to nobody else. Or, you can be somebody who doesn't spend their time consuming trash and filling their head with excuses as to why their vices are not as bad as the vices they don't partake in and realize that you are scum and you will always be scum unless you make an effort to not be scum.

These melancholic failures are the people who will have white collar careers. They will whine for their whole life, from high school to college to work to retirement and to death and whatever comes after that. They get uglier and uglier, increasingly desperate to prove that they aren't cowards and that their life is actually a beautiful tragedy rather than a mindless comedy about a fool. These are the people who will whine on social media and whine at home and whine at their job and look down on the people who are willing to take risks and make things and fail and look foolish for a short time in the pursuit of excellence and life.

How To Do Things On A Daily Basis

Many people have no structure to their life at all. They do things when they have to do things. They get up when it's time to get ready for work or school and they go to bed whenever they get tired of browsing the internet or playing video games. Then, there are some people who have structure to their life. They have set amounts of time they spend on various activities on a daily or weekly basis. This is good, in theory, but it turns out that the vast majority of the tiny minority of people with structure have their structure structured in an unstructured manner, which is arguably worse than being unstructured in an unstructured manner, because it gives the illusion of structure rather than the internal honesty of self-apparent ignorance.

A proper life, like everything else, is fractal in nature. What this means is that you can see each day as its own lifetime. In the morning we are born, the afternoon we are in our prime, and late in the evening: we die. This can be further extrapolated, and we will do that in this essay. Essentially, each day should resemble a proper workout, in that you start with something easy, then increase the stress of your workout until its peak and then you rest (literally in the case of a daily schedule.)

What does this daily philosophy look like in practice? In the morning and early afternoon, you should do things that are enjoyable. You should eat, drink, and be merry. Read some of a book and chat with friends. Then, when it is three or four in the afternoon, or fifteen-sixteen hours in military time, your work should begin in earnest. For me, this is when I start my writing and programming for the day. You do whatever work you have with increasing intensity until you are finished, taking very minimal breaks if any breaks at all. You should finish anywhere from ten at night to three in the morning of the following day. Then, you address your friends on the internet and tell them you are going to sleep, and you sleep. Then you do the same thing the next day.

There are no weekends with this schedule. Weekends are built in for slaves who sit in offices and work in the morning and early afternoon and need some time to recover from their abuse. This schedule has no abuse and is structured like any stuttered resistance training, where you are are finishing your daily recovery from your daily activities just as you start in earnest in the late afternoon of the following day. You don't feel dead and trapped with this sort of schedule, and you don't slip into the unhealthy breaks that weekends afford. You are always active every day and get much more accomplished than people who work a five day work week.

Remember, you need to have everything in moderation; even moderation. You need a short period towards the end of every day where you are hard at work and completely absorbed in your task. This keeps your mind (and your body since you are doing daily exercise in the same manner) sharp and active, which allows you to always be on top of your game and make better decisions. This healthy predictable variance within a set pattern allows for personal freedom and forms discipline, which ripples out into all other areas of life.

Over time, your daily schedule will become easy for you and you'll crave the initial challenge that you felt when you first started. This is very similar to what any avid gym member will tell you is their experience. You'll increase the amount of things you accomplish on a daily basis and you'll keep on getting better and better at everything, accomplishing things you never thought possible when you were trapped in the normal way of doing things. You'll get rich, women will love you, and you'll finally feel happy. You'll have kids and those kids will have grandkids. Life will be perfect for you once you start following this system. You will never die.

Reputation Management Theory

Look around you at all the unhappy people who get made fun of and mocked publicly: Some are young, some are old, some are straight or gay, some are male, some are female, some are high IQ, some are low IQ. What do they all have in common? The answer to that question is that they try to talk themselves up. They try to be respected. They try to convince people that they are good or quality individuals, so whenever anything comes out that is contrary to that reputation, the discrepancy becomes very noticeable to onlookers who then adjust their opinion of the individual in question in a negative direction. Then, the individual in question usually reacts in a manner which increases the downward momentum of their perception. This causes a sort of feedback loop that gradually drives the value of the public individual into the ground over time, especially if they make repeated mistakes.

Now, look around at the successful individuals: They have oftentimes done much worse things than the people who are mocked and looked down on. Why is this the case? People who do bad things and make public mistakes but are still successful are a different breed than the first example. They know how to interact with the public. Most importantly, they know to put themselves in the worst possible light possible (within reason) whenever they represent themselves, and to go out of their way to make sure people think lowly about them. That way, when bad things come out, it doesn't matter. In fact, a lot of the times the bad things can even boost the reputation of the individual and speak to a supposed authenticity.

Another aspect to how you portray yourself is that it selects the type of individual who gives you the time of day. If you spend your time acting pious and trying to show that you are a good individual, you will attract a lot of dishonest and very slimy individuals who are also playing a sort of deceptive game where they feel the need to project some form of holiness or virtue to strangers. As a result, you will cultivate a very fragile and sensitive audience of the worst sort of individual. If you show yourself to be a flawed and not all that great person, the people who will look up to you will be people who appreciate honesty as well as individuals who go out of their way to give you the benefit of the doubt. These are genuinely good, albeit naive, people who are a benefit to have listening to you, and they will not gossip or turn on you like pious freaks and manipulative deviants will.

As long as you stay away from being painted as something objectively disgusting, like a pedophile or zoophile or child molester, you will not be harmed by playing up your negative attributes. This is not to say to justify or treat them like they aren't negatives, that is just another way to attract the fake moral crowd and set yourself up to ridicule, but rather to be unapologetic and open about your problems. This sort of honesty will end up benefiting you long term, because people who have similar issues will be attracted to you, you won't have to hide or pretend you don't have problems that you do, and anything you stop doing that was bad will be inspirational and also cause a positive reaction to anybody who finds out how you are now as compared to how you were in the past.

As said in previous essays, the vast majority of humans are reactive rather than proactive. If you hide problems and flaws and people figure them out, then those problems and flaws will seem more noteworthy than they really are and you will suffer for them being discovered. If you play up all the bad things about you without trying to justify them, then people will see you as somebody without insecurities and view your problems as not really problems and ignore them and the "insults" people will try will be to state that you are actually a better person than you say you are, which is no insult at all.

Suicide Threat

I thought you'd like to know that I'm really going to do it this time. I'm really going to kill myself soon. Just watch, this is the time I really end up killing myself. I know you don't believe that I will do it, but I really will do it. I will kill myself and you will be the one to blame.

Once I am dead and gone, everybody will see that I was valuable. Once I am dead then my absence will be felt. Then people like you will wish you were nicer to me. Than I will be vindicated. Of course, I'll be dead and you'll be alive so it won't matter, but that doesn't matter.

I might have faked being suicidal in the past for emotional manipulation reason, but I'm serious this time. I'm really super serious this time. I have sleeping pills and a knife. I'm just working up to actually doing it, because I'm so serious about it.

I'm really serious about killing myself this time, and you are still ignoring me? This speaks to your inhumanity. If I were dead, would you even care? I doubt it. I think you would just go on your way and do whatever it is you do each day and be happy that I'm gone. You are such an evil person.

OK, so I really tried to kill myself, but it didn't work. I tried so hard, but it's just too hard for me to die. I guess I was meant for more. Where were you? Why didn't you stop me from almost dying? Why do you act like you knew I wouldn't die? Why do you call me an "attention whore"? Why do you treat me so poorly? I'm going to fail at killing myself again.

Things That Don't Exist

There is a funny sort of trick that you can play on other people as well as yourself, but this trick can also be quite dangerous. It's not complicated or really anything special, but it is very real and definitely is a thing that can be utilized by anybody who really understands what it is and how it works? What is it? It's nothing, but at the same time it's something. You can make things that aren't real real by simply tricking somebody (yourself or somebody else) into feeling the need to prove that those things aren't real.

This is the trick of dialectic and debates. This is also the trick of mass fictions that might or might not have happened. By making something up, you can either go unchallenged (the thing is accepted), refuted (the thing is denied), or ignored. As long as you are not ignored, then the thing that you have said exists now exists, if only partially, by a conception and rejection. After all, if something is not real, it cannot be denied. The denial, no matter how factually correct, leads to some degree of positive affirmation.

Once there is a modicum of incongruence between claims and reality, there is a sort of energy created. Most people don't know what they're doing when they say things or think things, so they haphazardly create this energy or rather amplify it in negative and harmful directions, but in the care of somebody who is thinking of terms of momentum and triangles, this very real effect is a very useful and very noticeable phenomenon.

If I say "the chair is red" in a public setting when there is no chair and somebody mentions how there is no chair but I insist on a chair, a whole chain reaction of people who try to figure out what I mean and people in the future who will actually think the chair was there will be created. This will create ripple effects in tons of different ways, and once you have let the cat out of the bag by repeated obvious tricks like this, then you create even more ripple effects, so it is important to be mindful of what you are doing when you are stating blatant untruths as truths.

You can shape reality in this as well as many other ways. It is a form of manipulation, like everything else is (even honesty is manipulation), and most people who are involved in it are doing it from a position of weakness and laziness, always trying to cover up some misdeed or exaggerate their worth due to some insecurity, but if you behave in this manner from a position of strength you will quickly see how well it can benefit you. Like anything, this is simply a tool that can be used or misused, even though the most visible users of it tend to misuse it and end up harming themselves in the process.

Sisyphus

There is a myth of Sisyphus. I don't really remember the details of the myth but the gist of it is that Sisyphus a man who is eventually cursed by some gods to roll a rock up a hill and once the rock gets to the top of the hill it always falls down again and the whole process starts over. This is supposed to demonstrate the absurdity and futility of life, and I can definitely see that point of view, but the real takeaway for me was the fact that Sisyphus should have just refused to roll the rock and sat down instead of rolling the rock or walked away.

Sometimes in life you are placed in a situation where there is no way to go on and benefit. The people who want you to go on will talk of your duty and how you have to do this or that or you'll be a failure, but the reality is that if they need to rely on somebody who doesn't benefit by their actions and also have to goad them on, then the people talking to you don't really know what they're doing. Since these people are stupid and have placed themselves in a position where they have to rely on you essentially being a slave, there could even be argued that there is a moral obligation to neglect whatever it is that you have told is your duty in order to teach these people a lesson and make them better individuals who are more in line with how reality actually works.

The myth of Sisyphus can be applied to most of modern life. Most people will spend every month and every year doing some task that doesn't objectively benefit them, knowing full well that they will keep on doing this task without a final resolution until some natural disaster, they retire, or they die. These people have bought into the myth of selfless duty and self-destructive sacrifice. They feel the need to impress other people who feel the need to impress other people who feel the need to impress other people who don't deserve to be impressed. They never stop and realize that they can just stop.

You can just quit. You can just refuse to contribute to social contracts you never signed up for. People will whine and complain and talk down to you for a little while, then when they realize you won't be guilt tripped they'll get right back to their slavery all while feeling morally superior. They'll slowly wear themselves down and degrade themselves for their superiors and you will not. Of course, this is not an excuse to behave in an equally self destructive behavior of laziness and stupidity in the opposite direction. Don't waste the energy and free time you have gained, but rather funnel your energy into personal health and discipline and creative and business projects. Very quickly you'll find that you advance in life in ways that the people who scorned you covet, without even trying to. You'll also see that it's not really worth all that much and you won't be tied down to the same fate that all the losers around you are.

The social contract, just like the myth of Sisyphus, is a myth. It's not reality. There are certain realities to life that make sense in the context of a social contract, such as the fact that it's proper to treat friends, family, and your local (physical and now digital) communities with respect, but the reasons for doing so are for self interest, not because of any duty. You are not your family, you are not your friends, you are not your community. You are interacting with them, so generally you should treat them well and help them when it's feasible, but you should not feel like you have been tasked with some higher calling (unless you have been) to be the slave to reality.

Stop pushing the rock up the hill and watch when nothing objectively bad happens to you. Stop carrying water for other people unless there is some real benefit to you. Stop being a pushover in order to win the praise and worthless admiration of other pushovers. Stop treating the myth of Sisyphus like a reality rather than a myth. Work with people, not for people.

My Existential Pain

There are quite a number of things about reality that are constantly painful and saddening to me, but by far the most is my existential pain regarding the fact that very few people will ever actually understand what I write or what the point to everything I have done has been. With every essay I start and finish, I mentally note that maybe ten out of every hundred people who read what I have written will really look beyond the immediate surface for some coherence and that maybe one tenth of those people will actually ascertain the genuine point behind my communication.

This is the way things have to be. because if I were to make everything clear and obvious then the mental thought processes to actually understand them would be too boring and unenjoyable for the people I want to read them to read them, and only a few stuffy academic losers with no influence on the world around them would ever even see what I have created. Still, it is a very unsettling feeling and hints of the futility of long term communication and the entropy of information transfer that such a startlingly low amount of successful transfers of knowledge will occur even though hundreds of thousands of individuals in my lifetime will eventually pour over my words.

Life is a bit of a joke, to be quite honest, because the only people who get a reputation for being wise or clever are usually never wise nor clever, which is why they seek out recognition and reputation in the first place. I am well known and increasingly successful in various endeavors, but not for my admirable traits and talents and rather my more disgusting attributes that have enabled me to cut through a lot of obstacles that hamper other individuals. This is by my design, as I do not like people who try to come off as serious and intelligent to strangers, but it is still amusing to watch how poorly the general public is able to determine who has value and what their value is.

I am in constant pain, knowing that I know how reality works and will spend the rest of my life will be easy while most people suffer and labor under delusions that leave them unhappy and decrepit in old age. There is a sort of survivor's guilt when people look up to me or talk well about me because I know I am no better than the normal individual. If anything, I am a worse than average individual with worse than average inclinations, which is what has allowed me to outperform most if not all of my contemporaries to a consistently increasing degree. My profane acts have given me dominion over humanity as a whole, and I am constantly rewarded and praised for my worst habits.

How do people go about their life in such a fashion as what I see all around me? This is what haunts my my mind the most. How are normal people content to consume trash and waste away for decades? It makes no sense. It seems like the majority of normal people are in some trance and thus the only people who have autonomy are people like me; bad people. This is most likely the way reality has always worked, but it is especially strange to watch now that we have essentially psychic connections to all first and second world individuals via the internet and can read the minutia of the average mind.

There is no escape from where we find ourselves, and there will never be any escape from where we find ourselves, so it is best to treat the masses like one would treat a pet in the display exhibits in a zoo: You can't trust them, can't really connect with them on any equal level, can't rely on them, they aren't very useful, they aren't very smart, they have no real freedom, and they are kind of sad to observe. It's best to just let them do whatever it is they do, in peace, while making peace with the reality of just how stupid everything really is.

The Passage Of Time

It has been about three months since I started writing my second book. When I had started my first book, I had thought that I would most likely finish the first book this time next year, which is amusing to think about now that I know I will most likely have two or three more books finished in addition to this book by this time next year. It is also quite interesting to think about how much time I have wasted and how many more creative projects I could have created by now in various creative fields if I had had some form of exterior guidance. All in all, it is probably for the best that I had a lack of direction or mentorship, because if it wasn't for the best then some system would surely be set in place by people who are wiser and more accomplished than me, and there is no proper system like that.

Time is not real, but it is a good measurement, and life is very short by its measurement. I am at least one fourth (most likely more one half) finished with my life and I have barely started to do anything particularly interesting. Still, I am struck by how easily and quickly things may be done as long as they are done consistently. All it takes to get things done is to stop doing things that are stopping things from being done, which seems like a riddle or joke but is really not.

What is there to do with the passage of time? It cannot be successfully fought or beaten or reversed, no matter what doctors or scientists hungry for fame might hint at and indicate. It cannot be delayed or bargained with. Things are in a constant state of flux and the only way to deal with that without being destroyed is to learn to move with the passage of time. Once you start noticing cyclical patterns and start treating everything like a dance, you can start to move in time and with time. You'll start to see the beauty to the ephemerality of everything, but also the sadness inherent in death that accompanies everything and everyone by virtue of their interaction with the passage of time.

We are here for such a short time, and in that time we get constantly bombarded with people trying to take advantage of us or manipulate us. The people doing the predatory behaviors are almost all in the same situation as we are, although most of them think themselves above the rest of humanity while not forgetting to pay their phone bill and rent. There is so much noise drowning out the beauty and life all around us, and there is no guarantee that there is any positive resolution to any of this on a personal time-frame.

Human beings seem to suffer from the delusion that justice and cause and effect begins and ends when a human is born and when a human dies. What I mean by this is that they think that bad things happen to bad people, and that bad people get punished for bad behavior. Anything else seems unjust and immoral, and for most people it's impossible to function in a system they see as immoral. The flaw in this reasoning is that human beings are not our own systems. We are little cogs in a much bigger organism, which is bigger than humanity as a whole or even this planet. Just like a cancer that is destroying a human body can have great success while alive, a human being can have great success and joy over its lifespan while destroying its local community and doing horrible things. There is a cause and effect relationship to everything in the universe (and whatever else exists), but that cause and effect is not on the time-frame of one - or even a hundred - generations of human life.

Time will continue to pass and people who are winning will continue to win and the people who are losing will continue to lose. Then this generation will slowly lose its influence as the generation after us gains power and the whole process will start again. With each generation or every few generations there will be some general feeling that "things are about to change", but besides large advancements in technology which modify reward structures and thus behavior (automated delivery is most likely the most impactful next step in society), nothing ever really changes. Time goes on. You and I live, you and I die, but time goes on.

The Question Everybody Is Asking

Everybody is asking this question. They want to know the answer to the question, which is why they are asking it in the first place. If they didn't want to know the answer to the question, then they wouldn't be asking it. That wouldn't make any sense. Who would ask a question that they didn't care about knowing the answer to? Only people who are morons, and nobody who is asking this question is a moron. The people asking this question are smart; they're sophisticated. That's why they're asking the question in the first place.

The question, of course, is just how many of my "mistakes" or "mishaps" are really mistakes or mishaps. There has been a growing doubt as to whether or not I have ever done things in a truly spontaneous manner. I understand why people might suspect that I am a meticulous planner and genius mastermind. Who else could do what I have done? Who else would be able to not only survive but also thrive and turn nothing into something and something into more than most people will ever see in their life besides a bona-fide once in millennium savant?

I've seen conspiracy theories and charts that track my movements and statements across time. There are entire websites dedicated to me. Some have a theory that I am actually a team of individuals from the upper echelons of some government's intelligence agency. That is all understandable as well, because I have demonstrated an ungodly amount of range and versatility that should be impossible for some singular individual.

Did I make up being mentally ill? Did I do certain things with full awareness of what I was doing? Am I being advised by multiple high profile individuals? Am I really a millionaire? Was I really publicly involved in cryptocurrency as far back as 2013? Did I really make $80,000 bets when I was in high school? Am I still really a virgin? Did I actually go to jail? Do I actually have a criminal record? Am I multiple people? All these questions have taken the internet by storm, and that's understandable.

What is the truth to all of these rumors? Well, if I told you then you wouldn't believe me. I could lay out all the proof for everything that is true and false and it would be unbelievable. It would boggle the imagination. It would stymie the mind. It would make anybody normal go insane with cognitive dissonance and disbelief.

To be honest, the truth of the matter has driven me bonkers once or twice in the past few years. I cannot believe the position I have placed myself in. I cannot believe all that I have achieved. Even more, my constant humility amazes me. I don't think I have an ego, to tell the truth, or else I would be an egomaniac, and I am no egomaniac.

The answer to the question everybody is asking is out there, just like all the other answers to all the other questions. Whether you find out the truth or not is up to you. Here's a little hint: most if not everything I say I have done I have really done or kind of done. Some of the rumors about me are true and some of the rumors about me are false. There is truth out there, but there is also untruth.

Pure Insanity

Aaaaaaaaaaaaa, I'm going crazy! I'm losing my mind! I'm insane! I'm completely out of control! I'm saying things that don't make sense! I'm acting in ways that don't make sense! I'm scaring friends and relatives! Now I'm committing crimes! I'm never hurting anybody but I'm doing lots of crimes! Oh noooooooooo! Now I'm in jail!

OK, I'm normal now. I don't know what happened, but somehow now I'm more than normal. Now that I don't have to work or do anything and I have a captive audience, I'm the most sane person you will ever meet. Now I'm cool and collected. Now, I'm the most mentally and physically healthy person in all rooms.

It's funny how life works, isn't it? It's really funny now that I know who I can rely on and who I can't. What's funniest is being more productive and successful than people around me who think they're winning in life and I am in some bad spot in life. I've never felt as good as I do now and every day just keeps getting better and better.

Will I regress? Will my life end in ruins? Will I end up a failure? I think it's quite clear that it will not. I think with every passing day it becomes more obvious to the most dull onlooker that I'm going to end up on top and that I'm pretty much already on top.

There is nobody I know like me. I don't know if there ever was or if there ever will be anybody like me once I'm gone. I guess that's why I'm so humble, because I know that I'm special and everybody is beneath me, which leads me to look down on everybody and thus not get invested in the constant failures and mediocrity that most people get invested in.

Little Deaths

Every night, when you go to sleep, you die. When *you* wake up the next day, it isn't *you*, it is a new version of you. Every day is one lifetime. While you sleep, your brain is changing. You are changing. The way you process and remember things and make predictions is changing. You become something a little bit different than what you were before you closed your eyes.

You are your own parent you are your own child. This is very profound when you start to think about what it means. Will you be the parent that squanders what you have been given by your parent and leaves your child with less than what you were given, or will you be an improvement from the you that gave birth to you? Every day, a new version of you gets to decide a little bit for tomorrow's you.

Some days I'm a good parent, some days I'm a great parent, and some days I'm a bad parent. The thing is that over time I have gotten better and better at not wasting what has been given me, and most days I wake up at least a little better than I was the day before. It's all a matter of little deaths.

This is why sleep is so important to be done in the proper manner. Too much and you essentially are punishing yourself and making forward progress almost impossible as well as stunting how well you learn how to solve problems and process information, but too little and you are essentially not giving your daily you enough time to store up energy for its 24 hour life.

You can attempt to break this down further, into hours and minutes, but I feel like that is too short a time period. A day is a full cycle of sleep and being awake while hours and minutes are not and are just little snapshots in a daily life. With that said, you can essentially map hours to decades in what people assume life is (100 years at most) and find a good daily rhythm that benefits you and all future iterations of you.

Little Wedges
There is a way to easily succeed in social media. It is something that I have been testing for the last year and had great success with. All you need to do is just steal all the popular content and repost it and then share the reposted content with your friends on your normal account. Over time, the account that you have that reposts popular content will have thousands of followers, then you continue

to repost what other people make while also slipping in references to your creations.

I will be adding small watermarks to all memes I steal soon. These watermarks will then redirect to my stolen meme page which means that if anybody steals those stolen memes then they will be advertising my meme page and then I will essentially have hijacked all the accounts that steal my stolen material. I wouldn't be surprised if I don't have hundreds of thousands of followers on my account soon.

This strategy works in real life as well as online, as online is just a synthetic version of offline and everything is fractally connected and can be used to measure and determine how everything else in the universe works. All you have to do is figure out how this strategy works in the real world and soon you will be in control of the whole world. You're welcome.

More Thoughts On Video Game Streamers

I have already briefly touched on how unenjoyable it would be to be a video game streamer, but I neglected to mention that video game streaming is unhealthy on a physical level. If you look at any long term streamer you will see a very common hollow eyed look that they tend to have. While this can partially be explained by poor diet and lack of exercise, it cannot fully be explained by poor diet and lack of exercise, which means that there is some other element at play.

The long term video streamer tends to have a very similar look to a long term porn addict. It's like a less extreme version of a crackhead or junkie that has slowly screwed with the regulatory systems in their body for it to have visible effects on their exterior. What this is most likely due to is the fact that the games most professional streamers play are games that mess with emotions and psychological needs in order to give rewards through visual and auditory stimulation, similar in function but different in form to how porn functions.

The human brain is not built for getting constant feedback and reward and punishment based on very unimportant decisions. Video games that are addictive are created in a way to trick the brain and cause an unhealthy dependence on feedback from a computer of television screen, and this is essentially sort of drug. In the case of most normal people, they don't play video games enough for this sort of reward and punishment feedback loop to have any permanently harmful effects, but with the case of video game streamers, they are doing this as a full time job and thus are exposed to negative psychological and physical aspects that come from way too much interaction with digital entertainment.

I don't think I'm the only person to really notice this trend. I'm sure that the big companies who encourage streamers notice the unhealthy look that happens to nearly all video game players, and some of the people who notice it have figured out the correlation, but just like all other unhealthy products, the people making money from them are generally incentivized to not act in their market's objectively healthy interests. There's really nothing that can be done with regards to this problem. Video games are fine in small doses, just like gambling. The downsides are too vague and abstract to ever compete against the attractiveness of making money without doing any real work and "having fun" playing video games for viewers.

Conclusion
We have reached the end of this book, and so there must be a conclusion. The conclusion we have is this: HAHAHA

HAHAHA HAHAHA HAHAHA HAHAHA HAHAHA
HAHAHA HAHAHA HAHAHA HAHAHA HAHAHA
HAHAHA HAHAHA HAHAHA HAHAHA HAHAHA
HAHAHA
HAHAHA HAHAHA HAHAHA HAHAHA
HAHAHA HAHAHA HAHAHA HAHAHA HAHAHA
HAHAHA HAHAHA HAHAHA HAHAHA HAHAHA
HAHAHA HAHAHA HAHAHA HAHAHA HAHAHA
HAHAHA HAHAHA HAHAHA HAHAHA HAHAHA
HAHAHA HAHAHA HAHAHA HAHAHA HAHAHA
HAHAHA HAHAHA HAHAHA HAHAHA HAHAHA
HAHAHA HAHAHA HAHAHA HAHAHA HAHAHA
HAHAHA
HAHAHA HAHAHA HAHAHA HAHAHA
HAHAHA HAHAHA HAHAHA HAHAHA HAHAHA
HAHAHA HAHAHA HAHAHA HAHAHA HAHAHA
HAHAHA HAHAHA HAHAHA HAHAHA HAHAHA
HAHAHA HAHAHA HAHAHA HAHAHA HAHAHA
HAHAHA HAHAHA HAHAHA HAHAHA HAHAHA
HAHAHA HAHAHA HAHAHA HAHAHA HAHAHA
HAHAHA HAHAHA HAHAHA HAHAHA HAHAHA
HAHAHA
HAHAHA HAHAHA HAHAHA HAHAHA
HAHAHA HAHAHA HAHAHA HAHAHA HAHAHA
HAHAHA HAHAHA HAHAHA HAHAHA HAHAHA
HAHAHA HAHAHA HAHAHA HAHAHA HAHAHA
HAHAHA HAHAHA HAHAHA HAHAHA HAHAHA
HAHAHA HAHAHA HAHAHA HAHAHA HAHAHA
HAHAHA HAHAHA HAHAHA HAHAHA HAHAHA
HAHAHA HAHAHA HAHAHA HAHAHA HAHAHA
HAHAHA
HAHAHA HAHAHA HAHAHA HAHAHA
HAHAHA HAHAHA HAHAHA HAHAHA HAHAHA
HAHAHA HAHAHA HAHAHA HAHAHA HAHAHA
HAHAHA HAHAHA HAHAHA HAHAHA HAHAHA
HAHAHA HAHAHA HAHAHA HAHAHA HAHAHA
HAHAHA HAHAHA HAHAHA HAHAHA HAHAHA

HAHAHA HAHAHA HAHAHA HAHAHA HAHAHA
HAHAHA HAHAHA HAHAHA HAHAHA HAHAHA
HAHAHA
HAHAHA HAHAHA HAHAHA HAHAHA
HAHAHA HAHAHA HAHAHA HAHAHA HAHAHA
HAHAHA HAHAHA HAHAHA HAHAHA HAHAHA
HAHAHA HAHAHA HAHAHA HAHAHA HAHAHA
HAHAHA HAHAHA HAHAHA HAHAHA HAHAHA
HAHAHA HAHAHA HAHAHA HAHAHA HAHAHA
HAHAHA HAHAHA HAHAHA HAHAHA HAHAHA
HAHAHA HAHAHA HAHAHA HAHAHA HAHAHA
HAHAHA
HAHAHA HAHAHA HAHAHA HAHAHA
HAHAHA HAHAHA HAHAHA HAHAHA HAHAHA
HAHAHA HAHAHA HAHAHA HAHAHA HAHAHA
HAHAHA HAHAHA HAHAHA HAHAHA HAHAHA
HAHAHA HAHAHA HAHAHA HAHAHA HAHAHA
HAHAHA HAHAHA HAHAHA HAHAHA HAHAHA
HAHAHA HAHAHA HAHAHA HAHAHA HAHAHA
HAHAHA HAHAHA HAHAHA HAHAHA HAHAHA
HAHAHA
HAHAHA HAHAHA HAHAHA HAHAHA
HAHAHA HAHAHA HAHAHA HAHAHA HAHAHA
HAHAHA HAHAHA HAHAHA HAHAHA HAHAHA
HAHAHA HAHAHA HAHAHA HAHAHA HAHAHA
HAHAHA HAHAHA HAHAHA HAHAHA HAHAHA
HAHAHA HAHAHA HAHAHA HAHAHA HAHAHA
HAHAHA HAHAHA HAHAHA HAHAHA HAHAHA
HAHAHA HAHAHA HAHAHA HAHAHA HAHAHA
HAHAHA
HAHAHA HAHAHA HAHAHA HAHAHA
HAHAHA HAHAHA HAHAHA HAHAHA HAHAHA
HAHAHA HAHAHA HAHAHA HAHAHA HAHAHA
HAHAHA HAHAHA HAHAHA HAHAHA HAHAHA
HAHAHA HAHAHA HAHAHA HAHAHA HAHAHA
HAHAHA HAHAHA HAHAHA HAHAHA HAHAHA
HAHAHA HAHAHA HAHAHA HAHAHA HAHAHA
HAHAHA HAHAHA HAHAHA HAHAHA HAHAHA

HAHAHA HAHAHA HAHAHA HAHAHA HAHAHA
HAHAHA
HAHAHA HAHAHA HAHAHA HAHAHA
HAHAHA HAHAHA HAHAHA HAHAHA HAHAHA
HAHAHA HAHAHA HAHAHA HAHAHA HAHAHA
HAHAHA HAHAHA HAHAHA HAHAHA HAHAHA
HAHAHA HAHAHA HAHAHA HAHAHA HAHAHA
HAHAHA HAHAHA HAHAHA HAHAHA HAHAHA
HAHAHA HAHAHA HAHAHA HAHAHA HAHAHA
HAHAHA HAHAHA HAHAHA HAHAHA HAHAHA
HAHAHA

If you are somebody who dislikes me, there is still time to come over to the winning side. There is still time to join the side of life and laughter and love and success. There is no need for you to wallow in your self-destructive mediocrity.

To all the people who continue to support me I want to extend my thankfulness and genuine gratitude. As always, without you, I would not be able to do what I do as well as I do it. Always remember that my success is your success.

Made in the USA
Coppell, TX
16 May 2023

16911841R10233